DEVELOPMENTS IN
WATER QUALITY RESEARCH

PROCEEDINGS OF THE JERUSALEM INTERNATIONAL CONFERENCE
ON WATER QUALITY AND POLLUTION RESEARCH, JUNE 1969

DEVELOPMENTS IN
WATER QUALITY RESEARCH

General Editor

HILLEL I. SHUVAL

Associate Professor of Environmental Health
Hebrew University of Jerusalem

Editorial Board

YEHUDA GOLDSHMID   *Director, Water Quality Control Department, Mekorot Water Company, Tel Aviv*
GEDALIAHU SHELEF   *Chief Sanitary Engineer, Ministry of Health, Jerusalem*
ALBERTO WACHS   *Professor of Sanitary Engineering, Technion–Israel Institute of Technology, Haifa*

WITHDRAWN

ann arbor science publishers inc.

ANN ARBOR SCIENCE PUBLISHERS, INC.
P.O. Box 1425, Ann Arbor, Michigan 48106

©1970 Ann Arbor Science Publishers
Library of Congress Catalogue Card Number 79-109132
SBN 250 39961 X

Technical Editor: R. Amoils

Second Printing 1971

Third Printing 1973

Printed in U.S.A.

PREFACE

The ultimate amount of water annually at the disposal of a country is more or less a fixed volume. Its rate of development is dependent on the availability of financial resources and engineering technology. Into this fairly constant source of supply is spewed an ever-increasing quantity of organic and chemical wastes, disposed of into the environment by steadily growing populations massing in burgeoning urban centers and industrial complexes. This expanding populace requires more and more water for urban and industrial use, but its very own wastes continually contaminate the available supply, despoiling its quality. This process reaches, at times, a point where the water's utility for human consumption or industrial purposes is endangered. Thus a built-in paradox of modern society revolves around a situation where more and more water is needed but less and less becomes available at the required quality as a result of the self-destructive process of pollution.

Increasing water quality degradation has become a scourge of the developed countries of the world despite their generally plentiful water resources. Water pollution can present an even more serious drawback in those developing countries where, on the one hand, urbanization and industrialization are progressing at a rapid and often uncontrolled pace, while on the other hand the supply of water initially available is often more limited.

It is only fitting that The Jerusalem Conference on Water Quality and Pollution Research, June 1969, provided an international forum for reviewing some of these acute problems. Israel is a semi-arid country which is approaching the end of its possibilities to develop additional natural water resources. In such a situation, water pollution prevention and wastewater utilization assume a degree of urgency which emphasizes the extent to which the future of the national economy and

v

culture can be dependent on protecting and conserving precious water reserves.

Somewhat more than half of the papers presented are the outcome of the research efforts in these fields carried out by scientists and engineers from Israel. It is indicative of the degree of urgency assumed by the water pollution problem that so much excellent work is underway in this sphere in such a small country. However, the Conference was international in spirit and content, and the subjects dealt with and the research findings presented will find application in every country of the world which share the common problem of increasing pollution.

This work comprises twenty Conference papers which are divided here into three sections as follows:

1. Water Quality Management
2. Wastewater Treatment and Utilization
3. Marine Pollution

Three of the papers appearing herein were accepted by the program committee, but their authors were unable to come to Jerusalem to present them. The senior authors of these papers are G. Stander, R. J. Giglio and L. Klashman.

The Conference was sponsored and supported by: The National Council for Research and Development; The Technion–Israel Institute of Technology, Haifa; The Hebrew University of Jerusalem which served as host; The Israel Association of Architects and Engineers; and Mekorot Water Company.

Dr. Y. Goldshmid, Dr. G. Shelef and Professor A. Wachs made major contributions in their dual roles as members of the Conference Organizing Committee and of the Editorial Board of these Proceedings.

Mention must also be made of the group of leading scientists and engineers who so skillfully assisted in managing the Conference as session chairmen. They are listed alphabetically:

Professor I. Bear–Technion–Israel Institute of Technology, Haifa.
Ing. M. Kantor–Water Commissioner, Ministry of Agriculture, Tel Aviv
Ing. R. Gurevits–Tahal–Water Planning for Israel, Tel Aviv
Ing. S. Kishoni–Chairman, Organization of Water Engineers, Tel Aviv
Ing. Ch. Kosovsky–Deputy Chief Engineer, Mekorot Water Co, Tel Aviv
Dr. G. Shelef–Chief Sanitary Engineer, Ministry of Health, Jerusalem

Special acknowledgements are due to Mr. B. Kleter and Mrs. R. Dicker for their faithful assistance and untiring efforts in organizing the Conference in such an efficient and smooth manner.

So many other people contributed to the success of the Conference and to the preparation of these Proceedings that a collective acknowledgment of their help is the only possible solution.

It is hoped that this Conference will be the first of a series of such international meetings on water quality and pollution research to be held in Israel at regular intervals.

Jerusalem   Hillel I. Shuval
December 1969

LIST OF CONTRIBUTORS

ADRIAN, DONALD D., Ph.D.
Associate Professor of Civil Engineering
University of Massachusetts, Amherst, Mass., USA

BERMAN, THOMAS, Ph.D.
Director, Kinneret Limnological Laboratory
P.O.B. 345, Tiberias, Israel

COHEN, HAIM, B.Sc.
Director, Chemical Engineering Laboratories
Negev Institute for Arid Zone Research, P.O.B. 1025, Beer-Sheva, Israel

COHEN, NAFTALI, M.Sc.
Deputy District Sanitary Engineer
Ministry of Health, Tel Aviv District Public Health Office, Tel Aviv, Israel

DALINSKY, PAUL, M.C.E.
Project Engineer, Long-Range Planning Section
Tahal–Water Planning for Israel, Ltd., 37 Ibn Gvirol Street, Tel Aviv, Israel

DEWLING, RICHARD T., M.C.E.
Laboratory Director, Hudson Delaware Basins Office
U.S. Dept. of the Interior, FWPCA, Edison, N.J. 08817, USA

DONAGI, ALEXANDER, D.Sc.
Head, Air Pollution and Radiation Control Laboratories
Ministry of Health, 27 Prof. Shorr Street, Tel Aviv, Israel

DREWS, R.J.L.C., Ph.D.
National Institute for Water Research
South African Council for Scientific and Industrial Research, Pretoria, South Africa

EREN, JACOB, Ph.D.
Head of Research Team, Water Quality Control Department
Mekorot Water Company, 9 Lincoln Street, Tel Aviv, Israel

FOX, MICHAEL ANDREW, M.Sc.
Chief Chemist, Miles Laboratories Israel, Ltd.
P.O.B. 288, Haifa, Israel

GIGLIO, RICHARD J., Ph.D.
Associate Professor of Civil Engineering
University of Massachusetts, Amherst, Mass., USA

GILAT, CHAIM, M.Sc.
Head, Radioactive Tracers Application Group
Soreq Nuclear Research Center, Yavneh, Israel

GOLDSHMID, YEHUDA, Ph.D.
Director, Water Quality Control Department
Mekorot Water Company, 9 Lincoln Street, Tel Aviv, Israel

GRUENER, NACHMAN, Ph.D.
Research Biochemist, Environmental Health Laboratory
Hebrew University–Hadassah Medical School, Jerusalem, Israel

HALPERIN, RAMY, M.Sc.
District Sanitary Engineer
Ministry of Health, Southern District Office, Beer-Sheva, Israel

HIRSCH, LAWRENCE, C.E.
President, Hirsch & Koptionak
5106 Federal Boulevard, San Diego, California, USA

KAMINSKY, FRANK C., Ph.D.
Associate Professor of Industrial Engineering
University of Massachusetts, Amherst, Mass., USA

KENDLER, JOSEPH, Ph.D.
Director, Central Laboratory for Prevention of Air Pollution and Radiation Hazards
Ministry of Health, 27 Prof. Shorr Street, Tel Aviv, Israel

KLASHMAN, LESTER M., B.Sc.
Regional Director, Northwest Region
U.S. Dept. of the Interior, FWPCA, John F. Kennedy Fed. Bldg., Boston, Mass., USA

KLIGFIELD, GEORGE, B.M.E.
General Manager, Hanford Engineering Services, a division of Vitro Corp. of America
P.O.B. 296, Richland, Washington 99352, USA

KOTT, YEHUDA, Ph.D.
Associate Professor, Sanitary Engineering Laboratories
Technion–Israel Institute of Technology, Haifa, Israel

LEVENTER, HAIM, B.Sc.
Reservoir Biologist, Water Quality Control Department
Mekorot Water Company, 9 Lincoln Street, Tel Aviv, Israel

MEIRING, P.G.J., Ph.D.
Chief Research Officer, National Institute for Water Research
South African Council for Scientific and Industrial Research, Pretoria, South Africa

MELAMED, ABRAHAM, Ph.D.
Consulting Engineer
32 Bloch Street, Tel Aviv, Israel

REBHUN, MENAHEM, D.Sc.
Associate Professor, Sanitary Engineering Laboratories
Technion–Israel Institute of Technology, Haifa, Israel

RIKKERS, ROBERT F., Ph.D.
Assistant Professor of Civil Engineering
University of Massachusetts, Amherst, Mass., USA

SALITERNIK, CHEN, M.Sc.
Head, Water Quality Unit
Tahal–Water Planning for Israel Ltd., 37 Ibn Gvirol Street, Tel Aviv

SERRUYA, COLETTE, Ph.D.
Senior Research Worker, Kinneret Limnological Laboratory
P.O.B. 345, Tiberias, Israel

SHELEF, GEDALIAHU, Ph.D.
Chief Sanitary Engineer and Head of Division of Environmental Health
Ministry of Health, Jerusalem, Israel

SHUVAL, HILLEL I., B.S.C.E., M.P.H.
Associate Professor, Director of Environmental Health Laboratory
Hebrew University–Hadassah Medical School, Jerusalem, Israel

SLESS, J.B., Ph.D.
Biologist, Sanitary Engineering Laboratories
Technion–Israel Institute of Technology, Haifa, Israel

STANDER, GERT JOHANNES, Ph.D.
Director, National Institute for Water Research
South African Council for Scientific and Industrial Research, Pretoria, South Africa

VAN ECK, H., Ph.D.
National Institute for Water Research
South African Council for Scientific and Industrial Research, Pretoria, South Africa

WACHS, ALBERTO M., M.Sc.
Professor, Head of Sanitary Engineering Laboratories
Technion–Israel Institute of Technology, Haifa, Israel

WALKER, KENNETH H., B.S.C.E.
Director, Hudson-Delaware Basins Office
U.S. Dept. of the Interior, FWPCA, Edison, N.J. 08817, USA

WIXSON, BOBBY G., Ph.D.
Associate Professor of Environmental Health, Dept. of Civil Engineering; Associate
  Director, Center for International Programs and Studies
University of Missouri-Rolla, Rolla, Missouri, USA

YOSHPE-PURER, YONA, M.Sc.
Bacteriologist, Tel Aviv District Public Health Laboratory
Ministry of Health, Tel Aviv, Israel

CONTENTS

xiii

SECTION 2. *Wastewater Treatment and Utilization*

SECTION 3. *Marine Pollution*

WATER QUALITY MANAGEMENT

Water Quality Management of the

Israel National Water System

Y. Goldshmid

INTRODUCTION

The Jordan System is the largest single water supply project ever built in Israel. It is designed to transport 320 million m³ each year from Lake Kinneret, where water is in abundance, to central and southern Israel, where most of the cultivable land is located and where there is insufficient rainfall. The importance of the Jordan Project extends far beyond the quantity of water it transfers, owing to the central position it occupies in the Israel National Water System (INWS).

Water quality problems influenced the design of the Jordan Project and required an approach that was somewhat unorthodox and tailor-made to the specific properties and conditions which prevailed at the time of the design. Now that the Jordan Project has been in operation for over five years, it is worthwhile analyzing the water quality concepts in light of the experience gained during operation.

This paper reviews the water quality considerations and concepts in the design of the Jordan Project and discusses these features in light of operational experience.

3

THE JORDAN PROJECT — GENERAL DESCRIPTION

Lake Kinneret Watershed

The area of the watershed (Figure 1) is approximately 2,730 square kilometers. Its major hydrological components are the Jordan River and its tributaries—the Dan, Snir, Hermon and Ayun rivers, several springs, surface runoff and rains. The inhabitants of the watershed area live mainly in small villages and towns. The total population of 100,000 is employed chiefly in agriculture and some industry (SALIK, 1965). Annually, the watershed discharges to the lake about 4.5 million m³ of domestic sewage, about 54 million m³ of fish pond effluent and about 14 million m³ of runoff from agricultural fields (GOLDSHMID, 1966). Most of these flow directly into Lake Kinneret without any treatment at all, increasing the nutrient concentration of the lake. In coming years, with the growth in population density, the watershed will have an increasing deleterious effect on Lake Kinneret water quality.

Lake Kinneret

The sweet-water lake, situated 209 meters below sea level, has a volume of about 4,400 million m³, a surface area of 169 square kilometers, a maximum depth of 45 meters, a mean depth of 25.4 meters and a total inflow of 770 million m³ per year (SHAPIRO, 1962). It is a warm monomictic lake with pronounced anaerobic conditions below the thermocline for seven to eight months each year. Sulfides develop in the hypolimnion and during spring may appear in the epilimnion following strong winds. The lake's chemical composition differs considerably from that of other lakes with an outflow. Chlorides predominate over carbonates and alkalis over calcium due to the inflow of salt water from springs on the bottom of the lake and along its shores. These saline springs increase the TDS and the concentration of sodium, chloride and other ions. The lake water has a chloride ion concentration about 15 times greater than that of the incoming Jordan water. The measured primary productivity is as high as in the most productive lakes and Lake Kinneret may be classified as a eutrophic lake (GOLDSHMID, 1968).

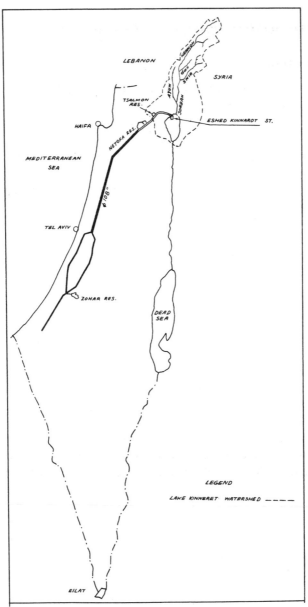

Figure 1
The Israel National Water System — Jordan Project

The Open Conduit, the Reservoirs, and the Pressure Line

The water intake is about nine meters below the surface when the water level is at -209 m, and is located about 500 meters from the lake shore. At Eshed Kinnarot, the water is pumped to the Jordan canal, 250 meters above the lake. This canal, 16 kilometers long, carries the water to the Tsalmon reservoir which has a capacity of 800,000 m^3. The Tsalmon pumping station raises the water another 110 meters to the Netofa canal which is 17 kilometers in length. At the end of the Netofa canal, the water flows to the two Eshkol (Netofa) reservoirs, with a total capacity of 6 million m^3. The first of the Eshkol reservoirs is a settling basin, the second is for storage. From the storage reservoir, the water flows into the 108″-diameter pipeline to Rosh Ha'ayin, then through the two Yarqon lines to the southern part of the country (TAHAL, WATER PLANNING FOR ISRAEL LTD., 1963).

The Jordan Project as Part of the INWS

The 108″ pipeline and the more southerly Yarqon lines form the backbone of the INWS. Many regional projects are connected to this pipeline, thus making it a large network. Water may flow in or out of the Jordan System, depending on the needs developing in the local projects. It serves as a major supply and storage for balancing the regional projects and is of special importance because it integrates these individual projects into a national water supply system and serves as the mainstay of this system, contributing over 20% of the total annual national supply (and in winter a much larger proportion). The operation of the Jordan Project has completely changed the water supply situation in Israel.

PARAMETERS INFLUENCING WATER QUALITY DESIGN OF THE JORDAN PROJECT

The water quality design of the project took into account historical and political aspects in addition to the usual engineering and economic considerations.

From the outset it was decided that although 80% of the water pumped from the lake was intended for agriculture, all the water would be treated and maintained at drinking-water standards. This was found to be more advantageous than providing treatment units at the connections to cities and villages. Moreover, this was the only way to unify the water supply projects into a single national system (TAHAL, 1963). This concept of a unified national network, maintained at potable-water quality, is new not only in Israel but also possibly in the rest of the world.

Historical and Political Considerations

Prior to the operation of the Jordan Project, Israel received almost all of its water supply from wells and springs. The quality problems were limited to the presence of H_2S in water, corrosivity and bacteriological considerations. The operation of the new Jordan Project, a surface supply, presented new problems with which designers were not fully familiar theoretically and practically. Also there was a certain hidden fear of water quality problems which would arise when the Jordan System was operated. This situation called for the establishment of a scientifically qualified water quality control unit which was not in existence at that time.

The type and location of the intake were influenced by security and political considerations. Originally, the Jordan River was to have been diverted at the Bnot Ya'aqov Bridge. Later, due to political pressure from neighboring countries, the intake was moved downstream to Lake Kinneret (KALLEE, 1965). A comparison of the effect on water treatment requirements of these two different intakes (one planned near the Bnot Ya'aqov Bridge and the other submerged in the lake) can be made immediately from the following data summarized in Table 1.

As can be seen, at the Bnot Ya'aqov Bridge a conventional treatment plant would have been required, while pumping from Lake Kinneret calls for only

Table 1. Comparison of water quality at Bnot Ya'aqov Bridge
and in Lake Kinneret

Property	Bnot Ya'aqov Bridge	Lake Kinneret
Turbidity J.U.	6–300	1–14
NO_3 mg/1	0.05–2.7	0.01–0.3
PO_4 mg/1	0.02–0.24	0.01–0.11
MPN/100 ml	10^4–10^7	2–240
Cl mg/1	14–24	235–390*
Total iron mg/1	0.01–6.0	0.02–0.34

* Concentration varies with the years due to operation of salt-water canal.

minor treatment facilities. It is difficult to evaluate the effect which the diversion of the Jordan at the Bnot Ya'aqov Bridge might have had on Lake Kinneret ecology.

Security considerations governed not only the intake's location but also its shape. Rather than building an intake tower which would enable pumping water of suitable quality from different lake depths, a submerged intake was constructed, pumping from one depth only.

Lake Kinneret

Research on Lake Kinneret has been carried out since 1812 (STEINITZ and OREN, 1968), but the survey required for the design of the Jordan Project was started only in the late fifties. The properties of the lake influenced the final water quality design of the Jordan Project. As shown in Table 1, Lake Kinneret is low in turbidity and color; MPN examinations, carried out over several years at different sampling stations and depths, indicated less than 240 coliforms/100 ml in most cases. The lake water contains very little iron or manganese and relatively high TDS, of which over 50% are made up of sodium and chloride ions originating in the saline springs entering the lake (MEKOROT WATER Co., 1966, 1968).

The high chloride concentration of 390 ppm in the lake in 1964 made the water unsuitable for some crops and necessitated special measures to decrease the chloride concentration. The water is relatively hard and does not contain agressive CO_2. Its corrosive properties stem from the high TDS and chloride concentration (Larson Index about 6.5) (LARSON and SKOLD, 1958).

The Kinneret watershed is an agricultural area with little industry, and includes some peat fields formed as a result of the drainage of the Hula Lake; these factors influence the nutrients entering the Kinneret and increase their concentration in the water, thus making the lake a productive one.

At the time the project was designed, data on ecological properties, such as change of primary productivity with depth, quantities of nutrients which might reach the Jordan Project reservoirs and their effect on these reservoirs, were not yet available. Emphasis was placed on turbidity due to the poor quality of the water of the Jordan River entering the lake. Many steps were taken to minimize turbidity in the Jordan Project, some of which were later to become the source of much trouble.

The Reservoirs

Once the high rate of percolation in the Netofa Valley was determined, Lake Kinneret became the natural alternative site for the storage basin of capacity 1,000 million m³ needed for safe operation of the Jordan Project. Two more operational reservoirs, Tsalmon and Eshkol (Netofa), were required to insure proper operation. The first serves as a holding reservoir for the Tsalmon pumping station, while the Eshkol reservoir, at the head of the pressure line, was built to hold the finished water.

In 1959 fish from the Zohar reservoir, at the southern end of the Yarqon lines, entered the supply system and appeared at the consumers' taps. This spoke against introduction of fish into the Tsalmon and Eshkol reservoirs.

These and other factors constituted the basis for the sanitary design of the Jordan Project.

THE WATER QUALITY CONCEPT IN THE DESIGN OF THE JORDAN PROJECT

It was decided to view the lake, its watershed, the open canal and the reservoirs as one unit. Nutrients and other contaminants entering the lake were to be held to a minimum. The lake's self-purifying power was intended to be the major treatment, and chlorination was introduced to reduce bacterial load and maintain the water in the reservoirs and distribution systems at the required bacterial quality. Water in the Tsalmon and Eshkol reservoirs would be of high quality and efforts were made to keep it from deteriorating. However, other problems, such as turbidity, algal blooms in the lake, open canal or reservoirs, and removal of coarse objects and fish, were not overlooked, and treatment facilities were incorporated into the project. In order to implement this scheme of water quality control, a highly qualified and well-equipped water quality control unit was to be established.

The high chloride content of the water would be a problem in irrigation, and a system was thus designed for dilution of the Kinneret water in transit to the south by injecting low-chloride aquifer water.

Let us now describe how the water quality control concepts outlined above were implemented in engineering terms.

Measures to Improve Water Quality in the Jordan Project

To preserve the quality of Lake Kinneret water, decrease the organic and bacterial load, and slow down the lake's eutrophication process, it was advised to establish a watershed authority. This authority was to be entrusted with all watershed operations concerning the preservation of the lake as a water source.

The water enters the Eshed Kinnarot pumping station through a submerged intake. The intake is so placed as to ensure that only epilimnion water enters the Jordan System. It was built as a polygon, any side of which can be shut if pollution arrives predominantly from that direction. Before reaching the pumps, the water passes through 4 mm-mesh rotating screens to prevent the entry of large objects and fish into the system. The water is chlorinated and pumped to the Jordan canal.

At the head of the Jordan canal a $CuSO_4$ treatment plant was installed. This was intended to operate only when algal blooms appeared in the Eshkol and Tsalmon reservoirs or when large masses of algae entered the system from Lake Kinneret. In order to prevent sand and silt from entering the canal during heavy rains, drainage channels were constructed along the main canal and the artificially created slopes were planted.

A second chlorination station for emergency use was built at the exit from the Tsalmon reservoir.

Three recording turbidimeters were installed—one each at Eshed Kinnarot, Tsalmon and the Yiftah-El siphon some two kilometers upstream of the Eshkol reservoirs. At the last-mentioned site the alum addition plant was erected with the idea that fast and slow mixing would be provided by the flow in the canal.

Part of the first Eshkol reservoir was designed to serve as a settling basin; the water flows out of this reservoir via a collecting trough.

Upon leaving the Eshkol storage reservoir (the second one), the water is again chlorinated and screened (4 mm-mesh rotating screens) prior to its entrance into the 108″-diameter pipeline. At the Eshkol complex, the storage reservoir was placed downstream of the settling basin in spite of the possibility of additional contamination during the stay at the reservoir, so as to prevent water level changes in the settling basin and to assure its proper operation.

A mobile chlorinator was supplied to be used at different localities along the Jordan System in cases of emergency.

A bypass canal to the two Eshkol reservoirs was built mainly for operational reasons, but also as part of the sanitary design. The Eshkol reservoirs were to be bypassed if the quality of the water in them deteriorated.

To overcome the problem of high chloride concentrations, two types of dilution stations were built along the pressure pipe. The first serves to introduce aquifer water low in chlorides into the pipeline, thus reducing the salinity of the Kinneret water. At the second type of mixing point, Kinneret water is diluted with water of the regional project and the mixture supplied at a predetermined chloride concentration. In order to reduce the overall salinity of the lake water body, a salt-water diversion canal was built along the western shore of the lake to collect the water from the saline springs emerging along the shore and divert it away from the lake.

To provide for water quality control and technical and scientific knowhow, much emphasis was placed on a well-trained and well-equipped water quality control unit. A laboratory was built at the site of the Eshkol reservoirs and was staffed with qualified people.

The water quality control scheme calls for the following groups of tests: a) operational tests, such as residual chlorine, turbidity, chloride concentration, etc., which call for immediate action and are carried out by the plant operators; b) water quality control tests—all examinations determining the quality of the water for comparison with the Israel Drinking Water Standard; c) survey and research tests—aimed at understanding or solving special problems.

WATER QUALITY OPERATIONAL EXPERIENCE

The Jordan Project was commissioned in June 1964. Since then it has been in continuous operation except for two planned interruptions. However, the water supplied did not always comply with standards set up by Mekorot, and on several occasions it was decided to supply water with a Threshold Odor Number (TON) > 10 and not to shut down the Project.

Agreement Between Design and Operation

For the most part, the problems anticipated by the designer were those actually encountered. In most cases the design was adequate.

The chemical, physical and bacteriological properties of the Project water supplied to the consumers were at all times in full accord with the Israel Drinking Water Standard (ISRAEL STANDARDS INSTITUTE, 1963). The chloride concentration in Lake Kinneret water surpassed that recommended for agriculture, but the measures taken adequately solved the short- and long-term problems. The chloride concentration in the lake now stands at 240 ppm and should continue to drop, except in the event of a dry winter, until a lower equilibrium point is reached (TAUSSIG, 1965).

A reduction in the number of algae and in the organic load has been observed between Eshed Kinnarot and Rosh Ha'ayin (KATZ, 1967). This decrease is achieved by chlorination, settling in the Tsalmon and Eshkol reservoirs, and sporadic $CuSO_4$ treatment. The algae developing on the canal banks also settle in these reservoirs. The treatment applied in the Jordan System effects the algae in all the reservoirs connected to the national system. We usually find species resistant to chlorination dominant throughout the system. These species and the concentrations observed are of no sanitary significance (LEVENTER, 1969).

The Eshkol settling basin at Netofa reduces the algal and organic load by sedimentation without the addition of alum.

The rotating screens at the exit from the Eshkol reservoirs prevent small shrimp, algae and *Potamogeton* masses from entering the distribution system. Chlorination at Netofa and persistence of residual chlorine down to Rosh Ha'ayin prevent the growth of microorganisms in the 108″ pipeline. Two inspections inside the 108″ pipeline showed it to be completely free of algae, sponges and slimes. The lengthy contact time, from Netofa to Rosh Ha'ayin, ensures bacteriologically satisfactory water.

Shortcomings of the Design

The creation of a watershed authority, which is a fundamental aspect of the water quality control concept for the Jordan Project, has not come about, owing to technical and legal difficulties. Thus, one of the basic tools for maintaining and preserving water quality in the Project is not available.

The problem of turbid water, given considerable attention in the design of the project, was found to be of secondary importance and alum treatment was never applied, whereas the major problem of taste and odor, which we now attribute to *Peridinium* bloom in the Kinneret in winter and to a benthic community of *Oscillatoria* in summer, was not given due consideration.

The rotating screens did not prevent entry of fish into the reservoirs. In November 1968, when the reservoirs were emptied, many tons of fish were removed from the Tsalmon and Eshkol reservoirs.

Hypolimnion water high in sulfides reached the Eshed Kinnarot pumping station on several occasions. This usually occurred in early summer, several hours after the onset of heavy western winds (MIZRAHI, 1966; COHEN, 1968).

The lake water recharged into wells for seasonal and long-term storage is of great value in improving groundwater reserves. However, problems such as well-clogging during recharge, taste, odor, and bacterial contamination during first days of pumping (SCHWARTZ, 1967) necessitate treatment at the well site.

The copper sulfate treatment of the Jordan Project reservoirs was found to have "aftereffects" which are difficult to predict. In view of this, more thorough study is required, notwithstanding the fact that the treatment achieves its primary objective of reducing the algae in the water.

DISCUSSION

The water quality design—equipment, processes, methods, manpower, etc.—has been discussed along with the experience gained during five years of operation of the Jordan Project. Let us compare the initial planning with actual operation.

It is an established fact that the Jordan Project has been in operation for five years and has not once been shut down for reasons of poor product quality, although it was close to being stopped several times.

Treatment Principles

The water quality engineering design's basic approach to problems of the Jordan Project was preventive rather than corrective. Preventive treatment never offers simple solutions; it invariably calls for ingenuity and innovation. Suggestions from the literature do not generally lend themselves to direct application; however, even these aids are often unavailable and experimental work must start from basic principles. These investigations require scientific and technical manpower of a higher level, trained in all aspects of sanitary engineering, especially in biology, ecology and limnology, and in the application of general knowhow to this specific water system. Such a highly qualified staff is usually not needed when corrective treatment is employed to improve water quality. To illustrate this point, let us examine the following, as yet unsolved problem: should the lake water be treated so as to precipitate as much organic matter as possible in the Jordan Project's reservoirs, and let water low in organic load flow southward, or should treatment be delayed as long as possible, allowing water with a heavier organic load to run to the south? If the first method is followed, the organic matter accumulating and decomposing in the Tsalmon and Eshkol reservoirs would increase the nutrient content and cause algal blooms in these reservoirs. If the water is left with a heavier organic load, as suggested by the second method, the organic matter would accumulate in the smaller distribution reservoirs and recharge wells, and cause nuisances in the central and southern part of the country.

We are limited by the treatment facilities provided in the original design. Some manipulation, such as superchlorination and dechlorination, or the injection of chlorine dioxide, is possible, but treatment completely new to the system, such as filtration, ozonation, etc., is economically prohibitive. This limits the possible methods of treatment and leads to more preventive methods.

Water quality control based on preventive measures calls for careful observation of changes in the entire system, supported by a tight sampling program. A thorough knowledge of the behavior of the system, which takes many years to acquire, is necessary. Operational flexibility is required when available means and knowledge are inadequate. A good example of this is the bypass canal at the Eshkol reservoirs, which can divert the flow when difficulties arise. The lack of such a bypass canal at the Tsalmon reservoir is felt every time this reservoir or Lake Kinneret shows signs of trouble. An intake tower in Lake Kinneret instead of the submerged inlet would have afforded greater flexibility. Because of the absence of operational latitude, there is always the danger of encountering a problem which might require the shutting down of the Jordan Project for a prolonged period.

Lake Kinneret Watershed

A watershed authority vested with executive powers should be an organic part of the water quality control of the Jordan Project, to ensure against future degradation of the lake's water quality. It should also be able to prevent possible catastrophies. Failure to establish such an authority will impair the future quality of Lake Kinneret water and may necessitate large expenses to maintain the present water quality of the Jordan Project.

Lake Kinneret

The most important component of the Jordan Project is the lake. In order to operate the system intelligently and gain the maximum benefits from it, a thorough understanding of this water body is necessary. The same applies to proper watershed management. Determination of the proper degree of treatment necessary in the watershed is reliant on intimate knowledge of the lake.

A study of Lake Kinneret was started before the operation of the Jordan Project and has been extended in both breadth and depth over the years. A limnological laboratory was established at Eshed Kinnarot and has been entrusted with the major role of studying and understanding the lake.

The present intake was designed at an elevation which would ensure the pumping of only epilimnion water at all times. In this way, the "good" water is being continually removed, while the water of poorer grade remains in the lake. We are not sure that this is the best policy. It now seems more logical to pump such water as can still be converted into drinking water by the treatment facilities available in the Jordan System. This calls for an intake tower that would draw also from the hypolimnion.

Peridinium blooms have been noticed in Lake Kinneret during January through May for many years. It is also known that large masses of algae cause taste and odor problems, and copper sulfate treatment was provided to overcome this problem. This treatment has been largely abandoned due to its aftereffects, and we recently started to study chlorination at different times and places as a means of settling the *Peridinium* in the Jordan Project reservoirs.

Reservoirs

A large number of algae are destroyed, one way or another, when water leaves the lake, and the organic debris settles to the bottom of the Tsalmon reservoir or at the Netofa settling basin. The Tsalmon reservoir was not designed as a settling basin, and no provisions were made for easy cleaning. There is no way to bypass the Tsalmon reservoir and cleaning involves stopping the pumping at Eshed Kinnarot for one to three weeks. The reservoir floor is made of basalt gravel which must be dried before it can be cleaned.

As already mentioned, a large part of the algae accumulating on the reservoir floor of the Tsalmon reservoir and the settling basin is made up of *Peridinium*. The *Peridinium* cell wall decomposes slowly in winter, and in spring we find an accumulation of 10^2–10^5 cell wall units (thecae) per cm^2 of reservoir floor mud. When the water temperature rises, the cell wall decomposes much more rapidly, discharging nutrients into the water (EREN, 1968).

This large concentration of nutrients on the reservoir floor, coupled with a water depth of only 3–6 meters (which allows light to reach the bottom) and the special construction of the reservoir floor made up of coarse gravel, makes the bottom of the reservoir a favorable site for the development of benthic algal blooms. Usually during May–July, *Oscillatoria* sp. dominate the reservoir floor and an earthy-musty taste and odor appear in the Jordan Project water supply.

An investigation of the phenomena indicates a close relationship between *Oscillatoria*—mainly *O. chalybea*—and the earthy-musty taste and odor.

The high concentration of algae and nutrients on the reservoir floor sustains large populations of small water insects, shrimp, daphnia, etc. These have not yet created a problem but may do so one day. Their large number is also attributed to the absence of fish from the reservoir.

We have learned from experience that if a reservoir is not emptied at least once a year, fish are found in it. The measures provided in the Jordan Project, namely rotating screens and chlorination at Eshed Kinnarot, are ineffective in keeping fish from entering the reservoirs. The artificial introduction of fish into reservoirs is now advocated because this presents possibilities of selecting species most suitable for a particular task, such as reduction of planktonic *Peridinium* cells in winter or reduction of growth of benthic algae and other small organisms in summer.

CONCLUSION

1. During five years of operation, the Jordan Project was never shut down due to poor water quality, though in some instances water with a relatively high TON was supplied.
2. The water quality design of the Jordan Project is based on preventive rather than corrective treatment.
3. The control of water quality by preventive measures requires the following:
   a. skilled personnel for research and engineering work, and thorough aquaintance with the entire water supply system;
   b. operational flexibility in the water supply system;
   c. a thorough understanding of the major components—in our case chiefly Lake Kinneret, its watershed and the reservoirs;
   d. shutdown of the Jordan Project when the limited corrective measures available fail.
4. In the original design, turbidity control was emphasized while the problems of high productivity on the reservoir bottom were not studied sufficiently.
5. Treatment is limited by the facilities provided in the original design.
6. Fish are an asset to the reservoir, not a disadvantage.

REFERENCES

COHEN, D. (1968): *Sulfide Survey and Aeration of Lake Kinnereth Water 1965–1967* (in Hebrew).

EREN, J. (1968): *Peridinium Cultivation and Destruction*, Progress Report (in Hebrew).

GOLDSHMID, Y. (1966): "Water quality control in the Jordan project," A paper presented before the Association of Engineers and Architects In Israel (in Hebrew).

GOLDSHMID, Y. (1968): "Chemical characteristics of Lake Kinnereth," Presented at the 17th Limnological Congress, Jerusalem.

ISRAEL STANDARD INSTITUTE (1963): Information Sheet 183 (in Hebrew).

KALLEE, E. (1965): *The Struggle for Water*, p. 22, Hakibbutz Hameuchad Publishing House Ltd. (in Hebrew).

KATZ, D. (1967): 1967 Annual Report—The B.C. Nesin Water Quality Control Laboratory (in Hebrew).

LARSON, T.E. and SKOLD, R.V. (1958): "Laboratory studies relating mineral quality of water to corrosion of steel and cast iron," Corrosion, **14,** 285.

LEVENTER, H. (1969): *A Limnological Survey in the Reservoirs of the National Water System 1966–1967* (in Hebrew).

MEKOROTH WATER CO. LTD. (1966): *Summary of Investigations—Lake Kinnereth* 1964.

MEKOROTH WATER CO. LTD. (1968): *Summary of Investigations—Lake Kinnereth 1965, 1966*.

MIZRAHI, S. (1966): "The appearance of sulfides at Eshed Kinnaroth pumping station and fish kill in Lake Kinnereth" (in Hebrew.)

SALIK, D. (1965): Water Pollution Control in Lake Kinnereth (in Hebrew), a Seminar given at the Sanitary Engineering Dept., Technion, Haifa.

SCHWARTZ, J. (1967): *Clogging and Pollution of Wells Recharged with Kinnereth Water.* Tahal, Water Planning for Israel, P.N. 550 (in Hebrew).

SHAPIRO, J. (1962): First report to Tahal on the present and future conditions in Lake Tiberias.

STEINITZ, H., and OREN, O.H. (1968): *Bibliography on Lake Kinnereth,* The Israel Academy of Sciences and Humanities.

TAHAL, WATER PLANNING FOR ISRAEL LTD. (1963): *The Jordan Project—General Description*, P.N. 265.

TAUSSIG, K. (1965): "The Kinnereth System," Report submitted to Mekorot Water Co.

Taste and Odor in the Reservoirs

of the Israel National Water System

H. Leventer and J. Eren

INTRODUCTION

In recent years, more and more attention has been drawn to the problem of tastes and odors of drinking water. Rapid growth of population and increase in consumption of water per capita have dictated utilization of water sources of marginal quality, which were not used in the past for drinking purposes. Another cause for increased concern about taste and odor of water is the generally higher expectations of consumers, making them more sensitive to aesthetic and organoleptic properties of water.

The growing scope of the problem necessitates increased research into the causes of taste and odor in each case, and the best way to prevent them.

In this presentation we shall describe the occurrence of taste and odor in the open reservoirs of the Israel National Water System and our search for the causative agent.

THE NATIONAL WATER SYSTEM AND ITS RESERVOIRS

The Israel National Water System (INWS) has been in operation since 1964 and consists of open channels, pipelines and open reservoirs (Figure 1). The water is pumped from Lake Kinneret at an altitude of 209 meters below sea level, and flows through open channels for 16 km to the Tsalmon reservoir, located 38 meters above sea level. The Tsalmon reservoir has an area of 20 ha, a maximum depth of 4.5 m and a maximum volume of 800,000 m³. Here a second pumping station raises the water to an altitude of 145 m, whence it flows through an additional 17 km of open channel to the Netofa reservoirs.

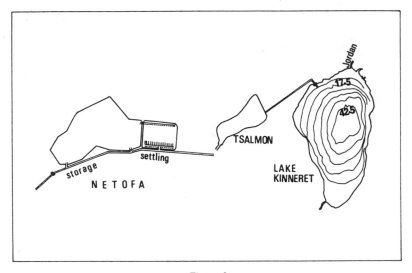

Figure 1
Scheme of the Tsalmon and Netofa reservoirs (not to scale)

At Netofa the first reservoir is a settling basin with a capacity of 1.5 million cubic meters and an area of 40 ha. The second reservoir, with a volume of 4.5 million cubic meters and an area of 100 ha, serves as a storage reservoir. The maximum depths of the first and second reservoirs are 4.5 m and 7.5 m, respectively.

From the Netofa storage reservoir, the water flows through a pipeline to the central and southern parts of the country, where it is used for both irrigation and domestic consumption.

The reservoirs have concrete walls; the bottom is a heavy soil covered by a layer of basalt gravel 30–50 cm thick to prevent turbidity.

The INWS annually conveys about 250 million cubic meters of water from the lake through the reservoirs. Table 1 shows the chemical composition of the lake water.

Table 1. Composition of Lake Kinneret water, July, 1967

Na	150	mg/l	Cl	314	mg/l
K	8.0	mg/l	HCO$_3$	117	mg/l
Ca	51	mg/l	SO$_4$	60	mg/l
Mg	35	mg/l	NO$_3$	0.44	mg/l
NH$_4$	0.05	mg/l	NO$_2$	0.01	mg/l
			PO$_4$	0.01	mg/l

In the spring, there is a heavy bloom of the dinoflagelate *Peridinium cinctum fa. Westii* in the lake, and large quantities of this organism are carried from the lake via the INWS and settle on the bottom of the reservoirs. The composition of the reservoir sediments is given in Table 2.

Table 2. Chemical composition of the sediments in Tsalmon and Netofa reservoirs during the period 12.1966–7.1967 (% of dry weight)

	Tsalmon	Netofa
Organic matter	9.5 –16.8	10.3 --15.4
Nitrogen (Kjeldahl)	0.69– 1.28	0.61– 1.37
PO$_4$	0.24– 0.52	0.34– 0.54
H$_2$S	0.07– 0.35	0.08– 0.23

OCCURRENCE OF TASTE AND ODOR IN RESERVOIRS

The first complaints from consumers about unpleasant taste and odor in water from the INWS were received at the end of June 1966—the second summer of operation of the Netofa storage reservoir. Most of the complaints were that the water had an earthy-musty taste and odor.

Surveys along the INWS showed that the water leaving Lake Kinneret and Tsalmon reservoir was of good quality, with no exceptional taste and odor. On the other hand, the water in the storage reservoir at Netofa developed an earthy-musty smell. Later, the musty odor appeared also in the settling reservoir.

There was no uniformity in the distribution of the odorous water in the reservoir. When the weather was fine, without winds, the odor gradient increased with depth. During windy periods when the reservoirs were thoroughly mixed, the odor was evenly distributed and even the air had a musty smell.

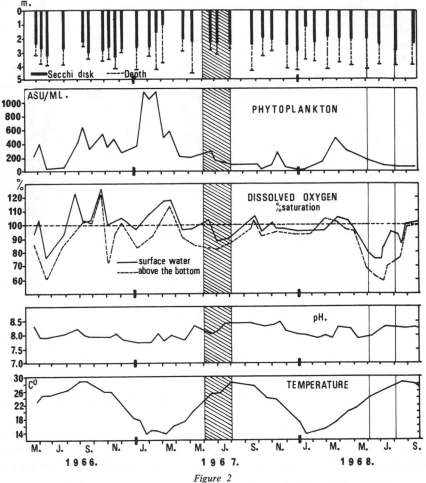

Figure 2

Tsalmon reservoir. Changes of temperature, pH, dissolved oxygen, phytoplankton and Secchi disk during the years 1966–1968. The hatched area represents the taste and odor period

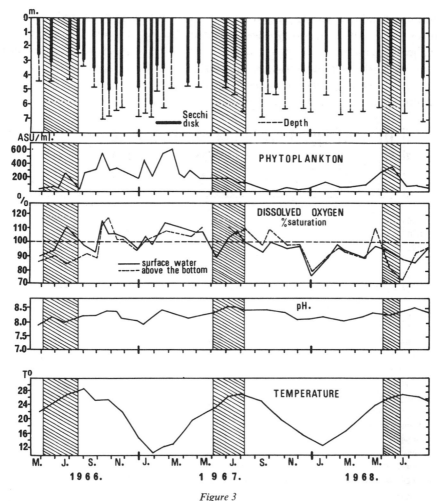

Figure 3
Netofa reservoir. Changes of temperature, pH, dissolved oxygen, phytoplankton
and Secchi disk during the years 1966–1968. The hatched area represents the taste
and odor period

The intensity of taste and odor reached its peak at the end of June and the
beginning of July. Later, there was a gradual decrease in the strength of the odor
and it disappeared from the reservoirs after they were drained and dried at
the end of summer (August–September).

The following summer, 1967, a musty taste and odor were again noticed, this time first in the Tsalmon reservoir and later in the Netofa reservoirs. Although many complaints were forthcoming from consumers, intensity was less than in the previous year.

In the summer of 1968, the taste and odor reappeared, this time in the Netofa reservoirs only. The intensity was about the same as in 1967 but it lasted for a shorter period (about five weeks only).

For each of the seasons described, the taste and odor appeared during the period when the water temperature was 22–26°C. At the same time, there was a drop in dissolved oxygen, which was especially noticeable close to the reservoir bottom (see Figures 2 and 3).

In our first efforts to trace the cause of the nuisance, we attempted to localize the source of the taste and odor compounds. The higher intensities of taste and

Table 3. The phytoplankton in Netofa reservoir during May–August, 1966

DATE	24.5			26.6			3.7			20.7			19.8		
Sampling point	1	2	4	1	2	4	1	2	4	1	2	4	1	2	4
Algae ASU/ml.															
Chlorococcum								6	3				2		2
Cosmarium	4	x	x	2	x	4	2	2	2	3		3	22	8	12
Coelastrum			2			2	2	x							
Gleocystis	2	x	4												
Lagerheimia				2	8		2	2	2				2		
Mougeotia							x								
Oocystis		138	12	88	42	126	144	256	330	595	368	954	138	136	166
Pediastrum			x		2			x		x			x		
Scenedesmus	2	2	2	6	x	6	2	4	4				2	2	2
Tetraedron	10	4	4	18	36	48	20	26	28	11	18		6	2	4
Euglena										x					
Chroococcus		10	x										2		
Oscillatoria*		8	x	10	8	32	x		x	46	14	25	x	2	
Navicula			x		2					x	3	3	2		x
Synedra	x	4	10			2		4	4						
Ceratium					2										
Peridinium	22	x	4												
No. cells/ml.	40	166	38	126	96	224	172	296	390	658	403	976	178	154	186
ASU/ml.	81	32	21	47	31	149	37	51	68	267	160	385	34	23	29

x less than 1 cell/ml.

* most of the cells were damaged.

odor at the lower layer suggested the reservoir bottom as a possible source. The fact that there were no significant changes among plankton organisms during spring and summer 1966 supported this view. Neither was there any sudden increase in the number of any one organism which could be suspected as a source of this nuisance.

Unfortunately, no quantitative determination of benthos organisms was made, but the qualitative tests showed changes in population with considerable increase in *Oscillatoria* and *Beggiatoa*.

Table 4. The benthos algae in the Netofa reservoir, May–August 1966

Algae	24.5	26.6	3.7	20.7	14.8
Coelastrum	x	x	x	x	x
Cosmarium	x	x	x	x	x
Oocystis	xx	xx	xx	x	xx
Pediastrum	x	x	x	x	x
Scenedesmus	x	x	x	x	x
Tetraedron	x	x	x	x	x
Euglena			x	x	x
Microcystis					x
Oscillatoria°	x	x	xx	xx	xx
Spirulina			x	x	x
Cymbella					x
Diatoma				x	x
Navicula	x	x	x	x	x
Nitzschia					x
Pinnularia	x	x	x	x	x
Synedra	x	x	x	x	x
Beggiatoa		x	x	xx	xx

x   presence of organism

xx   organism present in large quantity

°   there are 4 species of this alga; the dominant species is *Oscillatoria chalybea*

The large quantities of *Oscillatoria* and the often-mentioned phenomenon of taste and odor caused by *Actinomycetes* in water bodies drew our attention to two suspected microorganisms—*Oscillatoria* and *Actinomycetes*.

ACTINOMYCETES

Actinomycetes are microorganisms morphologically resembling fungi; however, their physiological properties show close relationship with bacteria. Many species produce odorous substances and the well-known smell of freshly tilled soil is due to *Actinomycetes*.

The first to ascribe taste and odor in water to *Actinomycetes* was ADAMS (1929), who investigated the earthy odors appearing in the waters of the Blue Nile. Later, many cases of earthy-musty odor produced by *Actinomycetes* in rivers in various parts of the world were reported (ISSATCHENKO and EGOROVA, 1944; MORRIS, 1962; ROMANO and SAFFERMAN, 1963). Probably, the most intensely investigated cases of nuisance caused by *Actinomycetes* were the outbreaks of taste and odor in reservoirs in Texas and Oklahoma as described by Silvey and his group (SILVEY et al., 1950; SILVEY and ROACH, 1953).

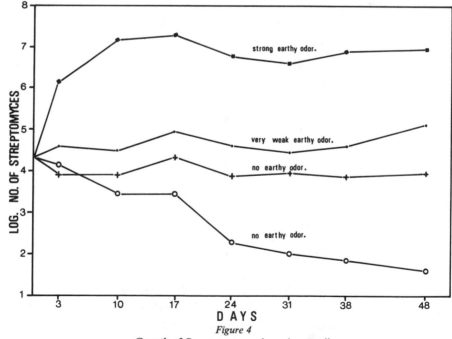

Figure 4

Growth of *Streptomyces* sp. in various media

■ 1% bottom mud in lake water (sterilized)   • lake water (sterilized)
+ 1% bottom mud in lake water (unsterilized)   ○ lake water (unsterilized)

It was only natural that, with the manifestation of an earthy-musty odor and taste in our reservoirs, our search was directed toward *Actinomycetes*.

Using methods described by Silvey, we isolated from the reservoir mud an actinomycete of the genus *Streptomyces* which produces an earthy odor in culture media.

Growth experiments were carried out with species of *Streptomyces* most commonly isolated from reservoir bottom; these species showed good growth and sporulation when supplied with nutrients available under natural conditions in the reservoirs. Good growth was possible only without competition from other microorganisms. In all cases, with unsterilized substrate, no increase in numbers of *Actinomycetes,* no sporulation and no production of an earthy musty odor occurred. Several growth experiments with *Streptomyces* sp. from reservoirs are summarized in Figure 4.

Since the spring of 1967, quantitative determinations of *Streptomyces* isolated from the bottom mud of the reservoirs have been made. A plating method on

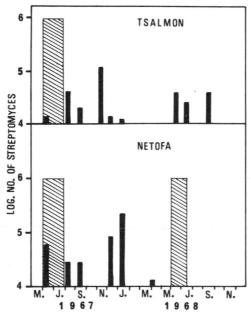

Figure 5
Actinomycetes and taste and odor in Tsalmon
and Netofa reservoirs. The hatched area
represents the period of taste and odor

a medium described by Silvey was used, and the number of organisms counted (more accurately the number of propagules of the organisms, both conidia and hyphal fragments) was related to unit of dry weight of bottom matter. The results are presented in Figure 5.

OSCILLATORIA

ASCHNER et al. (1967) reported an earthy taste in fish, caused by the benthic blue-green alga *O. tenuis*. They also showed the potential of this algal group to affect the taste and odor of water in a natural environment.

Similar findings were made earlier by CORNELIUS and BANDT (1933) in Germany, and by USPENSKAYA (1954) in Russia. This induced us to pay attention to the benthic algal population in the reservoirs.

Large populations of *Oscillatoria* sp. were present at the bottom of the INWS reservoirs in all cases of taste and odor. The dominant species resembles *O. chalybea*, although it differs in some aspects from the strains of the latter species received from the Cambridge Culture Collection. Our species produces a strong musty odor when grown in culture.

Our research was aimed at gaining an understanding of the ecological conditions which enable development of this alga. The investigation was conducted simultaneously *in situ* at the reservoirs, and in a simulated environment created in aquariums.

The laboratory work was performed in transparent plastic aquariums of dimensions $42 \times 17 \times 30$ cm. A layer of reservoir sediment 3–4 cm thick was introduced into each aquarium and overlain by 21 cm of reservoir water (about 15 liters.) From each aquarium water samples were taken periodically by means of a syphon fixed 1.5 cm above the surface of the sediment layer. Dissolved oxygen (DO) was determined using the Winkler Method as described in STANDARD METHODS FOR THE EXAMINATION OF WATER AND WASTEWATER (1965).

Analysis of the sediments was usually performed at the beginning and end of each experiment. Organic matter, Kjeldahl nitrogen and phosphate were determined according to STANDARD METHODS (1965). Sulfide was determined by iodometric titration after fixation by zinc-acetate, dehydration and liberation by H_2SO_4.

Planktonic and benthic flora were determined only semiquantitatively, as there was difficulty in quantitative determination of the filamentous *Oscillatoria*.

From the reservoirs, water samples were taken by a Kemmerer sampler.

Samples taken near the bottom represent a water layer 0 to 40 cm above the sediment and not the layer directly in contact with it.

Bottom samples were collected in a sack attached to a scraper. The Ekman dredge could not be used owing to the irregular surface of the gravel bottom.

DEVELOPMENT OF OSCILLATORIA IN THE BENTHOS

The experiment was carried out in four aquariums. Bottom mud was collected from the settling reservoir. It contained 17.4% organic matter, 0.99% N (Kjeldahl), 0.27% PO_4 and 0.18% S^{-2} (H_2S). The temperature of the water in the aquariums was 24–26°C and there was constant illumination (250 lux).

A few hours after the experiment was set up, the concentration of DO 1.5 cm above the sediments decreased to 20% of saturation, and after an additional 5 days the oxygen disappeared completely (see Figure 6). Total anaerobiosis prevailed for 5 days and then for 10–12 days there was very low DO concentration (less than 10% saturation). This last period was characterized by appearance of *Beggiatoa alba* which covered the sediment with a dense growth.

A gradual increase in the DO level was noted 24–28 days after the inception of the experiment, *O. chalybea* started to appear, and this alga rapidly expanded and became the dominant organism on the bottom. We also found *O. chalybea* growth on walls of the container, but not in the plankton. During this period the concentration of DO was 30–40% of saturation. The water had an earthy-musty odor and taste.

Tests for *Actinomycetes* at this time did not show increase in their numbers.

As the experiment progressed, the number of green algae and diatoms gradually increased, accompanied by a rise in the DO. Fifty-five days after the start of the experiment, the level of DO was about 70% of saturation, with only a few filaments of *Oscillatoria* still present. The upper layer of the mud (1–3 mm thick) was oxidized and changed in color from black to gray-brown, but below this layer the black reduced material remained unchanged. There was no noticeable musty odor.

The aquariums were left undisturbed for a further 110 days and the water was then replaced by fresh reservoir water (poor in algae) and the sediment thoroughly mixed. During the following days there was a sharp drop in DO, followed by reappearance of *O. chalybea,* and the musty odor.

Similar experiments were performed at different temperatures (range 16–26°C) and in all cases the same trend could be observed.

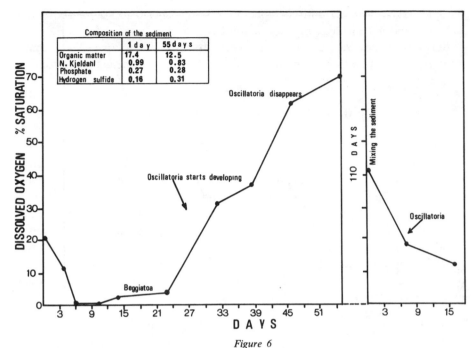

Figure 6
Change in dissolved oxygen in the aquarium containing Netofa sediment

INFLUENCE OF SUBSTRATE ON
DEVELOPMENT OF OSCILLATORIA

In this experiment sediments from the Tsalmon reservoir and the Netofa settling basin were compared as to their ability to support development of benthic *Oscillatoria*. The mud was collected during the month of October. At this season, the sediments of Tsalmon were partly oxidized, but those from the settling basin were still in a reduced state (due to larger accumulation of organic matter there). Some parameters of the bottom mud are compared below:

	Organic matter	Kjeldahl N	PO_4	S^{-2} as (H_2S)
Tsalmon sediment	14.7%	1.28%	0.5%	0.07%
Netofa sediment	19.5%	1.60%	0.42%	0.16%

The changes in dissolved oxygen with time are presented in Figure 7. In the aquariums with settling reservoir mud the process was similar to that in the pre-

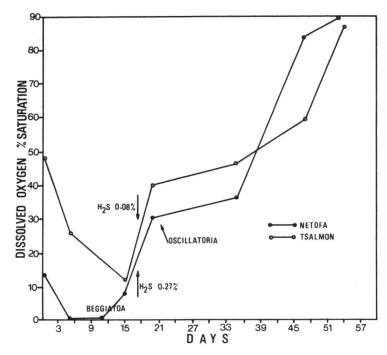

Figure 7
Change in dissolved oxygen in aquariums containing sediments from the
Netofa and Tsalmon reservoirs

viously described experiment. In containers with partly oxidized sediments from
Tsalmon, the oxygen drop was less pronounced, total anaerobiosis was not
reached, and there was no development of either *Beggiatoa* or *Oscillatoria*.

OXYGEN MANAGEMENT AND OSCILLATORIA
IN THE BENTHOS

In this series of experiments, the effects of aeration and illumination were
tested. Eight aquariums with Netofa settling basin mud were set up as described
previously. Two containers were constantly aerated by bubbling air. Two containers received higher light intensity (500 lux). The remaining containers served
as a control. Aeration of the aquariums maintained the dissolved oxygen at a

relatively high level (see Figure 8). No macroscopically visible growth of *O. chalybea* on the surface of the sediment was detected in the containers treated in this manner, but a few filaments were present immediately below the surface. No musty odor was detected in these aquariums.

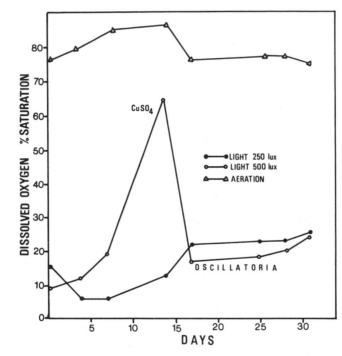

Figure 8
Influence of light and aeration on dissolved oxygen in
aquariums containing sediment from Netofa

In containers which received stronger illumination there was a noticeable growth of green algae and diatoms, and the concentration of DO was higher than in the control. Application of $CuSO_4$ (10 mg/l) killed this algal population. Subsequently, there was a sharp drop in DO followed by development of *Oscillatoria* (see Figure 8).

DEVELOPMENT OF O. CHALYBEA ON THE
BOTTOM OF TSALMON RESERVOIR

Because of difficulties in sampling, we were not able to follow the changes at the bottom of reservoirs as effectively as in the aquariums, with a single exception. In 1968, the bottom of the Tsalmon reservoir was covered by a relatively thick layer of mud and there was no growth of submerged plants, which usually interfered with sampling. The changes in dissolved oxygen, organic matter and sulfide are presented in Figure 9. In June, the DO dropped rather

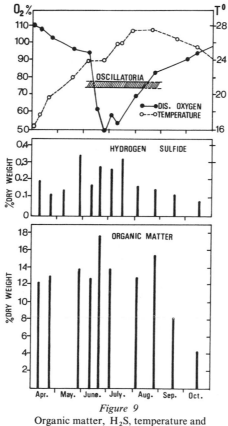

Figure 9

Organic matter, H_2S, temperature and
dissolved oxygen at the bottom of the
Tsalmon reservoir during summer 1968

suddenly (from above 90% saturation to about 50% saturation). At the same time, there was an increase in sulfide concentration (from about 0.1% to about 0.3% of dry weight of mud), accompanied by a fairly heavy growth of *O. chalybea.* For reasons not yet understood, this bloom of *Oscillatoria* had only a very slight effect on the taste and odor of the water.

In August we noted an increase in DO as well as a drop in sulfide, and *O. chalybea* disappeared gradually.

When, in October, the Tsalmon reservoir was drained and dried, the upper-most layer of sediment (1–2 mm thick) appeared oxidized and brown-gray in color. The sediment (20–30 mm thick) below the surface was still in a reduced state, black and rich in sulfides. This situation resembled that described previously in the aquariums.

DISCUSSION

When the taste and odor nuisance appeared for the first time in the INWS reservoirs, the suspected organisms were *Actinomycetes.*

Determinations of *Actinomycetes* in the reservoirs during the period 1967–68 did not show any correlation between the quantity of these organisms and taste and odor in water (Figure 5). Most of the cases of taste and odor caused by *Actinomycetes* were reported from rivers and reservoirs with an earth floor and large fluctuations of water level. The majority of odor-producing species of *Actinomycetes* are aerobic, soil-dwelling organisms, and in certain instances cited in the literature the taste-and-odor substances were apparently produced on the banks of rivers and reservoirs and washed into the water (ADAMS, 1929; ISSATCHENKO and EGOROVA, 1944). Our reservoirs have concrete walls; there is little fluctuation in water level and no drainage from surrounding areas occurred during the period of investigation. Laboratory investigations with odor-producing strains of *Actinomycetes* isolated from the reservoirs under simulated reservoir conditions did not indicate any noticeable effect of these organisms on the water quality.

On the other hand, in all cases of taste and odor in our reservoirs, large populations of *Oscillatoria* were present at the bottom of the reservoirs. These organisms also made their appearance in the experimentally prepared reservoir environment and produced under these conditions a very definite typical earthy-musty taste and odor in the water. It should be noted that in certain instances, their presence was not accompanied by any noticeable taste and odor in water.

The dependency between development of *Oscillatoria* and the state of oxidation of the sediment became evident when the reduced sediment from Netofa and the partially oxidized one from Tsalmon were compared (Figure 7). When a decrease in oxygen was prevented, either by aeration or by high photosynthetic activity, the necessary environment was not produced and there was no growth of *Oscillatoria*.

This information from laboratory experiments helped us understand the phenomenon of taste and odor in reservoirs. During the spring, heavy loads of organic matter (mostly cells of *Peridinium*) arrive from Lake Kinneret, settle in the reservoirs and decompose there. With the increase in temperature, there is an acceleration in degradation of this organic matter and the demand for oxygen is higher than its supply.

At the mud-water interface, a zone low in DO is formed. *Oscillatoria* develop and taste and odor substances are produced and released. During the following weeks the upper layer is oxidized, the higher level of DO is restored and, with the changes in the environment, the population of nuisance-causing *Oscillatoria* is reduced.

The dependence of *Oscillatoria* blooms on the state of oxidation (concentration of dissolved oxygen) is a well-known phenomenon. LUND (1959) reports blooms of *O. agardhii* in the metalimnion of lakes. Blooms of *Oscillatoria* in layers poor in oxygen were also described by FINDENEGG (1965) and ELSTER (1965). TASH (1967) suggests that development of *O. redecii* in the lower layers of lakes is due to reducing conditions and prevalent H_2S. USPENSKAYA (1954), who studied taste and odor production by *O. splendida* on the bottom of water bodies, noted that the growth of the alga varied with the organic contents of the mud and that the more oxidizable the mud, the stronger was the taste imparted to the water. Our strain of *O. chalybea* can be added to the above-mentioned species as an organism requiring a specific state of oxidation for development in a natural environment, although in the laboratory it can exist in partly purified culture without this specific condition (ASCHNER and CHORIN-KIRSCH, 1968). Studies on physiology of *O. chalybea* are necessary in order to understand the exact relationship between redox potential and growth of the alga.

In certain cases, we observed growth of *O. chalybea* in the laboratory and in nature without any accompanying noticeable taste and odor in the water. The reason for the absence of odor is unknown, and the production and mechanism of release of the odorous substances in water should be investigated.

CONCLUSIONS

From the investigations described we conclude that a blue-green alga labeled by us as *Oscillatoria chalybea* is the principal causative agent of the earthy-musty taste and odor in the reservoirs of the Israel National Water System. *Actinomycetes* of the genus *Streptomyces* do not seem to affect the water quality under the conditions prevailing in these reservoirs. They may, however, make a minor contribution to the taste and odor compounds released into the water.

There is a relationship between concentration of dissolved oxygen, sulfide level, and development of *Oscillatoria chalybea*. In our reservoirs the conditions supporting the growth of this benthic alga are apparently created by increased rate of decomposition of organic matter brought about by the temperature rise during late spring and early summer.

REFERENCES

ADAMS, B.A. (1929): "Odors in the water of Nile River," *Wat. & Wat. Eng.*, **31**: 309–314.

ASCHNER, M. and CHORIN-KIRSCH, I. (1968): "The Influence of *Oscillatoria* on taste and odor in water," Preliminary Report, May 1968 (In Hebrew).

ASCHNER, M., LEVENTER, H. and CHORIN-KIRSCH, I. (1967): "Off flavour in carp from fishponds in the coastal plain and the Galil," *Bull. Fish. Cult. Israel*, **19**: 23–25.

CORNELIUS, W.O. and BANDT, J.H. (1933): "Fischereischädigungen durch starke Vermehrung gewisser pflanzlicher Planktonen insbesondere Geschmacks-Beeinflussung der Fische durch Oscillatorien," *Zeitschrift für Fischerei und deren Hilfswissenschaften*.

ELSTER, J.H. (1965): "Absolute and relative assimilation rates in relation to phytoplankton population." In C.R. Goldman (ed.) *Primary Productivity in Aquatic Environments*, Mem. Inst. Ital. Idrobiol., 18 Suppl., pp. 79–103. University of California Press, Berkeley.

FINDENEGG, L. (1965): "Factors controlling primary productivity, especially with regard to water replenishment stratification and mixing," In C.R. Goldman (ed.) *Primary Productivity in Aquatic Environments*, Mem. Inst. Ital. Idrobiol., 18 Suppl., pp. 105–121, University of California Press, Berkeley.

ISSATCHENKO, B. and EGOROVA, A. (1944): "*Actinomycetes* in reservoirs as one of the causes responsible for the earthy smell of their waters," *Mikrobiologiya*, **13**: 224–230.

LUND, J.W.G. (1959): "Buoyancy in relation to the ecology of the freshwater phytoplankton," *Br. Phycol. Bul.*, No. 7, p. 17.

MORRIS, R.L. (1962): "*Actinomycetes* studied as taste and odor cause," *Wat. Sew. Works,* **109**:76–77.

ROMANO, A.H. and SAFFERMAN, R.S. (1963): "Studies on *Actinomycetes* and their odors," *Journ. A.W.W.A.,* **55**:169–176.

SAFFERMAN, S.R., ROSEN, A.A., MASHNI, I.C. and MORRIS, E.M. (1967): "Earthy-smelling substance from a blue-green alga," *Environ. Science and Technology,* **1**:429–430.

SILVEY, J.K.G. and ROACH, A.W. (1953): "*Actinomycetes* in the Oklahoma City water supply," *Journ. A.W.W.A.,* **45**:409–416.

SILVEY, J.K.G., RUSSEL, J.C., REDDEN, D.R. and McCORMICK, W.C. (1950): "Actinomycetes and common tastes and odors," *Journ. A.W.W.A.,* **42**:1018–1026.

STANDARD METHODS FOR THE EXAMINATION OF WATER AND WASTEWATER, A.P.H.A., A.W.W.A. & W.P.C.F., New York (12th ed. 1965).

TASH, C.J. (1967): "Environmental requirements of blue-green algae," U.S. Department of Interior, Pacific Northwest Water Lab., Corvallis, Oregon.

USPENSKAYA, V.I. (1954): "Physiology of nutrition in *Oscillatoria splendida* and *O. agardhii* as related to formation and accumulation of taste and odor in water," *Mikrobiologiya,* **22**:669.

Chlorination as a Means of

Controlling Earthy Odors in Reservoirs

M. Rebhun, M.A. Fox and J.B. Sless

Increasing exploitation of all available water supplies as necessitated by agricultural, industrial and urban requirements, poses problems of water quality which are now recognizable the world over.

Surface waters stored in reservoirs are particularly vulnerable to the appearance of undesirable tastes and odors which are often directly attributable to aquatic microorganisms (WHIPPLE, 1927; PALMER, 1959).

In the past, much empirical knowledge has been accumulated on ways of combating tastes and odors, and chlorination has always been one of the important means at our disposal for their control (MORRIS, 1966; RYCKMAN and GRIGOROPOULOS, 1961).

The appearance of earthy odors in the waters of rivers, reservoirs and other bodies of water has been attributed to the presence of various microorganisms, including species of *Actinomycetes* (SILVEY and ROACH, 1959) and *Oscillatoria* (SKASOVSKII et al., 1955). Species of *Oscillatoria* have also been shown to be the cause of an earthy taint in fish (ASCHNER et al., 1967) and *O. chalybea* has been identified as the source of the earthy odor which has appeared from time to time in the water of Israel's National Water System (INWS) (LEVENTER, 1968).

39

The action of chlorine on earthy odors due to *Oscillatoria* and *Actinomycetes* has been variously reported, but where the measurements of the Threshold Odor Number (TON) were made before and after chlorination, the effectiveness of chlorine in destroying the earthy odors was not always apparent (ROMANO and SAFFERMAN, 1963; MORRIS et al., 1963).

The present study deals with the effect of chlorine on the earthy odors occasionally present in the INWS. The investigation was carried out in two phases. In the first stage the effect of chlorination on samples of water from the reservoirs of the INWS was studied in order to obtain information on the changes in Threshold Odor brought about by chlorination of natural waters. In the second stage a model system was devised to provide information on the effect of chlorine on the odorant produced by a species of *Oscillatoria*.

All the determinations of chlorine demand of samples were made in accordance with Standard Methods (12th Edition), as were the measurements of TON.

Chlorination of reservoir waters possessing a typical earthy odor invariably brought about a reduction of the odor. This reduction was dependent on the dose and contact time but was only partial, inasmuch as that after the break

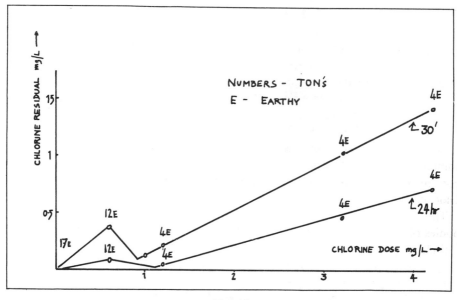

Figure 1
Effect of chlorine dose and contact time on TON of water from the Israel National Water System

point was reached no further reduction in the residual (earthy) odor was achieved, either by increasing the dose or extending the contact time.

A typical case is shown in Figure 1.

It will be noted that the earthy odor is present after chlorination to break point and beyond, with no subsequent decrease on continued contact up to 24 hours. However, a definite improvement with respect to the odor level was achieved, in this case a reduction from 17 to 4.

During the manifestation of earthy odors in March–July 1967, experiments on chlorination of the water from the Netofa reservoir at various TON levels showed that break-point chlorination (0.2 mg/l free residual) always reduced the TON level, but some residual (earthy) odor always remained.

On the occasion of a mixed odor (grassy-spicy) being present in the water,

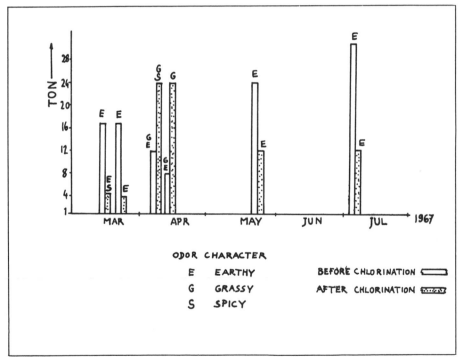

Figure 2

Threshold Odor Numbers of water from Netofa reservoir before and after chlorination
(March—July 1967)

chlorination to break point caused an increase in the TON of the water. However, it must be emphasized that such a phenomenon was never observed when the earthy odor alone was present.

Fig. 2 shows typical results from this period.

It will be noted that there is a tendency for the "residual odor" to be higher when the initial TON is higher.

In order to investigate more fully the effect of chlorination on the earthy odor, it was decided to exploit the odor-producing property of one of the *Oscillatoriae* and a model odor generator was assembled.

In this odor generator (Figure 3) the organism (*O. prolifica,* kindly supplied by Prof. M. Aschner, Department of Food and Biotechnology, Technion–Israel

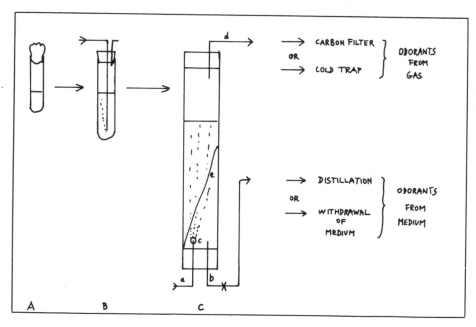

Figure 3

Scheme for culture of *Oscillatoria prolifica* and recovery of odorants

A represents the initial propagation of the organism in 10 ml volume

B represents the growths of inoculum for the column in 25 ml volume of medium through which air containing 5 % v/v of CO_2 is bubbled

C represents the "odor generator" consisting of a Pyrex column (4 cm in diameter × 150 cm in length) supplied with a diffusing stone (c); a gas mixture inlet (a) and outlet (d); an outlet tap for withdrawal of medium (b); glass rods for support of organism (e)

Institute of Technology) was cultivated in such a way that quantities of odorant could be withdrawn and applied to water to give samples of varying levels of TON, which could then be used for investigating the effect of chlorine on the earthy odor.

Results obtained by chlorinating samples of different initial TON's showed that the odor was always reduced by chlorination. The reduction achieved always reached an asymptotic value as shown in Figure 4.

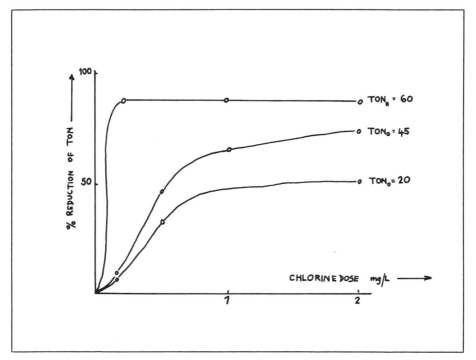

Figure 4
Effect of chlorination on odor of *O. prolifica* at various odor levels

In the range of initial TON values tested (from TON 60 to TON 20) the asymptotic value reached after chlorination was found to be proportional to the initial TON value of the sample prior to chlorine treatment; this is shown in Figure 5.

The great similarity of the results obtained by chlorination of natural waters having the earthy odor due to *O. chalybea* and by chlorination of the odorant produced in a model system by *O. prolifica* is very encouraging and implies that valid conclusions as to the use of chlorine in the field can be drawn from consideration of the results obtained from the model.

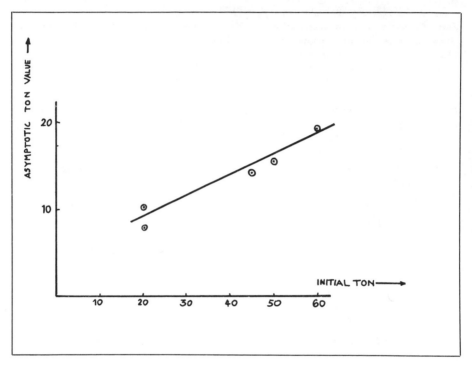

Figure 5
Asymptotic values of TON after chlorination of *O. prolifica* odorant as a function of initial TON's

The results obtained from the model system support the conclusion that chlorination can only ameliorate but not eliminate the earthy odor due to the presence of *Oscillatoria* in the waters of the INWS reservoirs, and that this reduction in odor is conditional on the initial TON level. However, the results obtained by chlorination are of significance when we consider that the reduction of TON achieved makes possible the consideration of other methods of control. For example, lowering of the TON by chlorination can often reach a degree where further reduction to an acceptable level can be obtained by simple dilution with water from another source.

REFERENCES

ASCHNER, M., LEVENTER, H. and CHORIN-KIRSCH, I. (1967): "Off-flavor in carp from fish ponds in the Coastal Plain and the Galil," *Bull. Fish. Cult. Israel,* **19**, 23.

LEVENTER, H. (1968): "Some characteristics of the operational reservoirs in the Israel National Water System," Paper presented at 17th Limn. Cong., Jerusalem.

MORRIS, J.C. (1966): "The future of chlorination," *J. Am. Wat. WKS. Ass.,* **58**, 1475.

MORRIS, R.L. et al. (1963): "Chemical aspects of *Actinomycete* metabolites as contributors of tastes and odors," *J. Am. Wat. WKS. Ass.,* **55**, 1380.

PALMER, C.M. (1959): "Algae in water supplies," *P.H.S. Publication No. 657.*

ROMANO, A.H. and SAFFERMAN, R.S. (1963): "Studies on *Actinomycetes* and their odors," *J. Am. Wat. WKS. Ass.,* **55**, 169.

RYCKMAN, D.W. and GRIGOROPOULOS, S.G. (1961): "The effect of chlorine and chlorine oxide on taste- and odor-causing substances in waters," Washington U., St. Louis.

SILVEY, J.K.G. and ROACH, A.W. (1959): "The laboratory culture of taste- and odor-producing aquatic *Actinomycetes,*" *J. Am. Wat. WKS. Ass.,* **51**, 20.

SKASOVSKII, S.N. et. al. (1955): *Trudy vsesoyuz. gidrobiol. obshch.,* **6**, 23 (quoted in *International Water Supply Association, Proceedings of the 4th Congress,* Brussels, 1958).

WHIPPLE, G.C. (1927): *Microscopy of Drinking Water,* 4th edition, John Wiley & Sons, N.Y.

Detection and Control

of Enteroviruses

in the Water Environment *

Hillel I. Shuval

INTRODUCTION

With the progress in the field of water purification in the more advanced countries of the world, and the resulting reduction or elimination of water-borne diseases, a well-earned feeling of confidence and security has been achieved. However, the massive water-borne outbreak of viral hepatitis that occurred in Delhi in 1955 (DENNIS, 1959) provided grounds for some second thoughts as to the effectiveness of standard water purification processes. It appears that in this case the treated water met the accepted chlorination and coliform bacteria standards, but that viruses were able to pass through the treatment plant when the latter was challenged by heavily polluted raw water.

An eminent panel of public health experts (U.S. DEPARTMENT OF HEALTH, EDUCATION AND WELFARE, 1962) summarized the situation as follows: "More

* The work reported on here was carried out under research agreement BSS-CDC-IS-10 of the Department of Health, Education and Welfare, as well as under research grants from Tahal–Water Planning for Israel and the Oceanographic and Limnological Research Co. of Israel.

than 70 viruses have been detected in human feces. All may be present in sewage. Viruses pass through sewage treatment plants, persist in contaminated waters, and may penetrate the water treatment plants. Numerous outbreaks of infectious hepatitis have been traced to contaminated drinking water. The occurrence of such incidents appears to be increasing." A later report (PRESIDENT'S SCIENCE ADVISORY COMMITTEE, 1965) stated that "The capability of present water pollution control technology is clearly inadequate as far as viruses are concerned."

This situation indicates the need for intensive study of all aspects of the detection and control of pathogenic viruses in the water environment. Engineers and scientists in the field of water quality control and pollution prevention can no longer rely solely on such standard and generally accepted parameters of microbial pollution as coliform bacteria, since there is now ample evidence that these indicator organisms can, under certain circumstances, be more sensitive to treatment processes or natural inactivation factors than some of the more resistant pathogenic enteroviruses (SHUVAL et al., 1967a).

There is a need to develop new and sensitive tools to detect small numbers of enteroviruses in large volumes of water in order to monitor drinking water supplies. Likewise it is imperative to re-evaluate the various water and wastewater treatment systems to determine their virus removal efficiency.

This paper will present some of the major findings of our studies on the detection and control of enteroviruses in the water environment. Included are a new method developed to concentrate and detect viruses in water; a survey of the levels of enteroviruses in water and wastewater in various communities; studies in which various wastewater treatment processes, including stabilization ponds, biological filtration and chlorination, have been evaluated for their virus removal efficiency; and the results of preliminary investigations of the dispersion and inactivation of viruses in seawater.

THE PHASE-SEPARATION METHOD FOR DETECTING VIRUSES IN WATER AND WASTEWATER

The Phase-Separation (PS) method for concentrating and detecting viruses in water was initially reported on at the Symposium on the Transmission of Viruses by the Water Route in Cincinnati in 1965 (SHUVAL et al., 1967b), while a full evaluation of the method as further developed and refined has subsequently been published (SHUVAL et al., 1969).

The method, which is described in full in Appendix I, is simple and inexpensive.

It involves adding appropriate chemicals (sodium dextran sulfate, polyethylene glycol and sodium chloride) to the water sample to be tested, which is then placed in a separatory funnel and held at 4°C overnight. The small bottom phase formed is drained off together with the interphase. This bottom phase has a volume of about 1/200 of the original water sample and has been shown to contain essentially all of the viruses present in the water sample. For further concentration, the concentrate is treated with sodium chloride, and once again a two-phase system is formed on standing for about 12–24 hours at 4°C. This time the viruses are concentrated in the small upper phase. By this two-step procedure it is possible to concentrate the viruses in a water sample by a factor of about 500.

The concentrate is then assayed for viruses by the plaque-forming technique (in disposable plastic petri dishes, on primary rhesus kidney cell (RKC) monolayers), with the results reported as Plaque-Forming Units (PFU) per liter of water tested. An alternative method of assaying the viruses in the concentrate, to be preferred when expected virus concentrations are very low, is to seed 1–2 ml of the concentrate in each of a series of five tissue culture bottles (milk dilution bottles). Bottles showing cytopathogenic effect (CPE) within 14 days are considered as presumptive positives for enterovirus, and the numerical virus concentration can be reported in a manner similar to the "most probable number" (MPN) commonly used in testing for coliform organisms.

In many instances water quality control laboratories will not be able to carry out independent virological assay work. However, with the PS method it is possible to freeze the concentrated sample at −20°C for later shipment to a specialized virus laboratory which can carry out the quantitative virus assay of the sample as well as identify any virus strains isolated.

Extensive laboratory and field testing of the PS method has shown it can effectively concentrate viruses in water and wastewater samples by a factor of 500 and that as few as one or two virus infectious units can be detected in one liter of water with about 85% reliability. For practical purposes, it is now possible to assay a 5-liter water sample and determine whether viruses are present in it.

Although the optimum virus monitoring method should be able to assay tens or even hundreds of liters of water for the presence of viruses, it is felt that the PS method can serve a useful purpose in initiating the routine virus monitoring of potable water supplies, since it is simple and inexpensive and can thus be employed by most routine water quality control laboratories. This would be particularly true if arrangements can be made with regional or national virological laboratories to assay the frozen concentrated samples sent in from local laboratories.

ENTEROVIRUS CONCENTRATIONS IN SEWAGE

In the absence of quantitative methods for evaluating the concentration of viruses in water and sewage, a number of authors have made estimates based on information from various experimental sources. In one such estimate it is assumed that the initial concentration of enteroviruses in raw wastewater varies between 20 and 700 PFU/100 ml, with considerable seasonal variation, while the concentration of viruses in polluted rivers and streams is taken to be lower by a factor of one hundred (CLARKE et al., 1964).

Studies carried out in Israel using the PS method have provided a preliminary picture of the concentrations of enteroviruses in wastewater from different communities as well as in surface water systems exposed to contamination. These findings tend to confirm the earlier estimates.

Table 1. Enteroviruses in raw sewage samples from
two neighborhoods in Jerusalem

Date	Katamon PFU/l	Rassco PFU/l
20.4.67	65	*
7.5.67	84	*
18.6.67	1165	9
7.9.67	109	104
25.9.67	682	*
12.10.67	119	216
18.8.68	4185	416
25.6.68	1213	28
2.7.68	4035	152
9.7.68	783	23
25.7.68	50	91
31.7.68	3375	101
7.8.68	101	339
14.8.68	—	26
27.8.68	7349	3159
4.9.68	1844	2977
	Av. 1677	Av. 480

* These samples produced no plaques but did produce CPE on multiple passages.

Table 1 shows the concentration of enteroviruses in raw sewage samples from two neighborhoods in Jerusalem, of differing socioeconomic levels, during the period April 1967–September 1968. It is noted that the enterovirus concentrations in the raw sewage samples from the Katamon area average 1,677 PFU/l, with a high of 7,349 PFU/l, while those of the Rassco area for the same period average 480 PFU/l, with a maximum of 3,159 PFU/l. The socioeconomic level in the Rassco area is considerably higher than that of the Katamon area.

Table 2. Enteroviruses in raw sewage samples from the Reading pumping station, Tel Aviv

Date	Viruses PFU/l
25.4.68	91
5.6.68	1094
12.6.68	280
26.6.68	371
3.7.68	476
17.7.68	367
14.8.68	1711
21.8.68	342
28.8.68	236
10.9.68	522
16.9.68	1055
10.10.68	779
17.10.68	392
24.10.68	1493
6.11.68	152
12.11.68	889
19.11.68	457
	Av. 663.5

Table 2 shows the enterovirus levels detected in raw sewage samples taken from the main pumping station at Reading in Tel Aviv during the period April to November 1968. The average enterovirus concentration was 663.5 PFU/l.

Table 3 shows the concentration of enteroviruses in the raw sewage of Kiryat Shmoneh in the Upper Galilee. This town, with a population of 18,000, disposes of its raw sewage to a drainage ditch which discharges into the Jordan River. During the period under study, from November 1968 to April 1969, the average virus concentration was 1,572 PFU/l, with a maximum of 11,184 PFU/l.

Table 3. Enteroviruses in raw sewage samples from Kiryat Shmoneh

Date	Viruses PFU/l
11.2.68	5
3.4.68	162
29.4.68	1327
26.5.68	11,184
30.12.68	614
13.1.69	1175
17.2.69	135
4.3.69	183
17.3.69	1292
31.3.69	652
21.4.69	565
	Av. 1572

Table 4 shows the concentration of enteroviruses in the raw sewage of the city of Tiberias (population 25,000) on the shores of Lake Kinneret. The average virus concentration was 1,135 PFU/l, with a range of 16–7,546 PFU/l.

Table 4. Enteroviruses in raw sewage samples from Tiberias

Date	Viruses PFU/l
5.5.68	114
9.6.68	1996
18.12.68	268
1.1.69	7546
13.1.69	161
3.2.69	362
17.2.69	1413
4.3.69	184
17.3.69	426
31.3.69	16
21.4.69	1269
	Av. 1135

From this survey of the enterovirus levels in raw sewage samples in a number of communities in Israel over a period of about one year, it appears that with the PS method it is possible to detect viruses in every case and that the average virus concentration is 1,050 PFU/l. No clear seasonal variations in enterovirus levels in raw sewage was evident. Parallel bacteriological tests during the same period indicate that the coliform counts of raw sewage average about $10^9/100$ ml. This indicates an enterovirus-to-coliform ratio in Israel raw sewage of roughly $1:10,000,000$, or about $1:1,000,000$ based on the maximum virus concentrations detected.

This ratio, which is much larger than the theoretical result of $1:65,000$ derived earlier (CLARKE et al., 1964), is based on over 70 quantitative virus assays and represents an actual field determination of this parameter.

In the course of this survey, hundreds of virus strains isolated were typed. All three types of poliovirus were detected, including wild and vaccine strains. In addition, echovirus and coxsackievirus strains were identified. As many as four different virus types were isolated from a single sewage sample.

ENTEROVIRUS CONCENTRATIONS IN WATER

Numerous water samples were assayed for viruses using the two-stage PS method. These included water supplies for human consumption as well as water from streams and rivers exposed to known sources of fecal contamination.

Some 70 samples of domestic water supplies were tested for viruses. These included samples from Jerusalem, Kiryat Shmoneh, Tiberias, the National Water Carrier, Petah Tiqwa and a number of small agricultural settlements. Only two samples proved to be positive for enteroviruses. Both samples were taken from the same municipal well in Petah Tiqwa, which was under suspicion by the health authorities as a possible common source of a localized infectious hepatitis epidemic. Bacteriologic tests confirmed that the well was contaminated with coliform organisms. Chemical tests also indicated a high concentration of nitrates, further confirming the hypothesis that the well was contaminated with sewage. The virus concentrations detected in the water were 7.2 PFU/l in one sample and 4.0 PFU/l in the second. The virus strains isolated were later identified as poliovirus type 1. To the best of our knowledge, this is the first recorded instance of the isolation of enteroviruses from a municipal water supply, under surveillance in a suspected common-source epidemic of infectious hepatitis. Although the evidence in this case is at best circumstantial, it does demonstrate the potential usefulness of the PS method in investigating virus epidemics suspected of being of a common-source water-borne type.

A series of water samples taken at various points along the Jordan River were also tested for the presence of enteroviruses during 1968 and 1969. These samples were taken at varying distances downstream from the main source of fecal contamination which is the inflow of raw sewage from the town of Kiryat Shmoneh. Of the 34 river samples tested, enteroviruses were detected in only three cases (28 PFU/l, 1.4 PFU/l and 1 PFU/l). It is interesting to note that the highest concentration of enteroviruses in the Jordan River water, at a point some 25 km downstream from the primary source of contamination, was detected on the same day that the highest concentration of enteroviruses was found in the raw sewage of Kiryat Shmoneh (11,184 PFU/l).

In another series of tests, enteroviruses were detected in one out of three samples taken from the Soreq stream. This heavily polluted stream carries the major portion of the untreated sewage of Jerusalem, with only minimal dilution. The sampling point was about 30 km downstream from Jerusalem. The stream is very sluggish and in places flows through large swampy areas. A rough estimate showed that the time of flow from the point of entry of fresh sewage to the point of sampling was about two days.

THE VIRUS REMOVAL EFFICIENCY OF WASTEWATER TREATMENT PLANTS

Two wastewater treatment plants were evaluated as to their virus removal efficiency. The first was the Mefachim stabilization ponds treating the sewage of an area in northeastern Jerusalem. This plant is made up of a series of four stabilization ponds providing about a 20-day detention period. The Biochemical Oxygen Demand (BOD) of the raw sewage has been shown to be 450, and the average BOD removal efficiency is about 80%. Coliform reductions of about 90% are obtained.

Table 5 shows the virus removal efficiency of the plant on eight different days of sampling in 1968. In three out of nine cases the removal was negative, i. e., the effluent showed higher virus concentrations than the influent. The average virus removal efficiency of the plant was 67.5%, taking the negative efficiencies as zero.

The second plant studied from May 1968 to April 1969 was the Tiberias municipal sewage treatment plant. This plant is a standard biological filter plant.

Table 5. Virus removal efficiency in the Mefachim stabilization ponds–
Jerusalem, 1968

Test No.	Virus concentration raw sewage PFU/l	Virus concentration effluent PFU/l	Virus removal efficiency %
1	1366	529	61.5
2	903	40	95.5
3	12	40	Negative
4	31	71	Negative
5	288	102	47.0
6	132	28	79.0
7	357	572	Negative
8	1185	300	75.0
9	3889	370	91.0
			Av. 67.5%

The primary sedimentation is in an Imhoff tank with the effluent passing through two biological filters in parallel. The effluent is led through a final sedimentation tank before being discharged. The BOD removal efficiency of the total plant is about 85%, with 92% removal of coliforms. Table 6 shows that the efficiency of virus removal in the Imhoff tank was negative in eight out of ten series of tests,

Table 6. Virus removal efficiency in the Tiberias biological filtration plant, 1968–1969

Test No.	Virus concentration in raw sewage PFU/l	Virus concentration in settled sewage PFU/l	Efficiency of primary sedimentation %	Virus concentration in final effluent PFU/l	Total plant efficiency %
1	114	275	Negative	103	9
2	1996	—	—	4487	Negative
3	268	1307	Negative	1286	Negative
4	7546	1200	84	1207	84
5	161	653	Negative	400	Negative
6	362	521	Negative	127	65
7	143	157	Negative	259	Negative
8	184	209	Negative	—	—
9	426	538	Negative	230	46
10	16	918	Negative	201	Negative
11	1269	551	56	858	32
					Av. 24 %

while the total plant efficiency for virus removal was negative in five out of ten tests. If the negative series are assumed to show zero efficiency, the overall average plant efficiency is calculated at 24%, i. e., an insignificant level of virus removal.

These two series of tests confirm the findings of other investigators that certain types of standard wastewater treatment plants have very low efficiencies in removing enteroviruses from sewage.

INACTIVATION OF ENTEROVIRUSES IN SEWAGE EFFLUENT BY CHLORINATION

A number of studies have pointed to the fact that certain of the enteroviruses are more resistant than coliform organisms to chlorination, both in sewage and water (CLARKE et al., 1954, SHUVAL et al., 1967a).

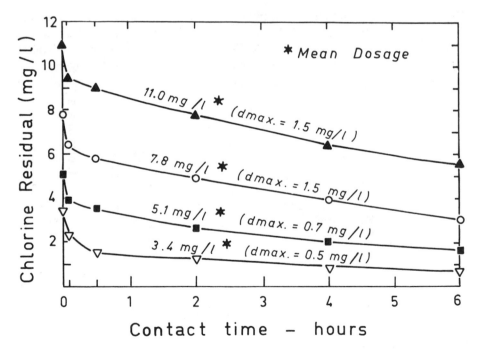

Figure 1
Chlorine residual in sewage effluent at varying contact times

In our studies we have attempted to compare the sensitivity of poliovirus, echovirus and coliforms to chlorination in sewage effluent. In these studies strains of poliovirus type 1 and echovirus type 9 were seeded into samples of effluent from the Haifa municipal high-rate biological filter, sewage treatment plant. The effluent has an average BOD of 45 mg/l, with an average of 50 mg/l of suspended solids. The pH ranged from 7.7 to 7.8 while the concentration of ammonia varied from 5 to 20 mg/l.

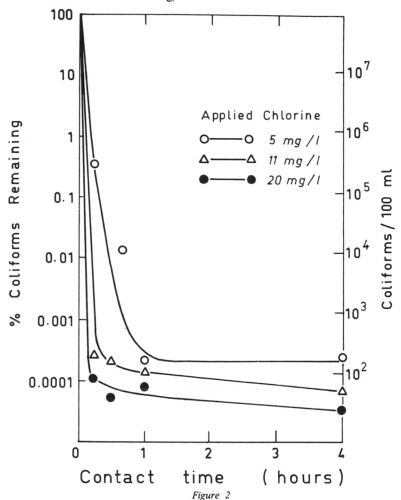

Figure 2
Inactivation of coliforms in sewage effluent at varying chlorine doses

Varying doses of chlorine were added to the samples of effluent after an appropriate virus seed was inoculated. The chlorine residuals were determined by the iodometric backtitration method (STANDARD METHODS FOR THE EXAMINATION OF WATER AND WASTEWATER, 1965).

In Figure 1 the chlorine residuals remaining in the effluent after varying contact times (up to 6 hours) are shown. Within one hour the residual was reduced by

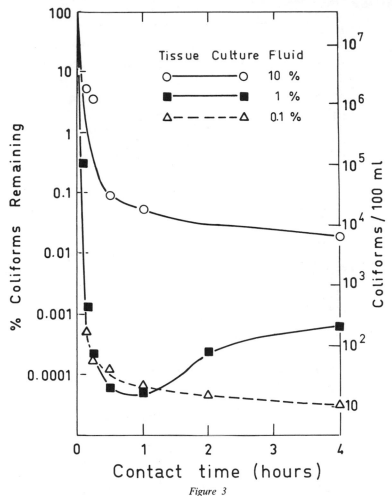

Figure 3

Inactivation of coliforms by 11 mg/l applied chlorine in sewage effluent in the presence of varying concentrations of tissue culture fluid

about 2 ppm, while in most cases the chlorine residual remaining at the end of 6 hours was between one half and one third of the original dose added. Under the conditions obtaining in these tests, it is assumed that essentially all the chlorine applied was transformed rapidly to chloramines because of the high concentration of ammonia and organic nitrogenous materials present.

Figure 2 shows the percent of coliforms remaining in the sewage effluent at varying chlorine doses. It can be seen that a five to six log reduction is achieved in one hour with applied chlorine doses of from 5–20 mg/l, the coliform levels being reduced to about 100/100 ml.

In our earlier experiments, the tissue culture fluids added together with the virus inoculum apparently interfered with the inactivation processes. In Figure 3 it can be seen that a mere three log reduction of coliforms takes place when 11 mg/l of chlorine are applied to effluent containing a 10% tissue culture fluid inoculum, while a six log reduction is obtained within one hour with 1% and 0.1% of inoculum and the same chlorine dose. The same interfering effect on poliovirus inactivation is shown in Figure 4.

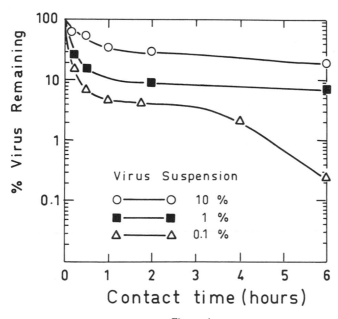

Figure 4
Inactivation of various concentrations of poliovirus suspensions
in sewage effluent treated with 11 mg/l chlorine

However, when 0.1% of concentrated poliovirus suspension was inoculated into the sewage effluent, poliovirus reductions in one hour were still very much less than the coliform reductions obtained under equivalent conditions (see Figure 5). Only about a one log reduction was obtained with 5 and 11 mg/l of chlorine, while a three log reduction was obtained with 20 mg/l of applied chlorine. Inactivation continued throughout the four-hour period of the test, reduction being improved somewhat with time.

In Figure 6 it can be seen that the ECHO 9 strain tested was inactivated more effectively than the poliovirus strain.

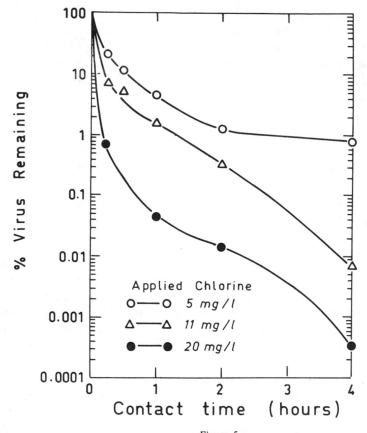

Figure 5

Inactivation of the 0.1% poliovirus suspension in sewage effluent
by various concentrations of applied chlorine

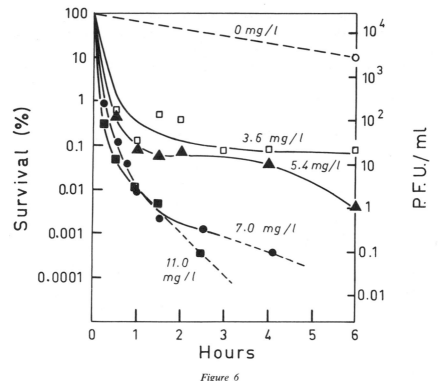

Figure 6
Survival of echovirus in sewage at varying chlorine doses

Figure 7 provides a comparison of the chlorine concentrations and contact times required to achieve a 99.9% inactivation of poliovirus, echovirus and coliforms. From this figure it can be seen that for a one-hour contact time 2 mg/l of applied chlorine are sufficient for coliforms, about 8 mg/l are needed for the echovirus, while about 20 mg/l of chlorine are required to achieve an equivalent inactivation of poliovirus. Under the conditions of this study, a chlorine dose, some ten times greater than that required for coliforms, was required for the inactivation of the poliovirus inoculum in the sewage effluent.

It can be clearly seen that usual wastewater chlorination practices are insufficient to provide effective inactivation of poliovirus, which can be considered as a model of the more resistant forms of enteric viruses. This also points out the possible dangers of a situation where coliform levels have been greatly reduced by chlorination but significant levels of enteroviruses remain.

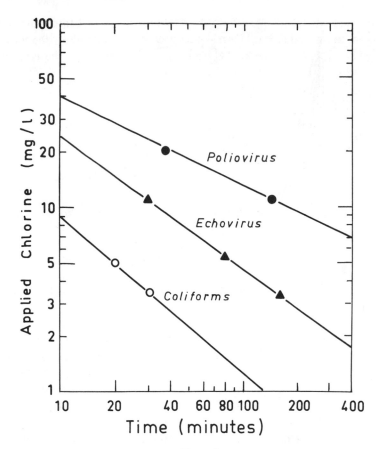

Figure 7
Concentration-time relationships for 99.9% inactivation of poliovirus,
echovirus and coliforms in sewage effluent by chlorine at 20°C

In addition to the experiments in which laboratory strains of viruses were
inoculated into sewage effluent, a number of experiments were carried out in
which the viruses naturally found in the effluent were tested by the PS method,
before and after chlorination. These tests more closely simulated true field conditions and avoided the many problems associated with inoculating higher concentrations of laboratory strains of viruses.

In these tests, with 11 mg/l of chlorine applied (Table 7), it can be seen that in
one case little virus inactivation occurred in 30 minutes while in the other an

81.5% reduction was achieved. However, after four hours of contact the viruses were reduced to an undetectable level. A conservative estimate of the virucidal efficiency of 11 mg/l of chlorine with 4 hours of contact is based on the assumption that the limit of detection of the phase separation method is 1 PFU/l. This would mean a virus reduction of something greater than 91.5% and 99.5%, respectively.

Table 7. Inactivation of natural virus flora in sewage effluent with chlorine (11 mg/l)

Exp. No.	Virus concentration in effluent PFU/l	Virus concentration after 30 min. PFU/l	Inactivation %	Virus concentration after 4 hrs. PFU/l	Inactivation %
1	12	10	16.5	<1	>91.5
2	244	45	81.5	<1	>99.5

THE DISPERSION AND INACTIVATION OF ENTEROVIRUSES IN COASTAL WATERS

The coliform index has served as an accepted parameter of pollution of coastal waters. The design of sewage outfall sewers is aimed at achieving certain coliform standards along bathing beaches (POMEROY, 1960; HARREMOES, 1966). Little attention has been paid in the past to the possible role of enteroviruses in the pollution of bathing beaches, although studies of the contamination of shellfish have pointed out that a satisfactory coliform index in seawater does not necessarily mean that the area is free of enteroviruses (METCALF et al., 1968).

A study of the dispersion and inactivation of enteroviruses in seawater was undertaken by our group in cooperation with the staff of the Ministry of Health and the Soreq Nuclear Research Center. Our earlier efforts had been limited to the study of bacterial parameters of pollution (SHUVAL et al., 1968). With the adaptation of the PS method for detecting enteroviruses in seawater samples, it was felt that a quantitative field study could be effectively carried out.

Preliminary studies initiated in the summer of 1968 demonstrated that enteroviruses could be detected routinely in seawater samples collected from a number of fixed stations marked by buoys placed at varying distances from the 880-meter-long Reading outfall sewer off the coast of Tel Aviv. Some 100,000 m^3 of sewage are discharged daily into the sea through this outfall. As shown previously in Table 2, the average virus concentration in the raw sewage at Reading is

663 PFU/l. The average virus concentration detected in the sea surface immediately above the diffusers at the end of the outfall, based on 15 samples, was 8 PFU/l. Tests using Br^{82} as a radioactive tracer, to determine the degree of physical dilution, tended to confirm this finding (GILAT et al., 1969). Virus tests on six out of 48 samples of seawater from more distant sampling stations gave positive results. It is interesting to note that two of these positive samples were taken from a buoy opposite the Tel Baruch bathing beach, some 1.5 km north of the point of sewage discharge. One of these samples showed a virus concentration of 32 PFU/l. On that same day, the seawater sample taken over the end of the outfall in the "boil" showed a virus concentration of 60 PFU/l. A series of bacteriological tests from the same sampling point showed that the water met the coliform standard of less than 2,400/100 ml. The radioisotope tracer studies indicated that the physical dilution between these two points might be as low as 1–10. These results can be considered only of a qualitative nature; however, they do indicate that with the virus detection methods now available it is possible to initiate quantitative evaluation of virus contamination in coastal waters. They also reinforce the doubt that the coliform index may not be satisfactory in seawater as far as assessing virus contamination is concerned.

MARINE ANTIVIRAL AGENT

Antibacterial factors in seawater have been studied for a number of years (MITCHELL, 1968), but there is little available information on the antiviral activity of seawater. Therefore, simultaneously with the field work, laboratory studies were initiated to determine the nature and extent of any antiviral factors in seawater.

Our studies, to be reported on in full elsewhere, have shown that there is a definite marine antiviral agent (MAVA) which appears to be of a biological nature. When poliovirus type 1 was seeded into seawater samples, taken from various points along the Mediterranean and Red Sea coasts, a three to six log reduction was obtained in seven days, at 22°C ± 3°. Parallel samples heated to 90°C for one hour and then seeded with an equal inoculum of poliovirus showed only about a one log reduction at the end of the seven-day period (see Figure 8). These findings parallel those of a group in Sweden studying this question, who feel that the microorganism, *Vibrio marinus*, is the responsible agent (MAGNUSSON et al., 1967). Our studies have shown that the antiviral agent in seawater is heat labile and ether sensitive. It is also removed from seawater samples by filtration

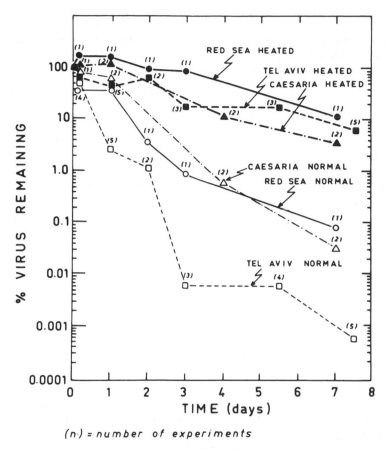

(n) = number of experiments

Figure 8
Inactivation of poliovirus in normal and heat-treated seawater samples
from the Mediterranean and Red Sea

through a membrane filter with a 0.45μ pore size. Interestingly enough, the agent is not completely removed from the supernatant of a seawater sample centrifuged at $60,000 \times g$; however, heat-treated seawater samples to which the centrifuged pellet of the above seawater sample was added showed a degree of antiviral activity similar to that of natural seawater samples. It is also noted that the MAVA in samples of Tel Aviv coastal waters appears stronger than that of sea samples taken at the relatively unpolluted areas of Caesaria on the Mediterranean or Eilat on the Red Sea. One explanation is that the agent may be stimulated by the higher nutrient levels resulting from the disposal of large volumes of sewage into the sea at Tel Aviv. There seems to be evidence that the MAVA is of a complex nature not completely explained by any reported findings to date.

Our preliminary laboratory findings indicate that the time required for a 90% decrease of poliovirus in seawater (T_{90}) may be somewhere between 12 and 48 hours. In view of the relatively rapid travel rate of sewage disposed of into the sea at Tel Aviv, which may range from one half to several km/hr, it can be assumed that pollution will reach nearby beaches within a few hours time at most. Thus, natural virus inactivation in seawater appears to be somewhat unreliable as a safeguard above and beyond actual physical dilution. A conservative estimate of the T_{90} for coliform organisms off the Tel Aviv coast, based on the radioisotope tracer experiments, is from one to three hours. This appears to be much more rapid than that found for poliovirus. Again this points to the possibility of enteroviruses being present in water of low coliform count.

Further intensive studies are being carried out to isolate and identify the marine antiviral agent or agents in seawater and to study their mode of action. Such studies may have broader applications than investigation of the ecological role of such agents in the self-purification capacity of seawater.

SUMMARY AND CONCLUSIONS

a) It has been felt for some time that there is a need to develop methods for the monitoring of water supplies for enterovirus contamination. The Phase-Separation (PS) method, which has been developed and extensively tested both in the laboratory and in the field, is both simple and inexpensive and should now provide local water quality control laboratories with a tool for carrying out such tests in collaboration with regional or national virus laboratories. It has been shown that this method can concentrate the viruses in a water sample by a factor of 500 and is capable of detecting as few as one or two virus infectious units per liter of water.

b) A survey of the enterovirus concentrations in raw sewage in four cities in Israel, based on regular tests carried out over a period of about one year, has shown that with the PS method it is possible to detect enteroviruses in all samples regardless of season. The average enterovirus concentration of raw sewage from cities in Israel is 1,050 PFU/1, while the average enterovirus-to-coliform ratio is about 1:10,000,000 or 1:1,000,000 based on the virus concentrations detected. In the course of this survey, all types of poliovirus as well as types of echovirus and coxsackievirus were detected. As many as four different types of virus have been isolated from one sewage sample.

c) In the course of examining some 70 samples of drinking water, enteroviruses were detected in two samples by the PS method. In this case the water came from a polluted municipal well suspected of being involved in a common-source epidemic of infectious hepatitis. This is thought to be the first reported isolation of viruses in a domestic water supply suspected of being involved in a water-borne epidemic.

d) A survey of surface water sources contaminated to varying degrees produced five samples positive for enteroviruses out of 37 tested. In three cases positive samples were detected in the Jordan River, one at a point some 25 km downstream from the main point of sewage inflow.

e) Standard methods of wastewater purification may be largely ineffective in removing enterovirus contamination. This was borne out during a study of a municipal biological filtration plant and a stabilization pond system. The virus removal in the primary sedimentation stage (Imhoff tank) was essentially zero, while only five out of ten tests revealed any virus reduction throughout the entire biological filtration plant. The average virus removal in the plant under study was negligible, although the plant was considered to be operating efficiently by the usual standard parameters. BOD reduction was 85% and coliform counts were reduced by 92%. The oxidation pond system with about 20 days detention was somewhat more effective. In three out of nine cases, there was no removal, the average virus removal efficiency being calculated as 67%. BOD and coliform reductions were 80% and 90%, respectively.

f) Chlorination of wastewater effluent by standard procedures was also shown to have a low degree of efficacy in inactivating enteroviruses. While chlorine doses of 11 mg/l added to treated sewage effluent resulted in a five log reduction of coliforms in one hr, a mere one log reduction was attained with a poliovirus. In order to achieve a 99.9% inactivation of poliovirus in the effluent, it was necessary to apply a chlorine dose ten times larger than the one required to obtain the equivalent degree of inactivation for coliforms.

g) The PS method has been adapted and tested for the detection of enteroviruses in seawater and has been found effective. Enteroviruses were detected in 14 out of 48 samples of seawater taken from points at varying distances from an outfall sewer. In two cases enteroviruses were detected at a point in the sea 1.5 km from the source of pollution, opposite a main bathing beach. Radioisotope tracer tests indicated that at that point the degree of physical dilution of raw sewage in the sea would be at least 1:1,000. This indicates both the sensitivity of the PS method and the degree of persistence of enteroviruses in the marine environment.

h) In laboratory studies, an apparently biological marine antiviral agent (MAVA) was detected in samples from both the Mediterranean and the Red Sea. Poliovirus type 1 inoculated into natural seawater samples was reduced by 3–6 logs in seven days, while in heat-treated seawater samples, used as controls, only a one-log reduction was detected in this period. The T_{90} of poliovirus in seawater, as determined from these laboratory experiments, was between 12 to 48 hours. This is considerably greater than that of coliforms in the same environment. Although the antiviral activity of seawater may constitute but a minor safety factor in preventing the contamination of bathing beaches, it is now under intensive study. This marine antiviral agent may prove of considerable interest in other areas of application once it has been isolated, identified and its mode of action established.

i)   In conclusion, a major re-evaluation of water quality control and water pollution prevention, based on the use of enterovirus parameters as illustrated in this paper, is called for. This is essential in the light of current knowledge on the risk of water-borne virus diseases, particularly infectious hepatitis, and the recognized inadequacy of such standard parameters as the coliform index.

ACKNOWLEDGEMENT

The research findings reported on in this paper are the result of a team effort made possible by the devoted collaboration of B. Fattal and S. Cymbalista together with the thoughtful advice and assistance of Prof. N. Goldblum. The active participation of Dr. Judith Cohen, Mrs. Y. Wiener and R. Kolodny are sincerely appreciated.

APPENDIX

PROPOSED PROCEDURE FOR DETERMINING THE PRESENCE OF ENTERIC VIRUSES IN WATER BY THE PHASE-SEPARATION (PS) METHOD

1. General Discussion

1.1 Principle: The "enteric virus" group in the broad sense includes all viruses known to be excreted in quantity in the feces of man. The group includes polioviruses, the coxsackieviruses, the echo (enteric cytopathogenic human orphan) viruses, the adenoviruses, and the virus of infectious hepatitis. The presence of members of this group of viruses in water can be considered as evidence of fecal pollution of human origin and as presumptive evidence that the consumption of such water by large nonimmune population groups might lead to human infections. In the PS method, water samples of several liters in volume are concentrated by a phase-separation technique; the obtained concentrate is about 1/500 of the original sample volume and contains essentially all of the viruses present in the original sample. This concentrate is assayed for enteric virus by standard quantitative tissue culture methods.

1.2 Minimum detectable contamination: This method should be able to detect as few as one or two virus infectious units of enteric viruses per liter of sample tested.

2. Apparatus

2.1 Separatory funnels, pear-shaped, of one- to five-liters capacity

2.2 Centrifuge, capable of centrifuging at 15,000 × g (this unit is not required if the virus assay is done in another laboratory)

2.3 Magnetic stirrer

3. Reagents

3.1 Sodium dextran sulfate 2000 (A. B. Pharmacia, Sweden)

3.2 Polyethylene glycol (Carbowax 4000)

3.3 Sodium chloride

3.4 Streptomycin

3.5 Penicillin

3.6 Fungizone (Amphototeriein, Squibb.)

4. Procedure

4.1 Place water sample to be tested in a sterile flask of a volume suitably large to allow for mixing of added chemicals.

4.2 To each liter of sample, the following chemicals are added: 2 g sodium dextran sulfate, 64.50 g polyethylene glycol and 17.50 g NaCl. Mix on a magnetic stirrer until the chemicals are dissolved.

4.3 Transfer solution to a sterile separatory funnel and hold at 4°C for 12–24 hours after which time the bottom and interphase are drained off into a sterile test tube.

4.4 Add NaCl to the concentrate to a final concentration of 1.0 M (50 mg NaCl per ml concentrate) and hold for an additional 12–24 hours at 4°C. Withdraw upper phase in sterile pipette for virus assay. Concentrate can also be frozen and held at −20°C for assay at a later date, or sent to a specialized virus laboratory for quantitative assay.

4.5 Centrifuge final concentrate at 15,000 g for 30 minutes and then add streptomycin (20,000 μg/ml), penicillin (20,000 u/ml) and Fungizone (60 μg/ml).

4.6 Assay concentrate on primary rhesus kidney cell monolayers by the plaque-forming method or in tissue culture tubes or bottles using standard virological procedures not to be covered here.

5. Calculation

When the plaque-forming technique for assaying viruses in the concentrate is used:

$$\text{PFU/liter} = \frac{A \times C}{B \times D}$$

where A = total number of plaque-forming units (PFU) on all plates assayed, B = ml of concentrate assayed, C = total ml of concentrate produced in final upper phase, and D = liters of original sample tested.

REFERENCES

CLARKE, N.A. and KABLER, P.W. (1954): "The inactivation of purified Coxsackie Virus in water by chlorine," *Amer. Jour. Hyg.,* **59**, 119.

CLARKE, N.A., BERG, G., KABLER, P.W. and CHANG, S.L. (1964): "Human enteric viruses in water: source, survival and removability," In: *Advances in Water Pollution Research,* Vol. 2, pp. 523–524, Pergamon Press, London.

DENNIS, J.M. (1959): "1955–56 infectious hepatitis epidemic in New Delhi, India," *J. Am. Wat. Wks. Ass.,* **51**: 1288–1296.

GILAT, C., SHUVAL, H.I., YOSHPE-PURER, Y. and COHEN, N. (1969): "The use of radioisotope tracers in the study of the dispersion and inactivation of bacteria discharged in coastal waters." These Proceedings, 269–288.

HARREMOES, P. (1966): "Prediction of pollution from planned wastewater outfalls," J.W.P.C. FED., **38**, 12, 23.

MAGNUSSON, S., GUNDERSEN, K., BRANDBERG, A. and LYCKE, E. (1967): "Marine bacteria and their possible relation to virus inactivation capacity of seawater," *Acta Path. et Microbiol. Scandinav.,* **71**: 274–280.

METCALF, T.G. and STILES, W.C. (1968): "Survival of enteric viruses in estuary waters and shellfish," *Jour. A.S.C.E. San. Eng. Div.,* **40**: 439–447.

MITCHELL, R. (1968): "Factors affecting the decline of non-marine microorganisms in seawater," *Water Research,* **2**: 535.

POMEROY, R. (1960): "The empirical approach for determining the required length of an ocean outfall," *Proc. 1st Conf. on Waste Disposal in the Marine Environment,* Pergamon Press, London.

PRESIDENT'S SCIENCE ADVISORY COMMITTEE (1955): "Restoring the quality of our environment," Report of the Environmental Pollution Panel, Washington.

SHUVAL, H.I., COHEN, N. and YOSHPE-PURER, Y. (1968): "The dispersion of bacterial pollution along the Tel Aviv shore," *Rev. Intern. Oceanogr. Med.,* **9**: 107–121.

SHUVAL, H.I., CYMBALISTA, S., FATTAL, B. and GOLDBLUM, N. (1967a): "The concentration of enteric viruses in water by hydroextraction and two-phase separation." In: *Transmission of Viruses by the Water Route* (Edited by Berg, G.), Interscience, New York.

SHUVAL, H.I., CYMBALISTA, S., WACH, A., ZOHAR, Y. and GOLDBLUM, N. (1967b): "The inactivation of enteroviruses in sewage by chlorination," *Proc. 3rd Int. Conf. Water Pollution Res.,* January 1967.

SHUVAL, H.I., FATTAL, B., CYMBALISTA, S. and GOLDBLUM, N. (1969): "The Phase-Separation method for the concentration and detection of viruses in water," *Water Research,* **3**: 225–240.

STANDARD METHODS FOR THE EXAMINATION OF WATER AND WASTEWATER (1965): Amer. Pub. Health Assn., New York.

U.S. DEPT. OF HEALTH, EDUCATION AND WELFARE (1962): Report to the Surgeon General of the Committee on Environmental Health Problems, Washington.

The Evolution of Nitrogen

Compounds in Lake Kinneret

C. Serruya and T. Berman

INTRODUCTION

The completion of the new Kinneret Limnological Laboratory has provided investigators with greatly improved facilities for research on Lake Kinneret (Lake Tiberias). An extensive study program, designed to elucidate the nutrient flows obtaining in the lake, has led to some preliminary results on the hydrome-chanics and macronutrient and other changes in the lake (SERRUYA et al., 1968). We present here an analysis of the seasonal evolution of nitrogen compounds in Lake Kinneret. Chemical data collected from 1963–1967 by the Mekorot Water Company have been kindly made available by E. Betser.

GENERAL PATTERN OF NITROGEN CYCLE IN LAKE KINNERET

The NH_4-N content increases in the hypolimnion throughout the summer. At the end of this period its concentration reaches 1 mg/l, while the epilimnion is completely depleted of NH_4-N. This high quantity of NH_4-N is probably derived partly from the decay of organic matter of the epilimnion passing through the thermocline, and partly from the sediments.

In December–January, the thermocline is destroyed and the general turnover of the lake takes place: all the water layers are mixed and the element concentrations homogenized. The concentration of NH_4-N in the entire water column is then about $200\mu g/l$.

This considerable quantity of NH_4-N from the hypolimnion is rapidly oxidized on entering oxygen-rich waters. We note a transitory period when NO_2-N appears, and then a high peak of NO_3-N replaces the NH_4-N. The quantities of NO_3-N are always greater than the NH_4-N concentrations of the previous period, for, at the same time, the lake receives the floods from the Jordan which are very rich in NO_3-N.

In the early spring, the NO_3-N is transformed into organic nitrogen through organic synthesis during the period of algal bloom, and in February–March–April the maximum of organic N is encountered in the epilimnion. From July on, the content of NO_3-N drops to below $10\mu g/l$. The epilimnion is then deficient in mineral nitrogen.

Two different mechanisms can influence the quantity of N in the lake:

1) release from the sediments;
2) supply from the Jordan.

The first mechanism depends on the redox potential (Eh) of the hypolimnion waters; it is known that the release of NH_4-N is enhanced by low redox potentials. The second is governed by the Jordan yield, i.e., meteorological factors and the water management policy in the watershed.

GENERAL PICTURE OF THE EVOLUTION OF NITRATE CONCENTRATION IN THE LAKE FROM 1964–1969

From the above outline of the transformation of NH_3-N into NO_3-N in the early summer, it appears that the concentration of NO_3-N is a good indication of the quantity of nitrogen supplied by the hypolimnion and the Jordan during the winter.

In the spring period of 1965–66–67, the NO_3-N content of the waters did not exceed $350\mu g/l$. In 1968, when the analyses of the epilimnion were only begun in May, the concentrations were not higher than $300\mu g/l$. In contrast, in the spring of 1964 the concentration reached as high as $800\mu g/l$, with a short maximum of $1,300\mu g/l$ in March. In the spring of 1969 we noted a very similar picture, with $600\mu g/l$ in February and a maximum of $740\mu g/l$ at the beginning of March.

In both cases the high quantities of nitrogen could be related to two main events:

1) Heavy floods coming from the Jordan.

2) Development in the lake of species of the blue-green algae group (*Micro-cystis* in 1964, *Microcystis* and *Anabaena* in 1969). It is likely that the large quantity of nitrogen introduced by the Jordan causes the development of blue-green algae.

THE SIGNIFICANCE OF THE HIGH CONCENTRATIONS OF NITROGEN IN THE WATER

It can be stated that during each normal year the Jordan brings to the lake about 1,600 tons of total N (data computed by Y. Gifman). Only 260 tons leave the lake via the Degania outflow yearly. If we add to this quantity the 200 tons led off by the Israel National Water Carrier, we see that about two-thirds of the yearly incoming nitrogen are stored in the lake. Two processes are operative in bringing about a *decrease* in the concentration of N in the water: a part of it is precipitated in the sediments where we find a nitrogen content of 0.1–0.3 % instead of 0.01 % in more oligotrophic lakes (AHLGREN, 1967); a denitrification takes place mainly in the hypolimnion water, transforming a certain amount of N into N_2 gas.

These processes are both reversible since the negative redox potentials of the mud-water interface in summer favor a considerable release of NH_4-N, and the N_2 gas stored in the hypolimnetic water might be used by the algae able to fix N_2 directly. The release of NH_4-N appears to be an important source of nitrogen nutrition to the lake. It is clear that nearly all the nitrogen nutrients that are added to the lake remain available for organic synthesis. If the present conditions persist, the N-nutrient concentrations will continuously rise.

In other words, the lake is acting as a trap for most of the nutrients received, and under the existing conditions of watershed drainage and water release this process is enhanced.

THE NITROGEN SITUATION IN 1968–69

For the 1968–69 period, quantities of the different kinds of nitrogen were computed for the whole lake. Weekly computations were made for each layer of 10 m. The results are presented in Figure 1. We note that in the summer months (May to November) the quantity of assimilable N (NH_4-N + NO_2-N + NO_3-N) is nearly constant and can be described as the minimum basic quantity of N in the lake. It amounts to about 650 tons, mostly in the form of NH_4-N in the

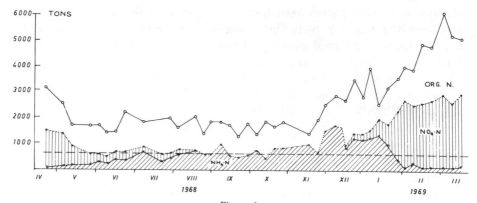

Figure 1
Lake Kinneret, absolute quantities of nitrogen, 1966–67

I	O—O—O	Total N
II	•—•—•	Assimilable N
III	×—×—×	NH_4-N
II—III		$NO_3 + NO_2$-N
I—II		Organic N
	— — — —	Basic quantity of assimilable N in the lake

hypolimnion. The total N attains about 1,125 tons, including organic nitrogen. At the end of November, *the quantity of* NH_4-N *rises suddenly*. The organic N remains unchanged. This rise in NH_4-N cannot be explained by the Jordan inflow, since the waters of this river are invariably very poor in ammonia. The most probable explanation is the following.

As the winter turnover includes ever-increasing quantities of hypolimnetic waters, the NH_4-N concentration of the hypolimnion decreases. Nevertheless, the redox potential at the interface is still very negative, -260 mV from 39 m to 43 m on the 10th January 1969. The diffusion from the lower layer rich in ammonia and the overlying layers depleted of ammonia increases as the entire temperature profile becomes more homogeneous. The more rapid depletion of ammonia from the lower layer enhances the release of this substance from the interstitial waters. We know from some analyses of interstitial waters that NH_4-N is stored there in large quantities. The increase in ammonia would then be due to accelerated release of NH_4-N by the interstitial waters from the sediments.

In December–January, the nitrate concentration began to rise; this is due partly to the oxidation of ammonia (we note the simultaneous decrease of NH_4-N) and partly to the Jordan floods. The assimilable N reaches the constant value of 3,000 tons. From February on, the organic nitrogen increases. In April the total nitrogen in the lake reaches 6,000 tons. A comparison with the year 1966–1967 is presented in Figure 2. Notwithstanding the less complete data, we observe: 1) an increase in the total quantity of ammonia in the middle of December; 2) an increase of NO_3-N from January on. However, the quantity of total N was between 4,000 and 4,500 tons; the assimilable N did not exceed 2,000 tons. Thus, in 1968–1969 we note a net increase in total N of 2,000 tons, which includes an increase of 1,000 tons of assimilable nitrogen.

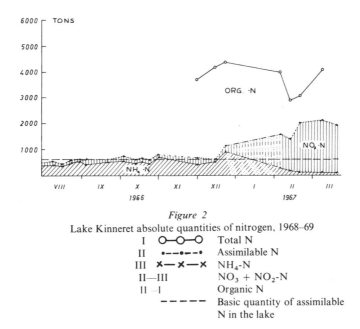

Figure 2
Lake Kinneret absolute quantities of nitrogen, 1968–69

I	O—O—O	Total N
II	•——•——•	Assimilable N
III	✗—✗—✗	NH_4-N
II—III		$NO_3 + NO_2$-N
II —I		Organic N
	— — — —	Basic quantity of assimilable N in the lake

It appears that similar general conditions obtain for the accumulation of other nutrients. Experiments examining the enzymatic release of soluble inorganic phosphate from total phosphate (soluble and particulate) indicate that, for the months March to June 1969, there was ample phosphate to satisfy all primary productivity needs in the epilimnion. The organisms in the 0–5-meter layer have an enzymatic *potential* to release about 3 tons of soluble inorganic phosphate daily. Between 40–60 % of the total phosphate is subject to this breakdown. The phosphate requirement for primary production at this period is about 1.2 tons daily (data from Professor W. Rodhe). During this season, there is a rapid epilimnic turnover of the phosphate fractions and, consequently, the demands for organic production appear to be adequately met by the existing levels of total phosphate.

In conclusion, it appears that nitrogen rather than phosphorus is the critical nutrient factor in the initiation and growth patterns of the phytoplankton during the major bloom period in Lake Kinneret.

ACKNOWLEDGEMENTS

We thank Professor Rodhe for useful discussion and criticism and MEKOROT WATER COMPANY for making available data.

REFERENCES

AHLGREN, I. (1967): "Limnological studies of Lake Norrviken, a eutrophicated Swedish lake," *Schw. Ztschr. für Hydrologie*, **29** (1): 53–90.

SERRUYA, C., SERRUYA, S. and BERMAN, T. (1968): "Preliminary observations of the hydromechanics. nutrient cycles and eutrophication status of Lake Kinneret (Lake Tiberias)," *Verh. internat. Verein. Limnol.*, **17**.

Soft Water Supply for Urban Consumption,

a Feasibility Study

P. Dalinsky

GENERAL

Municipal water supply in Israel was based—until the operation of the National Water Carrier—almost entirely on groundwater sources. The use of groundwater for urban needs has both advantages and disadvantages. We may, on the one hand, note that this water is generally superior to surface water in terms of its biological quality and availability; however, on the other hand, water supply based on groundwater usually has a high degree of hardness due to the chemical composition of the aquifers in Israel. A classification of natural waters in Israel, based on different concentrations of 5–6 common salts, has been proposed (TAUSSIG, 1961). Upon examining this classification, we see that more than half of all well water in Israel is classified in Group No. I, the salt content of which is made up largely of bicarbonates of calcium and magnesium, with smaller quantities of sulfates and chlorides of magnesium as well as NaCl. The main aquifers of this group have been found in Turonian sediments and in Pleistocene sand strata.

One of the compounds most frequently found in almost all the water groups under study is calcium bicarbonate $Ca(HCO_3)_2$. The frequent occurrence of this compound and other salts of the elements calcium and magnesium explains the high degree of water hardness in Israel. In contrast with the chloride content,

79

which may be subject to sharp changes, depending on the particular water source, the differences in hardness in parts per million of $CaCO_3$ are more moderate. The following table lists typical water supply sources together with data on hardness and chloride content.

Table 1. Chloride content and total hardness of typical waters

Source	Chloride	Total hardness as $CaCO_3$ (ppm)	Date of analysis
Ma'anit 1	60	320	15.8.1966
Rosh Ha'ayin 1	227	345	15.8.1966
Holon 3	40	250	30.4.1966
Kinneret, Station 1	317	267	27.11.1967

WATER HARDNESS

In a report issued by the World Health Organization in 1964, water supply is divided into the following classes:

Class	Hardness (ppm $CaCO_3$)
Soft water	50
Water with low degree of hardness	50–150
Hard water	150–300
Very hard water	over 300

The term "hardness" was first used in England and evolved in connection with soap waste which is a side effect of the use of water with high concentrations of the cations calcium and magnesium. The hardness caused by bicarbonates of calcium and magnesium is known as temporary hardness because it can be eliminated by raising the temperature. On the other hand, hardness caused by sulfates and chlorides of calcium and magnesium does not decrease on moderate heating and is therefore generally known as permanent hardness.

As mentioned above, the bicarbonate hardness of calcium is removed on raising the temperature, according to the following formula:

$$Ca(HCO_3)_2 \longrightarrow CaCO_3 + H_2O + CO_2$$

Calcium carbonate ($CaCO_3$) has a low solubility in water and precipitates. The following table gives the solubility of some common salts found in water supply (NORDELL, 1961).

Table 2. Solubility of salts found in water supply

Name of salt	Formula	Solubility at 100°C (ppm $CaCO_3$)
Calcium carbonate	$CaCO_3$	13
Magnesium carbonate	$MgCO_3$	75
Calcium sulfate	$CaSO_4$	1,246
Common salt	NaCl	243,000
Magnesium sulfate	$MgSO_4$	356,000
Calcium chloride	$CaCl_2$	554,000

As a result of the contact between hard water and soap, the cations of calcium and magnesium combine with the fatty acids of soap, forming a precipitate of calcium soap and magnesium soap. It follows, therefore, that a certain part of the soap acts as water softener; after disposing of the cations of calcium and magnesium, the soap is free to act upon the dirt. There is a direct connection between the quantity of soap consumed and water hardness.

In the case of hard water, synthetic detergents are preferable to soap. When detergents are used, the influence of calcium and magnesium cations is mainly on the polyphosphate sequestering agent, whose function is to hold the dirt particles in solution and prevent their adhering to the laundry. The sequestering agent also acts as a softener. Therefore, in hard water the polyphosphate concentration available for sequestering purposes is reduced, and an increased use of detergent may be in order.

If we divide the total annual sales by the number of inhabitants in Israel at the end of 1966, the per capita expenditure for soaps and detergents totals IL 22* per year.

It should be pointed out that the per capita expenditure for cleaning products is in reality smaller than the above-mentioned figure, due to the fact that the total sales include commercial and institutional consumption. We have also taken the recorded production to represent the 1966 consumption, an assumption which merits further study.

As an initial estimate, we will assume that 20% of the annual sale revenue of cleaning products can be attributed to the consumption of commercial and institutional laundries. It follows that the estimate of per capita expenditure

* 1 Israel lira (IL) = $0.29

Table 3. Production of soaps and detergents in Israel (1966)

Product	Production in tons	Prices per unit	Annual sale in millions IL
Laundry soap	5,491	0.80 IL per kg	4.4
Cosmetic soap	2,624	2.00 IL per kg	5.2
Liquid detergent	11,845	2.00 IL per kg	23.6
Detergent in powder form	9,631	2.00 IL per kg	19.4
Solid detergent	3,347	1.80 IL per kg	6.0
		Total	58.6

based on March 1968 prices of soap and detergent is IL 17.5. According to a study made in the United States (DEBEER, 1961), a saving of 20% in annual per capita expenditures can be expected in the case of a reduction of total hardness by 200 ppm (see Figure 1). A family of four may save about IL 14 per year in annual expenditure on detergent and soaps at prices of March 1968.

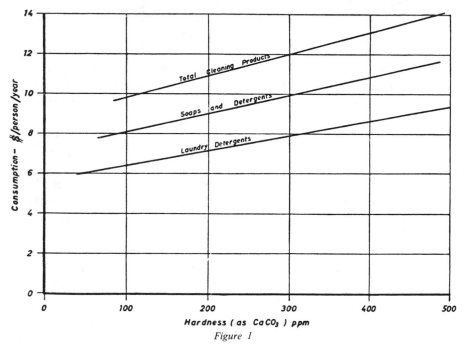

Figure 1

The influence of water hardness on the consumption of soaps and detergents (after DEBEER, 1961)

A report issued in California in 1959 attempts to estimate the influence of two qualities of water on annual expenditures per family on soap and detergent products. The saving per family due to the use of water with a total hardness of 100 (Feather River) in comparison with 343 (Colorado River) is estimated between $7 and $20.

There is a substantial gap between our initial evaluation and the American estimate, which, however, may narrow with time. It should be pointed out that we have omitted from our evaluation products such as chlorine bleach, shampoo, shaving cream, etc.

WATER HARDNESS AND THE WEAR AND TEAR OF CLOTHES

In August 1958, the Minister of Commerce and Industry appointed a committee to investigate the problems of textile wear due to laundering. The committee's findings and recommendations were published in June 1959. In order to compare the degree of wear in Israel with available pertinent data from abroad, a series of experiments were conducted by the "Institute of Fibres and Forest Products" with the cooperation of the Health Ministry. The following exerpt is taken from the committee's report: "the experiments were carried out on standard textiles ordered from Holland in order to be able to compare results obtained in Israel with those obtained in Holland. Various samples were sent by the Health Ministry to thirteen laundries (some under government auspices and others privately owned) and washed 25 times together with the white laundry of the Ministry. The laundries' managers were not informed of the experiments carried out, and the usual washing processes were employed so that the results are representative."

The total damage to textiles is made up of two components: chemical damage and mechanical damage.

Chemical damage effects the material of which the textile product is made and is expressed by the reduction of the polymerization level of the fiber. According to the above-mentioned report, this reduction precedes the drop in tearing strength of the cloth. Mechanical damage results from physical action such as rubbing and bending, and is determined by measuring textile tearing strength.

According to the Dutch standard, the total damage permitted after 25 washings was set at 11 %; included is a maximum chemical damage of 7 %. From a drawing included in the committee's report, it follows that the average total damage in Israel reached 40 % after 25 washings, compared with 11 % in Holland, and the chemical damage in Israel 24 %, compared with 7 %.

Due to climatic conditions, washing frequency in Israel surpasses that in Holland and hence the wear resulting from washing is greater in Israel, even if we do not take into consideration the committee's data pertaining to increased damage. In this context we read on p. 11 of the above report: "it follows that out of the total consumption of these mentioned textile products in Israel, only 25 % is necessary or justified consumption according to West European standards, whereas 75 % represents unjustified and unnecessary wear."

In the above experiment the rate of wear and tear in Israel has been compared to that accepted in Holland. Generally speaking, there is a long list of factors influencing the rate of wear, such as faulty textile production, sun radiation, etc. However, the data collected on this experiment were . . . . "obtained on standard cotton cloth of a very high quality and show that the superfluous laundry deterioration is considerable and it is probable that the factors originating in the washing process surpass in their importance all the other causes of wear" (Report and Recommendations of the Committee on Textile Wear and Tear in Laundering, June 1959, Jerusalem).

In the "Survey of Family Expenditures 1963/64," monthly outlays for various textile products have been specified. On the basis of this survey the per capita expenditure for washable textile products according to current prices is about IL 70.

No study has yet been carried out in Israel to establish the components which contribute to wear and tear due to laundering in water. Until data become available, we will refer to a short publication issued by the "American Institute of Laundering" (TEXTILE NOTES NUMBER 19), which estimated a 10 % reduction in wear as a result of washing in soft water as compared with hard water. The saving in clothing expenditure total is IL 7 per capita per year according to the above estimate.

WATER HARDNESS, ENERGY LOSS AND DETERIORATION IN HEAT TRANSFER SYSTEMS

Heat conductivity of hardness scale in water is on the average about 5 % that of steel. In order to transfer a given amount of heat across some partition, a temperature difference must be maintained between its inner and outer surfaces. The insulation qualities of the above-mentioned scale call for the creation of a temperature difference greater than that required for steel. As a result, the temperature in the heat-generating unit may reach a level which brings on the destruction of the steel. According to NORDELL (1961), cases of destruction have been recorded in modern boiler piping, resulting from the formation of a scale layer of only 1 mm in thickness.

Scale sediments formed in water pipes result in large losses to both the private consumer and the national water system due to the decrease in conveyance capacity of the pipes as a result of:

a. reduction in the effective flow area;

b. increase in the roughness of the inner pipe surface.

In pipes of medium and large diameters, the reduction in conveyance capacity can, to a certain extent, be compensated by an increase in energy expenditure. As an example, let us consider a 24″-pipe planned to carry $1,100 \text{m}^3/\text{hr}$, whose initial Hazen-Williams coefficient is 120. After the formation of a scale layer which results in a reduction in the Hazen-Williams coefficient to 90, the hourly discharge will decrease to $820 \text{m}^3/\text{hr}$. In order to maintain the planned hourly discharge of $1,100 \text{ m}^3$, it will be necessary to pay an extra IL 10,500 for additional energy for a 10-km length of pipe functioning 5,000 hours a year.

The influence of scale formation is especially evident in small-diameter pipes used in cooling and heating systems, owing to the great relative reduction in the flow area caused by the scale sediments. A 2″-pipe, for example, on which a 6-mm sediment layer is formed may lose up to two-thirds of its carrying capacity.

COMPARATIVE ECONOMIC ANALYSIS OF THREE SOURCES OF SOFT WATER

Table 4 summarizes the economic advantages of three alternative sources of soft-water supply. The 1980 population forecast for the 7-city Dan (Tel Aviv) Regional Scheme, with the inclusion of the cities of Ashdod and Rishon le Zion, is 1,120,000 (based on an annual anticipated growth rate of 2%). The population of these 9 cities totalled 866,000 at the end of 1966. The predicted annual water consumption stands at $118 \times 10^6 \text{ m}^3$. This forecast is based on studies published by TAHAL (see References). In the absence of other data, it has been assumed that the rates of saving in soaps and clothes of the two water-softening systems are proportional to the reduction in total hardness, assuming an initial hardness of 330 ppm $CaCO_3$.

Included in this economic comparison are savings in outlays, mainly in salt consumption, which can be realized by private operators of ion-exchange softening plants such as hospitals and certain types of industry. In addition, the supply

Table 4.   Summary of economic benefits due to the supply of softened water

Engineering Alternative	Total hardness ppm CaCO₃	Reduction in clothes wear-and-tear IL/capita/year	Saving in soap consumption IL/capita/year	Reduction in expenditures (salt) for softening IL/year	Saving in investments Dan Sewerage Project IL/year	Total sum of anticipated saving IL/year	Saving agorot*/m³
Water softening: lime	170	5.20	2.66	210,000		8.9 × 10⁶	7.6
Water softening: lime-soda	140	6.20	3.10	250,000		10.6 × 10⁶	9.0
Desalted water supply	115	7.00	3.50	280,000	150,000	12.2 × 10⁶	10.3

* 100 agorot = 1IL.

of desalted seawater entails specific benefits with respect to the Dan Sewage Recovery Project. These benefits are also considered in the calculation.

This report deals with some of the economic benefits derived from the supply of soft water to urban areas. However, it should be pointed out that soft water presents serious problems arising from internal corrosion of unlined pipes, water heaters, boilers, etc. Any cost-benefit analysis of the feasibility of supplying soft water to urban areas must include those expenditures required to assure minimum protection against corrosion.

REFERENCES

AMERICAN INSTITUTE OF LAUNDERING, Violet, Ill., "Textile Notes Number 19."

CENTRAL BUREAU OF STATISTICS, JERUSALEM (1963/64): *Survey of Families Expenditure.*

CENTRAL BUREAU OF STATISTICS, JERUSALEM (1966): *Monthly Statistical Bulletin of Israel,* Part B, Economy, March.

CENTRAL BUREAU OF STATISTICS, JERUSALEM (1966): *Israel's Foreign Trade,* Parts I and II.

CENTRAL BUREAU OF STATISTICS, JERUSALEM (1968): *Monthly Price Statistics,* February.

COMMITTEE ON SEWAGE DISPOSAL (1966): "Report on the Dan Area Sewage Project."

COMMITTEE ON TEXTILE WEAR AND TEAR IN LAUNDERING (1959): Report and Recommendations.

COX, C. (1964): *Operation and Control of Water Treatment Processes,* World Health Org., Geneva.

DEBEER, L. (1961): "Hardness and Detergent Use," *J.A.W.W.A.,* July.

DVIR, Y. and HALPERIN, L. (1967): "Use of Desalinated Water for Domestic Consumption," Technical Bulletin No. 3, Mekorot Water Co., Tel Aviv.

HOWSON (1951): "Economics of Water Softening," *J.A.W.W.A.*, April.

HUDSON, H. and BUSWELL, A. (1932): "Soap Consumption and Water Quality," *J.A.W.W.A.*, June.

LAWRENCE, C. (1965): "Quality Improvement," *J.A.W.W.A.*, May.

NORDELL, E. (1961): *Water Treatment for Industrial and Other Uses*, Reinhold Publishing Corp., New York.

RYZNER, J.W.: "A New Index for Determining Amount of Calcium Carbonate Scale Formed by a Water," Nalco Chemical Co., Chicago, Ill.

STATE OF CALIFORNIA, DEPT. OF WATER RESOURCES (1959): "Effects of Differences in Water Quality. Upper Santa Ana Valley and Coastal San Diego County," Bulletin 78, Appendix B.

TAHAL (1965): "Ashdod-Bitzaron Project. Water Supply from the Yarkon System."

TAHAL (1966): "Holon-Bat Yam Project. Water Supply from the Yarkon System."

TAHAL (1967): "Addition of Salt to Sewage of Dan Area, Dan Area Sewage Project."

TAHAL (1967): "Indirect Water Supply to Dan Area."

TAHAL (1968): "Corrosivity and Agressivity of Tel Aviv Water in 1980; Softened Tel Aviv Water; Desalinated Sea Water and Mixing Tel Aviv Water with Two Other Ones."

TAUSSIG, K. (1961): "Natural Groups of Groundwater and Their Origin," Mekorot Water Co., Tel Aviv.

TWORT, A.C. (1963): *A Textbook of Water Supply*, Edward Arnold Ltd., London.

Health Aspects of Nitrates

in Drinking Water*

Nachman Gruener and Hillel I. Shuval

INTRODUCTION

The increasing intervention by man in his environment has greatly increased the danger to public health. The rapid technological advances both in agriculture and industry are apt to cause harmful environmental changes of diverse origin, e.g., biological, chemical or radioactive. Such changing conditions often call for a re-evaluation of the existing and accepted health standards.

In this article we will deal with the danger of water contamination by nitrate salts. These salts may accumulate in surface and groundwater as a result of contamination by industrial or organic waste products and chemical fertilizers. Rapid urban growth with the intensification of agriculture and industry, on the one hand, and the increasing utilization of groundwater, on the other, are in some areas greatly accelerating the danger to public health from nitrates in drinking water.

In Israel the problem of nitrates in drinking water has become in recent years a cause for considerable concern among water supply agencies and public health authorities alike.

* This study has been supported in part by a research grant from The Mekorot Water Co.

Surveys of the nitrate levels in groundwater have indicated that there is a definite upward trend with time, which has now reached serious proportions (see Figure 1).* Approximately 180 water supply wells in the densely populated central and southern coastal plain area show nitrate concentrations equal to or greater than the limit recommended by the health authorities (45 mg/l of NO_3). Fifty other wells still supplying water with permissible nitrate concentrations have shown a nitrate increase of 2 mg/l or more per year.

Figure 2** gives the nitrate levels in the water supply wells of the town Nes Ziona for 1968, revealing that most of the town's wells have exceeded the recommended maximum concentration although they were at acceptable levels a few years ago.

A number of clinical cases of infant methemoglobinemia were detected in this town in recent years, and the possible association with the high nitrate concentrations in the water supply cannot be overlooked. A few years ago several cases of the disease were definitely traced to drinking water in the nearby town of Ramleh (WAGO, 1956).

The nitrate problem has become of even greater concern of late due to a major project for wastewater reuse by recharge into the aquifer. The Dan Region Water Reclamation project will infiltrate tens of thousands of cubic meters of treated wastewater high in nitrate content into the groundwater daily and will in that way further increase the nitrate burden on Israel's limited water resources (SHUVAL, 1962).

These developments have created the need to embark on a study to determine if present nitrate concentrations in drinking water are having any detrimental effects on the population exposed. In addition, it was felt that a basic re-evaluation of the nitrate standard in drinking water was called for, since this standard was originally based on very limited toxicological and epidemiological information and has been subject to criticism for some years. Of particular concern has been our suspicion that a form of subclinical chronic methemoglobinemia might exist in infants in those areas with moderately high nitrate concentrations in drinking water. First let us review the present state of knowledge concerning nitrate methemoglobinemia.

---

* The survey of nitrates in well water shown in Figure 1 was provided by Mrs. E. Foa of the Israel Hydrological Service and is based on data supplied by the Ministry of Health and Mekorot Water Co.
** Data based on report of Central District Health Office.

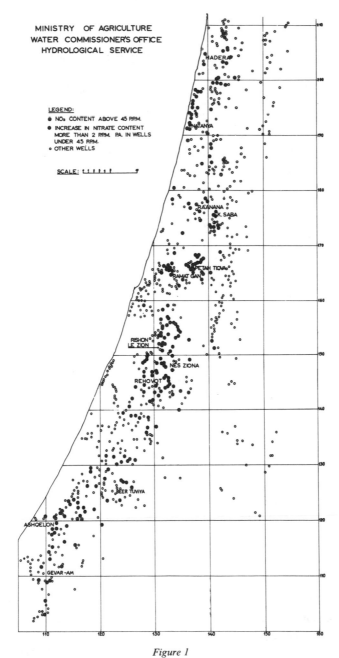

Figure 1

Nitrate radical (NO$_3$) content of pumped water in Central Israel
as of 1968

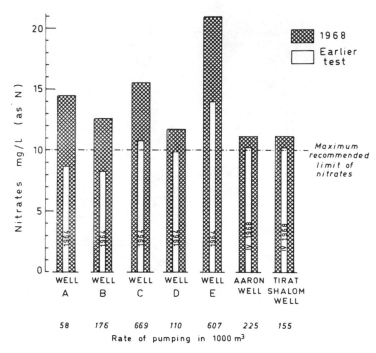

Figure 2

Concentration of nitrates (NO₃) in wells in Nes Ziona in 1968 in relation to
earlier tests

NITRATE STANDARDS IN DRINKING WATER

Infant methemoglobinemia resulting from the consumption of water with high
nitrate concentrations was first recognized clinically in 1945 (COMLY, 1945).
Since then about 2,000 cases, including many fatal poisonings in infants resulting from ingestion of water containing nitrates, have been reported in various
countries of the world.

This led the United States and later the World Health Organization to establish
maximum permissible limits for nitrates in water used for drinking purposes at
45 mg/l of NO_3 (10 mg/l of N). However, there is as yet no consensus of opinion
on the safety limits of nitrates in water. These limits vary in different countries
from 0.5–228 mg/l of NO_3 (CABALLERO, 1950), most of them lying in the range
of 20–100 mg/l NO_3 (U.S.P.H.S., 1962; RUMMEL, 1965).

Where nitrate limits in water are exceeded, it is generally recommended that infants up to the age of one year be supplied with low-nitrate water from other sources. These recommendations carry with them the tacit assumption that nitrates in water, irrespective of their concentration, are not harmful to children over one year of age or to adults.

In some areas where the water contains nitrate concentrations as high as 90 mg/l no clinical cases of the disease have been reported. This has led to pressure to relax the standard. On the other hand, clinical cases of the disease have more recently been reported in areas with less than 45 mg/l of NO_3 in the water (KNOTEK and SCHMIDT, 1964).

The existing standards are based on limited imperical evidence and leave many basic questions unanswered.

GENERAL ASPECTS OF METHEMOGLOBINEMIA

Methemoglobinemia can be caused by several chemicals such as nitrates, perchlorates, aminophenols, anilin, sulfonamides and others. Various endogenous forms of the disease are known. Nitrates do not directly convert hemoglobin to methemoglobin but can be converted to nitrites by intestinal microflora, with subsequent formation of methemoglobin. Hemoglobin (Hb) is the oxygen carrier of the blood. It is a protein of molecular weight 68,000, consisting of four identical sub-units, each containing a polypeptide chain (globin) and a heme group. Every heme contains at its center an atom of iron which, in the oxygenated form of Hb, oxyhemoglobin (HbO_2), is in the bivalent state (Fe^{2+} ferrous). Methemoglobin (MetHb) is the oxidized product of Hb in which the iron is in the trivalent state (ferric Fe^{3+}).

On transition from the ferrous to the ferric state the Hb loses its ability to combine with O_2. The exact molecular mechanism of the conversion of Hb to MetHb is still obscure.

Conversion of Hb to MetHb takes place all the time in the body, but the quantity of the latter is maintained at a low, steady-state level mainly by the action of an enzymatic system (JAFFE, 1964). Several enzymes with MetHb reduction capability have been purified, but the exact mechanism by which they operate *in vivo* has not yet been resolved. A direct, nonenzymatic reduction of methemoglobin is carried out by glutathion or ascorbic acid (LEMBERG and LEGGE, 1941). The normal concentration of methemoglobin is still a matter of dispute.

Methemoglobinemia constitutes a potential impairment of the proper supply of oxygen to the tissues. For example, it was found that in trained subjects who underwent work tests, 10–20% MetHb resulted in impaired oxygenation of muscles (TEPPERMAN et al., 1946). This phenomenon is a result of both less hemoglobin and the greater affinity of the residual Hb for oxygen.

PATHOGENESIS OF METHEMOGLOBINEMIA

It is accepted by many workers that under normal circumstances less than 2% of the total hemoglobin exists as MetHb (FERRANT, 1946; GROSS, 1964). No external signs or symptoms are generally noted under 5%. The first signs of cyanosis can be seen between 5 and 10% (KNOTEK and SCHMIDT, 1964).

The presence of high concentrations of nitrates in water is the principal determinant of the occurrence of methemoglobinemia in infants; however, it is not the only one. Other factors important in the pathogenesis of the disease are:

Age: Most of the cases of nitrate methemoglobinemia occur in infants below one year of age. In a review of 146 cases of methemoglobinemia in Minnesota, 90% of them were found to have occurred by the age of eight weeks. The youngest case was seven days and the oldest five months (ROSENFIELD and HUSTON, 1950). SCHMIDT and KNOTEK (1966) reported on a survey carried out in Czechoslovakia, in which 52% of the infants, 0–3 months old, in a high-nitrate area had elevated methemoglobin levels; in the age group from 3–12 months old the percentage reached 13. There are also reports on elevated MetHb levels in older children and adults who had consumed water with high nitrate concentrations but showed no symptoms of the disease (TEERHAAG and EYER, 1958). In a Russian study (SUBBOTIN, 1961) of 800 children in day nurseries, it was found that 92.2% of them who ingested water which contained 20–40 mg NO_3/l had elevated MetHb levels. In 50% of the cases the level was higher than 5%. Previously it was found that 8 mg/l nitrate did not raise the methemoglobin level (SUBBOTIN, 1958).

Presence of bacteria: CORNBLATH and HARTMAN (1948) emphasized the important role of bacteria in the production of methemoglobinemia. They studied the gastrointestinal flora with regard to nitrate reduction, gastric acidity, age and the level of intestinal absorption of nitrate. It was found that all microorganisms isolated from the mouth and from the gastrointestinal tract were capable of reducing nitrate to nitrite and grew in media of pH 5–7.

The invading bacteria must adapt themselves to nitrite formation if they were not previously in contact with nitrate. Consequently, it may take from four to five days after the first ingestion of nitrate until the full nitrate-reducing efficiency is reached. This may explain the commonly observed lag period of 1–3 weeks before the onset of the illness (TEERHAAG and EYER, 1958).

Gastric acidity: Examinations of gastric juice of infants who developed appreciable levels of MetHb revealed that the pH was usually higher than 4. It was found (MARRIOT et al., 1933) that the normal pH of infant gastric juice varied between 2–5, but with unspecific diarrhea, gastric pH increased and ranged between 4.6 and 6.5. MUCHA et al. (1965) examined the pH and bacterial flora of gastric juice from children. They found the gastric juice was sterile at pH < 4.6.

Gastrointestinal disturbances: DAUBNER (1962) has determined that all the members of the family Enterobacteriaceae are able to reduce nitrate to nitrite. Such organisms can gain access to the upper intestine during gastrointestinal disturbances (HORN, 1958). However, their ability to become established in the stomach is dependent on the pH, as mentioned in the preceding section. In the absence of nitrate-reducing bacteria in the stomach or upper intestine, most of the nitrate is probably absorbed as nitrate before reaching the colon in which the nitrate-reducing bacteria are normally found.

Type of powdered milk product: Studies in Czechoslovakia (KNOTEK and SCHMIDT, 1964; SCHMIDT and KNOTEK, 1966) indicated that the use of certain types of milk preparations has been suspected as the main cause for the development of methemoglobinemia in areas with high levels of nitrates in water. They reported on cases of methemoglobinemia in infants due to feeding with various brands of regular powdered milk which contained spores of *B. subtilis,* a nitrate-reducing bacteria; acidified milk powders which are often prepared by fermentation with *St. lactis* did not cause any disease. The acidified milk preparation can contain an antibiotic substance called nisin which inhibits the growth of nitrate-reducing bacteria. On the other hand, MUCHA et al. (1965) claimed that the main source of nitrate-reducing microorganisms could be eliminated by providing bacteria-free food to infants; however, under certain conditions, the ascent of bacteria from the colon to the duodenum and stomach cannot be prevented. *B. subtilis* spores are, however, not destroyed by normal milk pasteurization and drying processes. Little nitrate was found in the milk of cows drinking water with up to 800 mg NO_3/l (DAVISON, 1964). Many hold the opinion that mother's milk or cow's milk cannot be a cause of methemoglobinemia.

High fluid intake: Infants with an average fluid intake would ingest several times more nitrate per gram of hemoglobin than an adult due to their higher fluid intake per unit of body weight (GROSS, 1964). BURDON (1961), assuming that all nitrate is reduced to nitrite, sets the permissible level of nitrate for adults at 1,056 mg/l in England and 198 mg/l in the tropics; for infants the permissible levels would be 88 mg/l and 26 mg/l, respectively. His estimates are based on 13.2 mg NO_3/kg as the maximum daily amount which can be tolerated without giving rise to toxic symptoms. The governing factor would be the relative daily fluid intake which for infants would be 0.5 liter in England and 2.0 liters in the tropics.

Effect of nutrition: Food composition can also affect the severity of the illness. On the one hand, there are certain nutrients such as vitamin C that can cure or prevent methemoglobinemia. High vitamin C intake among infants in some areas may explain the scarcity of the disease even when waters rich in nitrates are consumed. On the other hand, certain vegetables such as spinach, rhubarb, etc. contain considerable amounts of nitrates. Several cases of nitrate poisoning in infants after eating spinach were reported (SINOIS and WODSAK, 1965). The nitrate content of selected food samples tested in Jerusalem are presented in Table 1 (SHUVAL and RAM, 1968). From this limited survey it can be seen for example that samples of spinach can contain as much as 1,330 ppm of nitrates. Such concentrations in food can become particularly toxic if exogenic bacterial activity converts the NO_3 to NO_2.

Fetal hemoglobin: Hemoglobin F is oxidized more readily to methemoglobin (BOI-DOKU and PICK, 1966). The fact that blood of newborn babies consists of more than 80% hemoglobin F might explain their increased tendency to develop methemoglobinemia.

Methemoglobin reduction: Methemoglobin reduction velocity in the presence of lactate or glucose is lower in cord blood erythrocytes than in adult blood. The lower methemoglobin reduction velocity in cord blood is explained by a temporary deficiency of DPNH—the methemoglobin reductase cofactor (ROSS and DESFORGES, 1959), or by low activity of the enzyme itself (BARTOS and DESFORGES, 1966). A positive correlation between DPNH diaphorase activity and methemoglobin reduction was shown in adult blood but not detected in cord blood (KANAZAWA et al., 1968).

Table 1. The concentration of nitrates [NO_3] in food samples in Jerusalem*

Type of Food	Concentration of NO_3 (ppm)
Butter	220
Onions, green	260
Orange drink	185
Tomato	140
Rhubarb	1050
Cabbage	600
Cauliflower	390
Strawberries	450
Spinach	1330
Artichoke	130
Spinach-potato (strained baby food)	400
Turnip	550
Asparagus	146
Cucumber	148
Carrot	500
Apple	380
Avocado	45
Potato	230
Tea	104
Coffee	540
Cocoa	100
Milk (from cows consuming water containing 90 mg/l NO_3)	17

* These analyses were carried out by Dr. E. Wiesenberg, the Institute for Control and Standardization of Pharmaceuticals, Ministry of Health, Jerusalem

RESEARCH PROGRAM IN ISRAEL

Our research activities concerned with the problem of the health effects of nitrates in drinking water were initiated in 1967 and are being carried out both in the field and in the laboratory.

Field Studies

The first question investigated was the possible health effects of medium to high levels of nitrates in drinking water (45–90 mg/l) on the infant populations exposed to such water.

Since only a few clinical cases of methemoglobinemia have been reported in the study areas, it was our intention to attempt to determine whether cases of chronic subclinical disease could be detected in such infant populations. This required a sensitive test for MetHb that had a high degree of precision capable of detecting small differences between normal and slightly raised levels of MetHb. It also had to be a micromethod simple enough to be used under field conditions.

Since blood samples in such surveys often have to be taken in communities distant from the laboratory, it is essential that the blood sample drawn be preserved for periods of up to 24 hours. MetHb is known to be unstable and it is generally recommended that blood be examined promptly (BODANSKY, 1951).

Previous reports have indicated the stability of MetHb in blood samples stored in buffers which contained a special detergent, even at room temperature (PASSANNANTE and GERARDE, 1966). In our initial testing of various methods of preservation of blood samples we found that with this method methemoglobin levels increased considerably on storage and that it was not reliable for the conditions of our study. Freezing of blood samples also proved unreliable.

The commonly accepted clinical methods are also not sufficiently accurate for this purpose (EVELYN and MALLOY, 1938) or call for the use of large volumes of blood, a requirement considered impractical for a survey of this kind (CRUZ, 1951). Therefore, an effort was made to develop a micromethod using samples of finger blood which would meet all the above-mentioned criteria.

The method developed in conjunction with Dr. E. Hegesh and his group at Kaplan Hospital requires only 0.2 ml of finger blood and is sensitive enough to detect 10 mg% of MetHb. Blood samples taken in the field are immediately hemolyzed in water and stored on ice. It has been shown that MetHb varies by no more than 10% of its initial concentration within 24 hours when treated by this method. Full details will be published elsewhere.

A field study of MetHb levels in infants up to one year of age has been initiated in two areas: Nes Ziona-Rehovot coastal plain area, having nitrate concentrations of between 45–90 mg/l; Jerusalem area, as a control, with a negligible nitrate content in the drinking water.

A questionnaire providing background information on milk and water consumption, nutrition and disease history is filled out for each infant tested. The results of this survey are as yet incomplete and it is too early to be able to draw any conclusions.

Toxicology of Nitrites

In the laboratory phase of our studies we decided to concentrate on the acute and chronic effects of nitrites on experimental animals. We were particularly interested in investigating the possible physiological significance of low levels of methemoglobinemia such as might exist in cases of chronic subclinical intoxication. As mentioned previously, it is the nitrite form rather than the nitrate form that causes the formation of MetHb. *In vivo* conversion of NO_3 to NO_2 apparently is an essential step in the pathogenesis of the disease. Since we were not yet in a position to regulate or control the conversion of nitrates to nitrites in experimental animals, we felt that as a first step it would be best to work directly with nitrites. The need to establish permissible limits for nitrites in water has also been suggested (NICHOLS, 1965); however, nitrites usually occur in water in amounts too small to be of physiological importance.

Initially we studied lethal doses and the kinetics of MetHb formation in Hebrew University albino sabra rats. Lethal doses were found to be approximately 200 mg/kg. When a single sublethal dose of nitrite is administered to a rat by oral intubation, the MetHb level reaches a peak in about 45 minutes to one hour and returns to normal within about 3–4 hours, indicating the effectiveness of the MetHb reductase system (see Figure 3). We also found that the rats' body temperature is depressed as the MetHb levels increase and returns to normal as the MetHb disappears.

A preliminary chronic test of rats (initially weighing about 110 g) supplied with water containing 4.5 g/l of $NaNO_2$ (Group A) and 3.0 g/l of $NaNO_2$ (Group B) was carried out over a period of 56 days. The controls received no nitrites (Group C). The amount of water consumed daily was recorded and it was found during this chronic exposure study that rats showed some degree of rejection of water containing such high concentrations of NO_2.

On the basis of the concentration of nitrites in the water and average daily water intake, it was calculated that the nitrite dose of Group A ranged from 610–1,066 mg/kg/day while that of Group B ranged from 450–831 mg/kg/day. The MetHb blood levels were taken at various intervals during the study. Previous studies of rats given nitrites in drinking water throughout their life span did not reveal significant changes in MetHb levels. In pretests we also at first did not detect significantly elevated MetHb levels in blood samples taken during

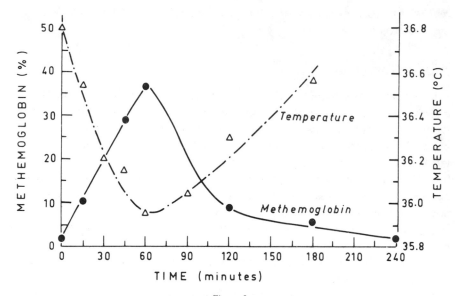

Figure 3

The effect of a single dose of 75 mg/kg $NaNO_2$ on methemoglobin development and body
temperature in rats

normal laboratory working hours, despite the very high nitrite doses. However,
it was decided to take blood samples at various times during the night on the
assumption that the rats' water consumption would be greatest during those
hours due to their nocturnal habits. Our measurements indicated that about 80%
of the daily water intake is consumed during the night. We have previously shown
that MetHb levels return to normal within a few hours after exposure to a dose
of nitrites. It was thus hypothesized that rats would have low MetHb levels
during the day, and higher levels at night. Our assumptions proved to be correct
and we have shown that MetHb levels in most rats under study reach a peak
during the night hours and might often return to normal during the day.

In Figure 4 it can be seen that the peak MetHb levels in Group A were about
20% while those for Group B were about 14%. Maximum MetHb values are
those for blood samples taken at about 4:30 a.m. The lower MetHb figures
represent samples drawn during various hours of the day. The MetHb of the
controls, Group C, ranged between 1 and 2%.

In Figure 5 the body weights of the rats consuming nitrites in their water are
given for the 56-day period. While the controls (Group C) increased in body

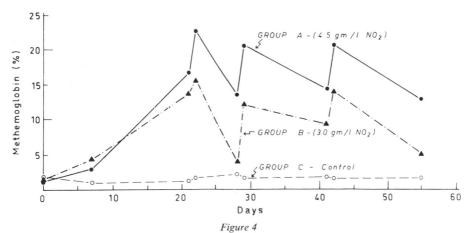

Figure 4
Methemoglobin levels in rats consuming nitrites in water

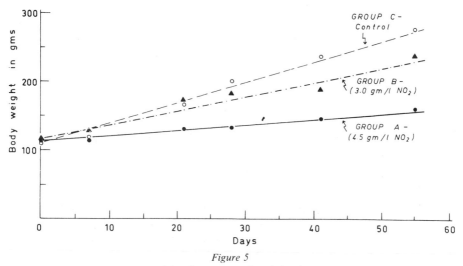

Figure 5
Body weight of rats consuming nitrites in water

weight from about 110 g at the beginning of the experiments to 270 g at the end, Group A increased to only 150 g and Group B to 235 g.

Further studies of the chronic effects of still lower nitrite levels on rats are being carried out in an effort to determine the possible long-term physiological impact of a chronic subclinical form of the disease.

Effects on Animal Behavior

Since the object of these experimental studies is to develop methods for evaluating the possible implications of chronic subclinical methemoglobinemia, it was felt that highly sensitive parameters should be studied. It was hypothesized that one of the effects of subclinical methemoglobinemia would be the reduction of the oxygen-carrying capacity of the blood system, which in turn would affect tissues particularly sensitive to reduced oxygen tension, such as the brain and muscles. This might lead to detectable behavioral changes in laboratory animals with induced chronic methemoglobinemia. A similar approach has been developed for the study of small doses of CO and found to be an effective toxicological tool (BEARD and WERTHEIM, 1967).

To study this possibility we carried out psychological experiments in a barrier activity box (LIEBLICH and GUTTMAN, 1965) using mice treated with nitrites. Preliminary experiments indicate the utility and sensitivity of this test. The treated animals showed significantly reduced activity patterns compared to the controls. Further experiments along these lines are being carried out. Following a similar line of approach, laboratory animals with implanted electrodes will be exposed to nitrites in their water for extended periods and checked regularly for changes in EEG patterns.

The Effects of Nitrites on Newborn and Suckling Rats

As noted previously, present nitrate standards for drinking water imply that the restrictions apply only to infants and that there is no need to limit the nitrate intake of adults. However, Donahoe reported what he considered to be a case of methemoglobinemia in a nursing infant who received no water. In this case the mother was consuming water high in nitrates and it was hypothesized that the nitrates may have been transferred through the mothers' milk (DONAHOE, 1949).

Such a possibility has been considered unlikely by other researchers. In order to study the possible transfer of nitrites in milk as well as possible direct transplacental transfer of nitrites to the fetus during pregnancy, we supplied pregnant rats with water containing 3.0 mg/l of $NaNO_2$ during the last week of pregnancy and during a period of three weeks after giving birth. In another test the same nitrite water was supplied to mother rats for a period of three weeks immediately after the birth of the litter.

In the former experiment it was found that the newborn rats showed MetHb levels of 5–10% at birth, while the mothers receiving nitrites in their water had

MetHb levels of 45%. However, after a few days the suckling rats showed normal MetHb levels while the mothers still had high levels. The birth weights and litter size of the controls and the experimental groups were equal.

In Figure 6 the body weights of the suckling rats of mothers consuming nitrites are compared with those of the controls. While the controls increased in weight from about 5 g at birth to 32 g after three weeks, the weight of the experimental group increased only to 22 g. Even more indicative of the possible negative effects of the nitrites supplied to the mothers before and after birth was the fact that of the 45 newborn rats in the experimental group only two remained alive at the end of the experimental period as against 17 in the control group of an original 38. Sixteen rats from each group were sacrificed at different times during the experiment for MetHb determination.

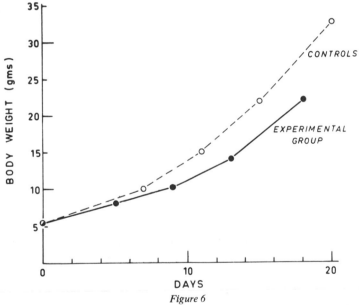

Figure 6

Body weight of suckling rats from mothers consuming nitrites in water before and after birth

In the latter experiment mother rats were given water containing 3.0 mg/l of $NaNO_2$ only after the birth of the litter. In this case MetHb developed in the mothers but not in the suckling rats, whose body weights paralleled the controls during the three-week period of the test. The results of these two experiments suggest that there is transplacental transfer of nitrites to the fetus, leading to the development of methemoglobinemia in the fetus, which was detected in the newborn rats on the day of birth. These same newborn rats showed very poor development and a high death rate, although their MetHb levels returned to normal a few days after birth. Suckling rats whose mothers were exposed to nitrite in water only after birth showed no detrimental effects, thus indicating that the nitrites are not transferred in the milk. A possible inference from these very preliminary experiments is that there is some form of irreversible damage to the fetuses of mother rats exposed to nitrites during pregnancy. Increased abortion rates in cows exposed to nitrites in feed have been reported (MURHRER et al., 1956).

Surprisingly, it is only in recent years that toxicologists have begun to pay serious attention to possible fetal damage. Only since 1966 has the United States Food and Drug Administration required that fetal toxicity tests be included in all drug evaluation studies (GOLDENTHAL, 1966). Our preliminary findings concerning possible fetal damage in cases where mothers are exposed to methemoglobinemia-causing agents point to the urgent need for a most careful evaluation of this phenomenon.

CONCLUSIONS

It has been shown that the problem of nitrates in drinking water is one of increasing concern in many areas. This is already the case in Israel. There is no certainty that the current level of knowledge of the pathogenesis of nitrate methemoglobinemia or of the toxic effects of nitrates on adults and infants is adequate to support the present maximum permissible concentration of nitrates recommended for drinking water.

What is the public health significance of chronic subclinical methemoglobinemia which has been reported to exist in some areas? What is the effect on the fetus when mothers ingest methemoglobinemia-causing agents? The research program described may in time help to answer some of the basic questions left open on this subject.

ACKNOWLEDGEMENTS

Mr. K. Behroozi and Mrs. S. Cohen participated actively in both the laboratory and field phases of the study and their valuable contribution to the success of this work is appreciated. The authors are also indebted to Professor G. Izak for his assistance in launching this study, and to Prof. I. Nir for his helpful advice.

REFERENCES

BARTOS, H.R. and DESFORGES, J.F. (1966): "Erythrocyte DPNH dependent diaphorase levels in infants," *Pediatrics*, 37, 991.

BEARD, R.R. and WERTHEIM, G.A. (1967): "Behavioral impairment associated with small doses of carbon monoxide," *A.J.P.H.*, 57:2012–2022.

BODANSKY, O. (1951): "Methemoglobinemia and methemoglobin-producing compounds," *Pharmacol. Rev.*, 3, 144.

BOI-DOKU, F.S. and PICK, C. (1966): "Spontaneous oxidation of the chain of the foetal haemoglobin component of cord blood," *Biochim. Biophys. Acta*, 115, 495.

BURDEN, E.H. (1961): *The Analyst*, 86, 429.

CABALLERO, P.J. (1950): "Discussion sobre las normas de calidad para aqua potable," *Organo Official de la Associacion Interamericana de Ingenieria Sanitaria*, 3, 53.

COMLY, H.H. (1945): "Cyanosis in infants caused by nitrates in well water," *J.A.M.A.*, 129, 112.

CORNBLATH, M. and HARTMAN, A.F. (1948): "Methemoglobinemia in young infants," *J. Pediat.* 33, 421.

CRUZ, W.O. (1951): "Colorimetric determination of methemoglobin in normal animals," *Acta Haemat.*, 6, 367.

DAVISON, K. (1964): "Nitrate toxicity in dairy heifers," *Dairy Science*, 47, 1065.

DONAHOE, W.E. (1949): "Cyanosis in infants with nitrates in drinking water as cause," *Pediatrics*, 3, 308.

DRUKERY, H. (1962): *Arzneimittel Forsch.*, 12.

EVELYN, K.A. and MALLOY, H.T. (1938): "Microdetermination of oxyhemoglobin, methemoglobin and sulfhemoglobin in a single sample of blood," *J. Biol. Chem.*, 126, 655.

FERRANT, M. (1946): "Methemoglobinemia: two cases in newborn infants caused by nitrates in well water," *J. Pediat.*, 29, 585.

GOLDENTHAL, E.I. (1966): "Guidelines for reproduction studies for safety evaluation of drugs for human use," A communication of the FDA.

GROSS, E. (1964): *Arch. Hyg.*, 148, 288.

HORN, K. (1958): "Über Gesundheitsstörungen durch nitrathaltiges Trinkwasser, vornehmlich bei Säuglingen unter Berücksichtigung der ortshygienischen Verhältnisse," *Städt. Hygiene*, 2, 2.

JAFFE, E.R. (1964): *The Red Blood Cell* (C.W. Bishop, ed.), p. 397, Academic Press, New York.

JUNG, F. and REMMER, H. (1949): "Über die Umsetzung zwischen Nitrit und Hämoglobin," *Arch. Exptl. Path. u. Pharmak.*, **206**, 459.

KAMAZAWA, Y., HATTORI, M., KOSAKA, K. and NAKAO, K. (1968): "The relationship of NADH-dependent diaphorase activity and methemoglobin reduction in human erythrocytes," *Clin. Chim. Acta*, **19**, 524.

KNOTEK, Z. and SCHMIDT, P. (1964): "Pathogenesis, incidence and possibilities of preventing alimentary nitrate methemoglobinemia in infants," *Pediatrics*, **34**, 78.

LEMBERG, R. and LEGGE, J.W. (1949): *Hematin Compounds and Bile Pigments*, p. 228, Interscience Publishers Inc., New York.

LIEBLICH, I. and GUTTMAN, R. (1965): "The relation between motor activity and risk of death in audiogenic seizure of DBA mica," *Life Sciences*, **4**, 2295.

MARRIOTT, W.M., HARTMAN, A.F. and SENN, M.J. (1933): "Observations on the nature and treatment of diarrhea and the associated systemic disturbances," *J. Pediatrics*, **3**, 181.

MUCHA, V., KAMENSKY, P. and KELETI, J. (1965): "Genesis and prevention of alimentary nitrate methemoglobinemia in babies," *Hygiene and Sanitation*, **30**, 185.

MURHRER, M.E., GARNER, G.B., PFANDER, W.H. and O'DELL, B.L. (1956): *J. Anim. Sci.*, **15**, 1291.

MUSIL, J. (1966): "Der Einfluss einer chronischen Natrium-nitrit-Intoxikation auf Ratten," *Acta biol. med. germ.*, **16**, 388.

NICHOLS, S.M. (1965): *J. A.W.W.A.*, **57**, 1319.

PASSANNANTE, A.J. and GERARDE, H.W. (1966): "A micro-method for the determination of methemoglobin," *Journal of Occupational Health*, **8**, 455.

ROSENFIELD, A.B. and HUSTON, R. (1950): "Infant methemoglobinemia in Minnesota due to nitrates in well-water," *Minn. Med.*, **33**, 787.

ROSS, J.D. and DESFORGES, J.F. (1959): "Reduction of methemoglobin by erythrocytes from cord blood," *Pediatrics*, **23**, 718.

RUMMEL, W. (1965): *Wasserwerk Wassertechnik*, **15**, 4.

SCHMIDT, P. and KNOTEK, Z. (1966): "Problems of nitrate food methemoglobinemia of infants in Czechoslovakia," *Gig. i San.*, **31**, 290.

SHUVAL, H.I. (1962): "Public Health aspects of wastewater utilization in Israel," *Proc. 17th Ind. Waste Conf., Purdue Univ.*

SHUVAL, H.I. and RAM, D. (1968): Research Report: Nitrates in drinking water and their effect on health, Department of Medical Ecology, Hebrew University—Hadassah Medical School.

SINIOS, A. and WODSAK, W. (1965): "Die Spinatvergiftung des Säuglins," *Dtsch. med. Wschr.*, **90**, 1856.

SUBBOTIN, F.N. (1959): *Gig. i San.*, **23**, 3.

SUBBOTIN, F.N. (1961): "The nitrates of drinking water and their effect on the formation of methemoglobin," *Gig. i San*, **2**, 13.

TEERHAAG, L. and EYER, A. (1958): "Nitrate in Trinkwasser," *Öff. Gesundheitsdienst*, **20**, 1.

TEPPERMAN, J., BODANSKY, O. and JANDORF, B.J. (1946): "Effect of para-aminopropiophenone-induced methemoglobinemia on oxygenation of working muscle in human subjects," *Am. J. Physiol.*, **146**, 702.

U.S. PUBLIC HEALTH SERVICE DRINKING WATER STANDARDS (1962): PHS Publ. No. 956,

WAGO, S. (1956): "Two cases of methemoglobinemia in infants," *Harefuah*, **50**, 35.

ZBINDEN, G. (1969): *Science*, **164**, 643.

Section 2

WASTEWATER TREATMENT
AND UTILIZATION

The Outlook for Wastewater

Utilization in Israel

Alberto M. Wachs

INTRODUCTION

A comprehensive outlook on wastewater reuse in Israel must include the following considerations:

The role of wastewater reuse in the general framework of water resources planning and development.

Analysis of different possibilities of wastewater reuse: general water supply, agricultural irrigation, industrial use, recreational use, etc.

Definition of problems which must be solved in order to achieve those objectives, whether technological, legal, financial, and those concerned with public acceptance of wastewater reuse projects.

Research, surveys and studies, as required for the solution of problems formulated in accordance with above paragraphs.

Since a thorough analysis of all the foregoing considerations is not possible in the context of this paper, an effort has been made to select for presentation those that are considered of general relevance or interest, and in relation to particular projects or situations, research performed at the Sanitary Engineering Laboratories of the Technion, Israel Institute of Technology. In this paper those laboratories will be henceforth referred to as TSEL.

In a situation where more than 85 percent of the water resources are already being exploited and demand continues to grow, as is the case in Israel, it becomes necessary to use water from natural resources more than once. In effect, since 1956, in the formulation of master plans for the development and management of the country's water resources, wastewater has been considered in this category, and this policy has been reflected in the increasing utilization of such resources.

Table 1 summarizes the results of a survey on wastewater reuse carried out by staff of the Water Commissioner's Office of the Ministry of Agriculture in the year 1967 (SURVEY ON SEWAGE RECLAMATION, 1967). It will be noted from the information presented in the table that, on a percentage basis, the utilization of wastewater produced in rural communities (kibutzim and moshavim) is higher than that produced in urban centers. This situation could be substantially changed during the next decade, when plans for the reuse of wastewater originating in the "Greater Tel Aviv" urban conglomerate are expected to be implemented. These plans will be discussed later in this paper.

Table 1. Wastewater reuse*

Sources of wastewater	Amounts produced m^3/day	Amount reused m^3/day	Percent reused (on daily basis)	Amount reused yearly (millions m^3)
Urban areas	343,000	79,000	23	20.6
Rural settlements (kibutzim and (moshavim)	64,000	42,000	65	8.5
Total	407,000	121,000	30	29.1

* From data presented in "Survey on Wastewater Reuse", Water Commissioner's Office, November 1967.

SOME ASPECTS OF WASTEWATER REUSE IN AGRICULTURE

In the great majority of cases, rural communities that reclaim their wastewater through agricultural irrigation treat their liquid wastes in stabilization ponds used also for short-term operational storage and located relatively close to fields requiring irrigation. However, in general, irrigation is needed only during the dry season (150 to 200 days per year), and the capacity of the ponds is not sufficient to store the effluent discharged during the rainy season. Consequently, not only is a considerable amount of wastewater lost, but in many situations a pollution problem is created by the disposal of pond effluents during the winter, aggravated by the fact that during this season the efficiency of pond treatment is at its lowest. The fact that irrigation needs of most of the country's cultivated land are limited to the dry season also restricts the agricultural utilization of effluents produced in urban centers. The use of reservoirs allowing for winter storage of treated wastewater, possibly on a regional basis, would undoubtedly provide a partial solution. The application of systems analysis techniques to the study of wastewater treatment and effluent storage, considered on a regional basis, would be of value in the search for optimal solutions to the problem.

As might be expected, taking into consideration the epidemiological implications, stringent conditions have been established by the Ministry of Health to regulate the utilization of treated wastewater in agriculture, and these restrictions preclude its more extensive utilization in irrigation, which is by far the largest component of water demand in Israel. Disinfection of those effluents would permit their use in agriculture for crops that at present are irrigated with fresh water, at the same time increasing the availability of the latter. In order to evaluate this possibility, it was considered necessary to obtain basic information on chlorine requirements for the disinfection of stabilization pond effluents which contain considerable amounts of algae. Research in this field has been carried out by Prof. Y. Kott of the TSEL (KOTT, 1969). Disinfection adds to the cost of treatment. Although estimates for the cost of chlorination arrive at figures that cannot be considered prohibitive, about 1.5 agorot* per m^3 (KOTT, 1968), it should be recalled here that most rural communities in Israel, such as "kibutzim" and "moshavim", are highly cost-conscious, having generally selected stabilization ponds for the treatment of their wastewater on the basis of their low capital investment and operational costs. Reluctance to invest in disinfection facilities and to use treated wastewater instead of the regular water supply can be overcome in instances where the cost-benefit ratio is sufficiently positive, and to this end another research project, commented upon in the following paragraph, may contribute significantly.

As explained above, stabilization pond effluents are widely used in Israel for agricultural irrigation. Surprisingly, in many cases where crops are thus irrigated, farmers have been adding chemical fertilizers in the same amounts as when fresh water is used. This may result not only in waste of fertilizers but could also cause the pollution of groundwater by excess nitrogen compounds, not utilized by plants and therefore reaching subjacent aquifers. As a matter of fact, in various

---

* 100 agorot = 1 Israel lira (IL) = $0.29.

areas of the country a significant increase in the concentration of nitrates in groundwater has been observed, and in some cases the upward trend is such as to cause serious concern. To prevent the excessive use of chemical fertilizers for land irrigated with pond effluents, it becomes necessary to determine experimentally the effluent's fertilizer value. Simple chemical analysis of dissolved PNK compounds is not sufficient, since, for instance, a significant part of the nitrogen and phosphorus is contained, as suspended solids, in algal cells. It is also desirable to determine the possibly favorable influence of organic matter and the possibly adverse affect of salt concentrations higher than those present in the original water supply. A study of this type is now being carried out at the TSEL with the participation of staff of the Faculty of Agricultural Engineering at the Technion. At this stage of the study, it has already been found that in certain types of soils and cultures irrigation with pond effluents satisfies a considerable part of the PNK requirements, and also that the nitrogen present in algal cells can be nitrified in the soil at relatively high rates.

Figure 1 illustrates results of one of the experiments in this project in which various amounts of ammonium sulfate were added to cultures irrigated with pond effluents in one group and with water in the other. It can be seen that under conditions corresponding to those in the experiment, addition of chemical nitrogen to soil irrigated with pond effluent does not significantly increase the crop yield, or, in other words, that the nitrogen requirement can be satisfied by the nitrogen compounds contained in the effluent.

It would be reasonable to expect that a better appreciation of the fertilizer value of those effluents, and the consequent saving in commercial fertilizers, would stimulate a wider use of the former in irrigation. In situations where the savings in commercial fertilizers would cover all or a considerable part of the cost of disinfection, the overall economics would promote the extension of irrigation with treated wastewater to those crops that at present are irrigated with fresh water.

DAN REGION PROJECT FOR WASTEWATER REUSE

Undoubtedly, the most ambitious plans for wastewater reuse in Israel are those concerning the Dan Region, formed by the association of Tel Aviv and six surrounding municipalities,* with the objective of finding regional solutions

---

* Ramat Gan, Giv'atayim, Petah Tiqwa, Bene Beraq, Holon and Bat Yam.

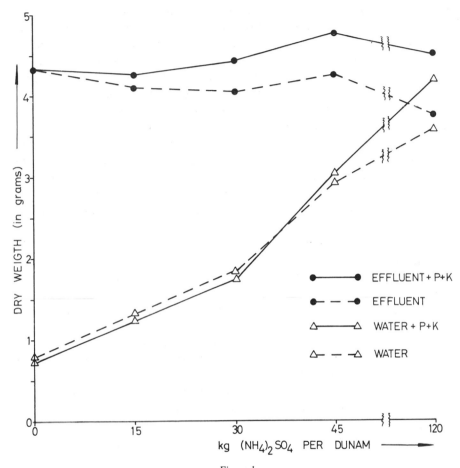

Figure 1

Dry weights of oats after 38 days of growth in "Hamra" soil (Sharon) when treated with pond effluents and with fresh water

to problems confronting the partner cities. The Region constitutes at present an urban conglomerate with a population of 800,000, and generates annually approximately 60 million m^3 of wastewater. The original wastewater reclamation project for the Dan Region was proposed in 1962 (AMRAMY et al., 1962), officially formulated in 1964 and again, with some modifications, in 1969 (PLANS FOR THE DAN REGION WATER RECLAMATION PROJECT, 1969). Two features of the project that favorably influence the estimated overall cost of the reclaimed water are related to the availability of large tracts of fiscal, relatively low-priced land in the area set aside for the project. This makes possible the treatment of the wastewater in series of stabilization ponds, allowing for a total residence time of 30 days. In conjunction with the favorable hydrogeological situation, this permits the recovery wells to be sited at a considerable distance from the basins where the effluent of the ponds is to be spread, thus providing for a period of approximately 400 days for the travel of the effluent in the ground.

In the first stage of the project, which is to become operational this year, only 7.5 million m^3 per annum will be treated for reclamation. This stage is considered to be of an experimental nature and is expected to provide valuable information for the construction and operation of the successive stages of the project which is expected to reach the design capacity of 50 million m^3 per annum in the year 1975.

Although circumstances in Israel do not correspond exactly to those in Southern California, it is of interest to consider the Dan Region Project in relation to criteria proposed by PARKHURST (1964) for evaluating the economic viability of wastewater reuse in that area. The four conditions that Parkhurst considers necessary to justify the construction of separate facilities intended for that purpose are the following:

1. The chemical quality of the water must be suitable for reuse.
2. The quantity available must be sufficient for economical production costs.
3. Reclaimable water must be produced near a project which can utilize it.
4. A benefit must be derived from the project in order to stimulate interest in the purchase of water at a reasonable price to compensate for all or a part of the cost of production.

Proceeding from the simple to the elaborate in our analysis of the foregoing criteria, conditions 2, 3 and 4 will be considered before condition 1.

The second condition is satisfactorily fulfilled, since more than 150,000 m^3 per day of wastewater are at present produced in the area. According to forecasts for the year 1990, this figure will be nearly doubled.

The proximity of the reclamation plant site to a major water conduit, the Western Yarqon-Negev Line, can be considered to satisfy the third condition, since this conduit constitutes "a project that can utilize" the renovated water.

As for the fourth condition, estimates of the cost of the renovated water compare favorably with alternative sources that could provide the amounts of water expected to be reclaimed by the project. In view of the almost complete exploitation of conventional resources, seawater desalination is virtually the sole alternative source. The cost of reclaiming the water from stabilization pond effluents, through lime treatment and long-term ground filtration, has been estimated at approximately 13 agorot per m^3 (14 cents per 1,000 gal.) for a system with a capacity of 50 million m^3 per year, a 25-year period of water production and an interest rate of 8%.*

Returning now to the first condition pertaining to the chemical quality of the water, Parkhurst assumes salinity to be the controlling factor, since desalination, even when partially applied, adds considerably to the costs of wastewater renovation. What are the salinity requirements for the renovated water in the Dan Region Project? It is interesting to note that in this case the main concern about salinity arises from the fact that water supplied by the Yarqon-Negev line, mentioned above, is used in the irrigation of citrus plantations in the southern part of the country. In consequence, a chloride-ion concentration exceeding 250 mg/l is not permissible.

The amounts and salinity of the wastewater undergoing renovation will vary at different stages of implementation of the project, and the low-salinity groundwater now available in the aquifer will be gradually displaced by the treated wastewater. Therefore, in order to predict changes of salinity in the water to be supplied through the Yarqon-Negev line, it has been necessary to formulate for each year of operation of the project material balances that take into consideration the following factors:

1. The salinity of the water supplied to each of the cities participating in the project.
2. The incremental salinity resulting from domestic and industrial water used in each of these cities.
3. The increasing salinity of the water pumped from the artificially recharged aquifer, as the treated wastewater gradually replaces the native groundwater.
4. The varying ratios between the pumped water and that supplied from other sources to the Yarqon-Negev line.

It will be noted from the foregoing considerations that the project is not aimed at attaining a salinity equilibrium in the recharged aquifer, since no partial desalination is to be practiced in the renovation of the wastewater, and natural recharge is only a fraction of the artificial one.

---

* The cost of water that could be produced in Israel by a dual-purpose, nuclear-fueled, seawater desalination plant of 100 MGD capacity was estimated in 1966 at 39.6 agorot per m^3 (36.7 cents per 1,000 gal.) on the basis of 7% fixed charge rate.

As a result, the salinity of the aquifer will gradually increase, but the designers consider that for a period of twenty years salinity can be satisfactorily controlled by dilution with water from other sources brought by the conduit to the point of admixture of the renovated water. It is expected that new sources of low salinity water, probably desalinated seawater, will already be available by that time. As explained in the final section of this paper, the project exemplifies a situation described by STEPHAN and WEINBERGER (1968), where "advanced wastewater treatment could postpone the time and reduce the total requirement for providing "new" freshwater to an area through importation or desalination."

RESEARCH RELATED TO THE DAN REGION PROJECT

Since in the Dan Region Project the spreading basins are to be intermittently operated, ammonia present in the effluent of the ponds would be biologically converted to nitrates, as was observed in similar projects elsewhere (MCMICHAEL and MCKEE, 1966). During the first stage of the project, control of nitrate concentration in the final water can be effected by dilution with groundwater in the aquifer and water introduced from other sources. In fact dilution will be required for the control of chloride concentrations, as explained elsewhere in this paper. However, for subsequent stages of implementation it is considered desirable to prevent objectionable nitrate concentrations in the renovated water through adequate treatment of the effluents before their introduction in the ground. Certain aspects of research related to this objective, currently being carried out at the TSEL, are described in the following paragraphs.

Although several meters of fine dune sand underlie the spreading basins, it has been shown that at high infiltration velocities the algae present in the pond effluents may be carried with the water to depths at which they may affect the quality of the water in the recharged aquifer (FOLKMAN, 1963). Removal of the algae from the effluents prior to their discharge into the spreading basins might therefore be required, and in 1962–63 investigations were carried out at the TSEL on algae removal by flocculation with alum, lime and polyelectrolytes. Lime treatment of pond effluents proved to be effective in removing, besides algae, significant amounts of phosphates, organic matter and bacteria. A comparative study of the efficiency of the flocculants mentioned above in the removal of viruses furnished the results presented in Table 2.

It was also found at that time that the efficiency of lime treatment was mainly conditioned by the presence of magnesium ions in the effluent. This can be ob-

Table 2. Removal of poliovirus type I from effluent of
stabilization ponds by flocculation and settling

Sample	Virus titer PFU/ml
Effluent + added virus	
Control	0.98×10^4
Control after 2 hrs	0.68×10^4
Treated with polyelectrolyte	4.78×10^2
Treated with alum	1.65
Treated with CaO	0.00

served in Figure 2 which shows that separation by lime treatment of algae suspended in a solution of magnesium bicarbonate gave much better results than separation of algae of the same type and concentration suspended in a calcium bicarbonate solution. The role of magnesium in the flocculation by lime can be explained in terms of the opposite surface charge of magnesium hydroxide particles (positive) and algae (negative). Further research on flocculation processes of algae by lime, as influenced by magnesium ions, is at present being carried out with the help of zeta potential measurements (FOLKMAN and WACHS, 1969), and results are to be published in the near future.

Presenting results of investigations carried out in small model-ponds at the TSEL in the years 1965–68, Dr. B. Sless observed that alkalinity and ammonia and orthophosphate contents in pond liquid decreased considerably when, as a result of intensive photosynthetic action, the pH in the ponds reached high values. It was inferred that carbonates and orthophosphates precipitated, while ammonia volatilized, when the pH reached values of 9.5 to 10.5, and therefore that significant part of the reduction in the concentration of major nutrients was due to the high pH caused by algal activity, rather than by direct uptake of those nutrients by the algae themselves (SLESS, 1968). The decrease in concentration of ammonia and orthophosphates with increase in pH (and temperature) can be seen in Figure 3, adapted from the work mentioned above, presenting data obtained throughout a 16-hour period on a summer day.

Those results indicated that significant amounts of ammonia could be transferred from a pond liquid to the atmosphere at high pH values resultant from intensive algal metabolic processes. However, such high pH values occur naturally only during a limited period of the day and then only in the summer season. The possibility of promoting ammonia transfer from ponds by artificially raising the pH merited exploration and, after corroborative laboratory work carried out on am-

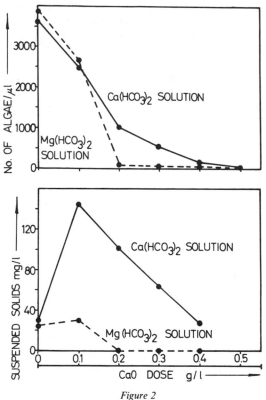

Figure 2
Separation, by lime treatment, of algae suspended in
solutions of calcium and magnesium bicarbonate

monia solutions by MELAMED and SALITERNIK (1969), research using model-ponds at Technion City was started by Y. Folkman, the present author and A. Melamed. Although the research program has not yet been completed, results from one experiment can be shown here to indicate that removal of considerable quantities of ammonia from pond liquids could in principle be effected without resort to more expensive methods such as forced air-scrubbing. This system of nitrogen removal is of particular interest when lime treatment is used for separation of algae from the pond effluent, since the pH of the supernatant is then above 10.8, adequate for promoting ammonia transfer to the atmosphere. In Figure 4 decreasing concentrations of ammonia are shown as functions of time, following lime treatment of the effluents of five model ponds operated in series. These

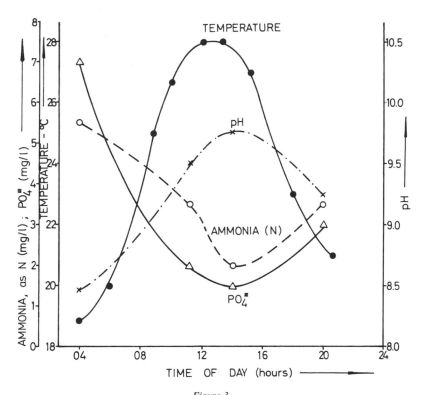

Figure 3
Variations in pH, ammonia and orthophosphate concentration during a 16-hour
period. Samples obtained near surface of pond. (Adapted from J. B. Sless)

ponds, shown in Figure 5, are operated at loadings proposed for the serial ponds
to be used in the Dan Region Project.

An interesting approach to the problem of nitrogen removal, relating to the
same Project, has been suggested by Melamed. Research required for its evaluation
is at present underway at the TSEL, being carried out by Saliternik under the
guidance of Melamed. In the proposed scheme, the ammonia present in the
effluent of an anaerobic pond would be nitrified in an activated sludge type of
installation, and the nitrified effluent consequently denitrified in the reducing
environment of an anaerobic pond. Results of the research stage dealing with the
nitrification of anaerobic pond effluents are promising and will be published
shortly.

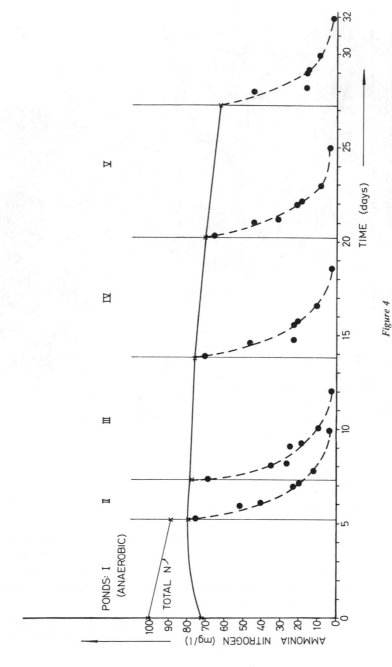

Figure 4

Changes in ammonia concentration subsequent to lime treatment of effluent of five ponds in series. (Lime dosage: 900 mg/l CaO)

Figure 5
Experimental stabilization ponds at Technion City

PROBLEMS OF THE FUTURE

By 1975 the design capacity of the first part of the Dan Region will be reached: 50 million m³ per year. But the amount of wastewater produced in that Region will continue to increase, and for the "nineties," when the population in the area is expected to reach 1.25 million, a yearly figure of 110 to 120 million m³ has been predicted.

It is possible that, as a result of research carried out during the early seventies, area requirements for pond treatment could be lowered and also that the absorption capacity of the spreading basins could be improved. However, a major expansion of the project, if designed on the basis of the main features of the first stage, will call for the construction of new ponds and spreading basins at a considerable distance southward from the present site. At any rate, investigations carried out during the first stage will be of considerable value for the development of the facilities that will be necessary when the design capacity of the system is exceeded. In the not so distant future the major problem to be solved, if wastewater reuse is to be continued, is that of salinity. The salinity problem could be alleviated if viable means could be found to control the relatively large salt input resulting from the discharge into municipal sewers of brines used in the regeneration of water softeners. It has been estimated that for most of the Dan Region's wastewater half of the sodium chloride increment is caused by such discharges.

It is generally agreed that a large seawater desalination plant, combined with electrical power production, will have to be erected in the next decade, not only to close the predictable gap between water demand and water potential, but also to solve the problem of increasing salinity already affecting a considerable portion of the country's water resources. Water produced in such plants could be used to control the salinity of water supply systems containing significant amounts of reclaimed wastewater. At the same time, the development of certain areas in the southern part of the country, not connected to the Israel National Water System, will necessitate the application of desalting methods to make possible the exploitation of locally available brackish groundwater. In this connection, two demonstration plants, one using electrodialysis and the other reverse osmosis, have been erected, at Zeelim and Yotvatah, respectively. Experience gained in the use of these processes will be of value in assessing the feasibility of desalinating renovated wastewater.

REFERENCES

AMRAMY, A., CASPI, B. and MELAMED, A. (1962): "Dan Region sewage reclamation project," Tahal (Water Planning for Israel, Ltd.), P.N. 241, Tel Aviv.

FOLKMAN, Y. (1963): "Filtration through dune sand of algae contained in stabilization pond effluent," Thesis for M.Sc. degree, Technion–Israel Institute of Technology, Sanitary Engineering Laboratories, Haifa (in Hebrew).

FOLKMAN, Y. and WACHS, A. (1969): "Reclamation of stabilization ponds effluents through lime treatment," Progress Report, Technion Research and Development Foundation, Haifa (in Hebrew).

KOTT, Y. (1968): "Reclamation of effluents of stabilization ponds for extended agriculture utilization," Research Report CV-262, Technion Research and Development Foundation, Haifa (in Hebrew).

KOTT, Y. (1969): "Chlorination of sewage oxidation ponds effluents," These Proceedings, pp. 189–197.

McMICHAEL, F. and McKEE, J.E. (1966): "Final report of research on wastewater reclamation at Whittier Narrows, California, via State Water Quality Control Board," Pub. No. 33, Pasadena.

MELAMED, A. and SALITERNIK, C. (1969): "Removal of nitrogen by ammonia emission from water surfaces," These Proceedings, pp. 165–172.

PARKHURST, J.D. (1964): "Progress in wastewater re-use in Southern California," A.S.C.E. Environmental Engineering Conference, Salt Lake City.

Plans for the Dan Region Water Reclamation Project (1969): Part "A"—Works North of Nahal Soreq, Designed by Tahal (Water Planning for Israel Ltd.), Mekorot Water Company Ltd. Publication No. 714, Tel Aviv (in Hebrew).

SLESS, J.B. (1968): "The role of algae in oxidation ponds in Israel," Report on Research Project CV–42, Technion Research and Development Foundation, Haifa (in Hebrew).

STEPHAN, D.G. and WEINBERGER, L.W. (1968): "Wastewater reuse—has it arrived?" J. Wat. Pollut. Control Fed., Vo. 40, No. 4.

Survey on Sewage Reclamation (1967): Ministry of Agriculture, Water Commissioner Office, Division for Agricultural Water and Sewage, Jerusalem (in Hebrew).

A Guide to Pond Systems

for Wastewater Purification

G. J. Stander, P. G. J. Meiring,

R. J. L. C. Drews, H. Van Eck

INTRODUCTION

The use of pond systems for the purification of wastewater is practiced widely in South Africa as an effective and low-cost method to relieve existing overloaded conventional sewage purification works, to provide additional polishing treatment for the purpose of obtaining an effluent with high bacteriological quality, to treat night-soil or as the sole wastewater treatment process.

Although this method varies in its efficiency according to the specific design and local conditions, instances can be quoted when the introduction of stabilization ponds for wastewater treatment has brought about a great improvement in the environmental situation, which, for practical economic reasons, would not otherwise be possible.

The economic advantages, simplicity of construction and ease of operation and maintenance of stabilization and maturation ponds for sewage purification and effluent beneficiation for reuse carry with them an inherent danger in that the systems are so simple they are not recognized as an engineering venture, such as a conventional sewage purification plant. Pond systems require proper planning and application, design maintenance and periodical review of pond loading.

A further factor responsible for laxity in pond management is the fact that these systems provide better barriers against pollution in the event of mismanagement than conventional sewage works.

As time passed, however, it appeared that through lack of knowledge, or misappreciation of essentials, there has been a deviation from suggested criteria for the design and construction of these ponds. These deviations have, in some instances, caused the ponds to fall into disrepute. The present document is, therefore, an attempt to combine knowledge and experience gained thus far with the results of further research. This document could thus serve as a reference for planning new systems and for improving existing installations.

In using maturation pond systems for humus tank effluent treatment, biological activity is harnessed: to minimize the hitherto uncontrolled eutrophication of rivers, natural lakes and impoundment reservoirs receiving purified effluents; to provide an effluent amenable to more advanced purification.

This guide is based on pilot plant and field research studies on pond systems carried out over the years by the National Institute for Water Research of the South African Council for Scientific and Industrial Research.

GENERAL CONSIDERATIONS FOR POND SYSTEMS

Definitions

Within the context of this guide, the following definitions of terms apply:

Pond system: Any pond system intended to fulfil a biological waste treatment requirement, utilizing bacteria and algae.

Stabilization pond: Pond used for biological stabilization of raw or partially treated wastewaters.

Maturation pond: Pond used for treatment of well-nitrified humus tank (final settling tank) or sand-filtered effluent.

Anaerobic pond: Stabilization pond with anaerobic conditions obtaining throughout.

Aerobic pond: Pond which is almost completely aerobic, with no or only a small anaerobic bottom layer.

Aerobic-anaerobic pond: Pond in which aerobic conditions prevail near the surface and anaerobic conditions in the bottom sediments and lower water levels. These ponds are also referred to as *facultative stabilization ponds* or simply as *facultative ponds*.

Anaerobic-aerobic stabilization pond system: A system in which anaerobic ponds are followed by facultative ponds from which oxygenated water is recirculated to the raw wastewater entering the anaerobic ponds. The system is considered as a primary unit in a series of ponds.

How a Pond Operates

A diagrammatic representation of different pond systems is given in Figure 1. The relative pond areas required are indicated. An improvement in effluent quality is represented by the relative movement across the spectrum to the right. The range varies from the completely anaerobic pond for treating raw sewage to completely aerobic maturation ponds treating sand-filtered humus tank effluent. Mechanically assisted ponds, in which all or much of the oxygen requirements are supplied by mechanical aeration, are not indicated in this diagram.

A pond system may be designed to treat either night-soil, raw sewage, settled sewage or sewage works effluent. The design depends on the treatment objectives, but this type of waste treatment process is most suitable for locations where land is inexpensive, climatic conditions are suitable, organic loadings fluctuate considerably, and funds are limited. Pond systems have often been used to satisfy interim waste treatment requirements for treatment of sewage in small quantities.

The process depends on the effective use of bacteria for degradation of putrescible organic material and, usually, green algae for oxygenation purposes. A mutual relationship exists between algae and bacteria. The bacteria are the primary workers, which have the ability to effectively break down and utilize many complex organic waste materials, whereas the algae, with the assistance of fungi, utilize the simpler degradation products. At the same time the algae produce oxygen for use by the aerobic bacteria.

As long as the algae can provide an excess of oxygen above that required by the bacteria, a relatively aerobic environment will at least be maintained in the upper layers of the pond. Under these conditions, aerobic organisms can degrade the organic material. Part of the substrate will be used to make new cells, and the remainder will provide the energy that is necessary to further the degradation reactions.

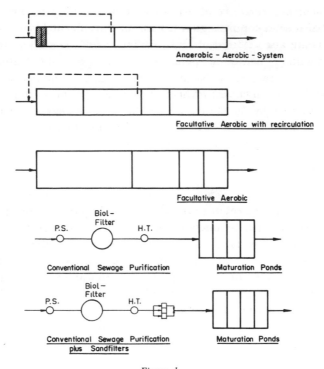

Figure 1
Range of applications of pond systems (pond areas approximately
proportional)

If sufficient oxygen is not provided, as in the bottom layer of a stabilization pond, anaerobic bacteria or facultative bacteria (i.e., bacteria which can function under either aerobic or anaerobic conditions) will obtain the required oxygen from chemical compounds and produce various types of organic acids, alcohols, etc. The anaerobic process, as compared with the aerobic process, is relatively more complex and will produce more odoriferous conditions. Except in completely anaerobic ponds, the anaerobic bottom layer is sealed off from the atmosphere by an aerobic surface layer.

Most ponds develop to varying degrees into combination anaerobic-aerobic treatment units. In this respect, ponds are very similar to rivers and lakes. Aerobic conditions are frequently maintained near the surface and sometimes throughout most of the pond. However, because organic debris frequently settles out, an anaerobic environment will persist near the bottom.

The effluent put into maturation ponds should already be well stabilized in a conventional sewage purification works. As the effluent from a series of stabilization ponds is also well stabilized, the final ponds in such a series also perform the function of maturation ponds. Purification effected in maturation ponds is primarily with respect to bacteriological quality, although some chemical improvement is also achieved. (When treating a humus tank effluent which contains very little suspended solids, a maturation pond may cause the apparent deterioration of this effluent because of algal development.)

Temperature

Temperature is of paramount importance in the design of pond systems. It affects photosynthetic oxygen production as well as other biological reactions. While optimum oxygen production is obtained at about 20°C, limiting lower and upper values, respectively, appear to be about 4°C and 35°C. Above 22°C increased anaerobic fermentation results in the formation of mats of sludge on the surface, buoyed up by occluded gases. When water temperatures approach 35°C in warmer climates, particularly when ponds are shallow, the beneficial algal population will be severely curtailed.

Topography and Siting

Any pond system for waste treatment should be well protected against washaways and the entry of natural runoff. Provided this can be ensured, there is no reason why the pond design should not be adapted to the surrounding topography, as it may cost less to include existing depressions or valleys in the scheme than to fill them in.

The least amount of earth-moving for the construction of ponds is usually required on land of gentle slope. However, it should be noted that this same land is not necessarily the most suitable for the construction of a sewage purification plant of conventional design, which may at a later stage replace the stabilization pond system as a sewage treatment facility.

Aerobic-anaerobic (facultative) stabilization ponds, properly maintained to keep mosquito-breeding in check, need not be sited more than 500′ away from a residential area. Anaerobic ponds can usually be operated to cause no odor nuisance. However, it is not always possible to eliminate fly-breeding in such ponds, and for this reason anaerobic ponds should be situated at least half a mile away from any residential area. All ponds should be fenced in.

Land Requirements

It is advisable that all land between the sewage purification plant—whether it be stabilization ponds or a conventional sewage purification plant—and the nearest watercourse should be acquired and owned by the owners of the purification plant.

A net pond area of facultative ponds of approximately 5 acres must be provided for a flow of domestic sewage of 100,000 gallons per day. Additional allowance for embankments, dividing walls and access roads must also be made. The above requirements of 5-acre pond area will differ with other wastes and other types of ponds. The extent of land required for irrigation purposes, if practiced, amounts to between 20 and 40 acres per 100,000 imperial gallons* per day of irrigation water.

Versatility of Application

Treatment of night-soil: Stabilization ponds can, in many instances, be put to excellent use to relieve existing conventional sewage purification works by treating night-soil and/or conservancy tank effluent rather than discharging these liquids to the sewer and thence to the sewage purification works (SHAW, 1963). If the ponds are sited adjacent to the existing sewage plant, humus tank effluent can be used profitably for topping up purposes.

Decentralized treatment facilities: Where stabilization ponds are to be used on an interim scheme (or even otherwise), it may be economically profitable to operate a number of small units on temporary sites close to the source of the effluent until such time as it becomes justifiable to install a main collecting sewer (STANDER and MEIRING, 1965).

Treatment of septic tank effluent: Facultative stabilization ponds can be profitably employed for the disposal of pretreated effluent such as that derived from septic tanks and aqua-privies or the effluent from a primary anaerobic pond with recirculation as described further on (VINCENT et al.).

Increased sewage treatment capacity: By introducing a quantity of settled sewage with the nitrified effluent from a conventional works to the first of a

---

* 1 imperial gallon = 4.545 liters.

series of maturation ponds, a marked reduction in the nitrate concentration can be achieved without otherwise materially affecting the quality of the final effluent (GAILLARD and CRAWFORD, 1964; BOLITHO, 1964).

Advanced effluent treatment (maturation ponds): The use of ponds for further treatment of humus tank effluent is being practised very widely in South Africa (STANDER and MEIRING, 1963; STANDER, 1955; CILLIE et al., 1966). Primarily, these ponds are used to obtain an effluent of high bacteriological quality, but it has been shown that advanced biochemical purification is also obtained in these ponds, as for instance illustrated by the further reduction of synthetic detergents. This improvement in chemical quality, as indicated by the normal sanitary parameters, is frequently masked by prolific algal activity.

The biological processes which improve a sewage effluent chemically and bacteriologically are unlikely to alter the virus content significantly, but ponds nevertheless have a gratifying ability to bring about virological purification (MALHERBE and COETZEE, 1965). The removal of viruses probably depends upon their adsorption onto static surfaces and their exposure to the rays of the sun. According to the aforementioned reference, it is concluded that, from the virological point of view, a pond system should be as shallow as possible and so extensive that the retention period exceeds the normal survival time of an infectious virus. This stresses the importance of preventing short-circuiting and points towards the necessity of having a number of ponds in series.

The development of an efficient technique to remove algae from pond effluents and the feasibility of denitrifying humus tank effluent in a pond system have opened new horizons for employing maturation ponds for effluent reclamation.

Contamination of Groundwater, Seepage Losses and Sealing of Ponds

Groundwater pollution from seepage must always be regarded as a possibility (MALAN, 1962). From tests reported in the literature, it would appear that where the pond bottom is in the zone of aeration above the water table, the migration of bacterial pollution would be slight (of the order of 20 feet). Where seepage from the pond is directly into an aquifer, bacteria may migrate for several hundred feet, the migration being generally in the direction of flow of the groundwater.

In certain geological formations, where the groundwater travels in fissures or channels, instead of permeating slowly through the soil or rock pores, the possibilities of dangerous pollution of underground waters are much greater.

It is obvious from the data presented in Table 1 that seepage losses can be high

Table 1. Reported seepage rates from pond systems

Literature source	Initial Rates					Eventual Rates				Geology of pond base	Place
	Initial seepage rate		Hydraulic load gals/acre/d	Seepage rate as % of hydraulic load	Settling-in period	Eventual seepage rate		Hydraulic load gals/acre/d	Seepage rate as % of hydraulic load		
	ins/day	gals/acre/d				ins/day	gals/acre/d				
California SWPCB (Nos. 15, 18)	8.8	199,000	316,000	63	9 months	0.35	7,940	±380,000	2.1	Desert soil (sandy soil)	Mojave, California
*Neel and Hopkins (1956)	5.5	127,850	141,970	90	1 year	0.61	13,810	47,323	29.2	Sand and gravel	Kearney, Nebraska
**Voights (1955)	—	—	—	—	Average over 5 years (1951–55)	0.34	7,660	9,160	84	Sandy soil	Filer City Michigan
Shaw (1962)	6	136,000	54,000	Exceeded inflow rate	±1 year	0.3	6,800	50,000	13.6	Clay loam and shale	Pretoria
Windhoek mun. †maturation ponds:											
nos. 5	0.16	3,500	776,000	0.45	Over period 14th–22nd June 1967 after all ponds in full operation	—	—	—	—	Mica and schist	Windhoek, S.W.A.
6	0.17	3,900	1,190,000	0.32		—	—	—	—	Mica and schist	
7	0.015	300	712,000	0.046		—	—	—	—	Mica	
8	0.06	1,400	715,000			—	—	—	—	Mica and schist	
9	0.23	5,300	455,000			—	—	—	—	Mica and schist with side wall seepage to river	

* Evaporation and rainfall effects were apparently not corrected for. Seepage losses were also influenced by a high water table at times.

** These lagoons were constructed in sandy soil with the *express purpose* of seeping away Paper Mill NSSC liquor.

† Ponds constructed for the *express purpose* of water reclamation.

and vary over a wide range according to the geology of the pond base and the composition of soil used in the construction of the walls. Consequently, the prevention of pollution of underground water supplies and the curtailment of losses where the reclamation of water for reuse is of primary importance necessitate that special attention be given to site selections and the sealing of pond base and walls.

If a pond is to be constructed in a soil of high porosity, i.e., having a very low clay content, or on an unsound geological formation such as found in dolomitic areas, the danger of groundwater pollution could be real. It would then be advisable to take steps to seal the pond bottom.

Such sealing could be effected by the importation and compaction of a layer of suitable soil on the floor of the pond, or otherwise with plastic sheeting. In the last instance, special care must be taken since the sheeting is easily ruptured and where it is exposed at the water's edge it should be covered over to protect it against hail stones and the perishing effect of ultraviolet light. Plastic sheeting is also subject to bulging if the soil underneath contains organic material which, because of anaerobic fermentations, would produce gas.

It will be noticed from Table 2 that sealing of a pond approximately doubles its capital coast.

Sludge Accumulation

The accumulation of sludge and its effect on the continued performance of a pond require further study. However, in a facultative pond, equilibrium between Biochemical Oxygen Demand (BOD) deposited and BOD released from the anaerobic sludge layer into the overlying water, as products of fermentation, is attained after about four years. Since there is a very slow build-up of stabilized sludge which is very resistant to further, biological degradation, it must be accepted that a primary facultative pond receiving raw sewage must either be cleaned out or replaced after about nine to twelve years of continued use since, after such period, the overlying water becomes too shallow (less than 2′6″) for continued satisfactory performance.

The removal of sludge from any of these ponds should present no problem since it is well stabilized and may be amenable to pumping by suction pump mounted on a raft, without need to empty the pond, or to lifting either manually or by mechanical means after emptying the pond and leaving the sludge to dry.

The sludge accumulation resulting from the treatment of primary and secondary treated domestic wastes is practically negligible.

Table 2. Relative costs of sewage treatment facilities

Population	Capital cost in rand/person			Running costs/year in rand*/person	
	Conventional purification works	Facultative pond systems		Conventional purification works	Pond system
		Without sealing of bottom**	With sealing of bottom†		
240	70	6	12	–	1.0
1,000	43	6	11	5	0.6
3,000	31	5	10	3	0.3
5,000	29	5	10	–	0.3

* 1 rand = $1.39
** Cost of construction estimated at ± R3,000 per acre.
† A rate of ± 60 cents per sq. yd. has been assumed for sealing of pond bottoms, both primary and secondaries.

Mosquito-Breeding

Mosquito-breeding in any of the ponds is best prevented by keeping the verges free from vegetation and the ponds open to wind action. See also "Health Aspects."

Fly-Breeding

Fly-breeding would normally not give rise to nuisance except in the case of anaerobic ponds.

Maintainance

It would seem that the less the maintenance required on a particular purification plant, the more likely it is to be totally neglected. A special appeal should, therefore, be made to operators to ensure that ponds are properly maintained in general, particularly by guarding against overloading, by keeping the verges free from vegetation, by removing vegetation from within the ponds, and generally by keeping the ponds in an aesthetically pleasing condition by removing and burying any unsightly floating debris. Leakage on the embankments from crab or rat holes must also be guarded against. Any neglect in this respect can impair the efficiency of purification.

Water-Borne Sanitation for Small and Isolated Communities

Table 2 is based on information obtained from various sources on actual existing installations. The cost data reveal an interesting comparison between the costs involved in the construction and running of conventional sewage purification systems and facultative pond systems for similar sized communities, and emphasize the fact that pond systems are ideally suited for providing water-borne sanitation for small and isolated communities which cannot afford the construction of conventional treatment facilities.

MATURATION PONDS

Maturation ponds as such are not intended to cater for underdesigned conventional sewage purification facilities or to obviate the extension of an overloaded works or to save on costs of operation and supervision. Maturation ponds are biological units in which a well-nitrified humus tank or sand-filter effluent is purified to give a water of high bacteriological quality (STANDER and MEIRING, 1963; STANDER, 1955; MALHERBE and COETZEE, 1965; MARAIS, 1963; DREWS, 1966).

Pond Appurtenances

Bodily displacement of the contents, i.e., river flow conditions, cannot readily be obtained in a pond since short-circuiting would inevitably occur. In view of this tendency, maximum *average* detention must be strived after. This can be achieved by setting the other extreme condition, that of complete mixing, as the ideal, and to this end pond appurtenances must be constructed and sited with great care. In this connection the following points are mentioned:

(1) Water discharging from the inlet pipe often has considerable momentum, which may result in short-circuiting. The inlet, which should preferably discharge near the bottom of the pond, should also be directed away from the outlet end of the pond and preferably into likely stagnant pockets, such as may occur in pond corners. This applies to the inlet to each pond. If this is not possible, some means of dispersion of the flow should be adopted.

(2) Outlets withdrawing water from the surface are not recommended, due to short-circuiting in winter caused by thermal effects of streaming and sheet-

spreading of the warmer influent along the surface. On the other hand, a deep subsurface draw-off facilitates short-circuiting in summer, since the cooler influent tends to move along the bottom. As a compromise, submerged or baffled outlets are preferable, as the effects due to thermal stratification will be reduced and floating scum will be prevented from passing out with the effluent. The baffle should reach to about one foot or eighteen inches below the surface. Examples of inlet and outlet arrangements are shown in Figure 2.

When succeeding ponds are at the same level, submerged oversized connection pipes could be used, thus greatly reducing the momentum of the outflowing water. This, however, may create new problems, as, despite the considerable retention time provided in pond systems, if oversized connection pipes or weirs are provided, it will be found that peak or surge discharges entering the first pond are not balanced out, and a similar peak outflow from the final pond will follow within a very short space of time.

This is due to the fact that very little build-up of head is needed to convey the peak or surge through the whole pond system. A highly variable rate of outflow would be undesirable where effluent is to be pumped to a point of reuse, or where chlorination or some other form of final treatment is to be practised, as equipment would have to be large enough to cope with peak loads, and would have to be adjustable to cope with constantly varying flows.

Under such circumstances, connection pipes or overflow weirs between ponds should be of the minimum permissible size; this will make it possible to use the capacity of the ponds themselves to balance out surges. For ponds having to deal with up to 150,000 gallons per day, when flow-balancing is needed, 4″ diameter pipes, or overflow weirs 6″ wide, are suggested. It is not expected that blockage of 4″ pipes or 6″ weirs will often occur, but emergency overflows should be provided.

An alternative to using the capacity of the ponds as balancing storage is, of course, to build an additional dam for storing effluent from the final pond, and to withdraw from the storage dam at a constant rate.

(3) Where possible or feasible, multiple inlets and outlets should be provided to counteract stagnation in certain corners of the pond.

Sizing and Arrangements of Maturation Ponds

The retention time in a maturation pond and the configuration of a series of ponds receiving humus tank effluent or sand-filter effluent are determined

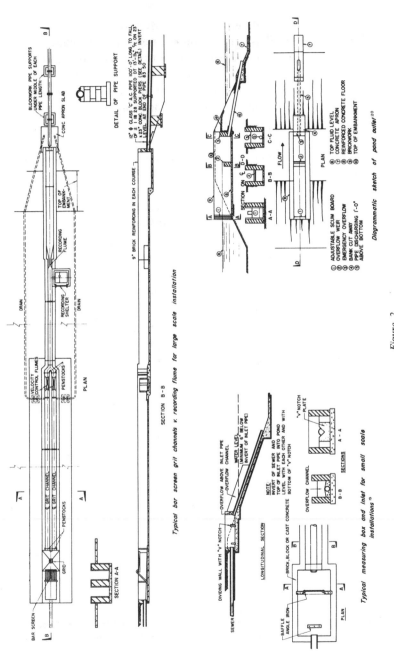

Typical bar screen grit channels v. recording flume for large scale installation

Typical measuring box and inlet for small scale installations [19]

Diagrammatic sketch of pond outlet [20]

① ADJUSTABLE SCUM BOARD
② OVERFLOW WEIR
③ EMERGENCY OVERFLOW
④ BANK CUT AWAY
⑤ PIPE DISCHARGING 1'-0"
   ABOVE BOTTOM
⑥ TOP FLUID LEVEL
⑦ CONCRETE APRON
⑧ REINFORCED CONCRETE FLOOR
⑨ BRICKWORK
⑩ TOP OF EMBANKMENT

Figure 2
Typical inlet and outlet arrangements

primarily by the measure of bacterial purification required. Unless the effluent which is to be treated has received only limited stabilization, a maturation pond cannot readily be overloaded to become anaerobic, and only practical considerations would therefore dictate the size of such ponds.

The die-off of fecal bacteria in aerobic ponds follows a monomolecular law provided good mixing is assured, i.e., the rate of die-off is more or less inversely proportional to the bacterial concentration (MARAIS and SHAW, 1961). This die-off is reflected in the following equation which gives the relationship, expressed as percentage, between the concentration of bacteria in a single pond N to the influent concentration N_o for varying detention times:

$$100\left(\frac{N}{N_o}\right) = \frac{100}{(KR + 1)}$$

where R = detention time in pond (days) and K = velocity constant (tentative value assumed to be 2).

The value of K has been established empirically and has been shown to vary considerably in sympathy with the extent to which short-circuiting and seasonal effects, such as hours of sunshine, influence pond performance. However, the value of K has never been observed to be less than 2.2, and until more data are available showing to what extent improved prevention of short-circuiting, for instance, would enable the designer to use an increased value for K, a K value of 2 is recommended for design purposes.

The advantageous effect of having a series of small ponds instead of a single large pond of the same overall size is illustrated by doubling the detention time in the above equation. The relationship then becomes:

$$100\left(\frac{N}{N_o}\right) = \frac{100}{(K2R_1 + 1)}$$

However, if instead a second pond of equal size is added in series, the relationship between the quality of the effluent from the second pond and the primary pond influent would become:

$$100\left(\frac{N}{N_o}\right) = 100\left(\frac{1}{KR_1 + 1}\right)\left(\frac{1}{KR_1 + 1}\right) = \frac{100}{(KR_1 + 1)}{}^2$$

By inserting any figure for R the superior performance of a series of ponds would become evident.

According to the above equation, four ponds in series, each having $4\frac{1}{2}$ days retention and properly operated, should give a 99.99% reduction in fecal bacteria concentration. Five ponds in series, each having three days retention, would perform even better.

Target Effluent Quality Requirement

Bacteriological: It has been established that the bacteria *E. coli* I, as determined by the MPN method and present in the effluent from any particular pond, have a log-normal distribution with a logarithmic standard deviation S not exceeding 0.45 (MARAIS, 1963). From this information it is therefore possible not only to set a quality requirement for a pond effluent, but also to stipulate an upper confidence limit on a rational basis. Since a biological system is being dealt with, a confidence limit is considered an essential feature of any quality requirement.

For design purposes, it should be accepted that an effluent bacteriological count of 1,000 *E. coli* I per 100 ml should be considered the upper limit of the 97.5% confidence range (exceeded by only 2.5%) of effluent quality. In most instances, such effluents should be acceptable for flood irrigation of crops for human consumption that are not likely to be eaten raw, for flood irrigation of fruit and trellised vines, for irrigation of pastures for grazing, for irrigation of golf courses, parks and sport fields, and for discharge into streams.

It can be shown that if the requirement stipulates that the effluent concentration, as measured by the MPN method, must not exceed 1,000/100 ml with 97.5% confidence, then, assuming a logarithmic standard deviation $S = 0.45$, the pond must be designed to give a mean effluent concentration of 132 *E. coli* I per 100 ml.

Referring to the suggested sizing of ponds, it is interesting to note that if a humus tank effluent with an assumed *E. coli* I MPN of 1.32×10^6 per 100 ml is treated in a well-designed system of four ponds in series (each with $4\frac{1}{2}$ days detention), an effluent of the desired quality should be produced, since this system should be sufficient to bring about a 99.99% reduction. In order to bring more highly polluted effluents to the desired bacteriological standard, the bacterial reduction in this system would be insufficient.

Chemical: The chemical quality of the effluent is affected by influent quality. A general survey (DREWS, 1966) has indicated that four ponds in series, four feet deep, with $4\frac{1}{2}$ days retention each, would produce an effluent with an OA of less than 10 ppm and a Chemical Oxygen Demand (COD) of less than 100 ppm on a *filtered* pond effluent sample, provided the unfiltered humus tank effluent does not exceed an OA of 20 ppm and a COD of 175 ppm.

Measuring Devices

Knowledge of the flow to the maturation pond system will assist in keeping a check on the pond loading. An integrating flow recorder would not be essential for the influent to the maturation ponds, if the raw sewage is measured. If, however, some of the total flow is diverted for other purposes before reaching the ponds, flow measurements to the ponds would be desirable.

Embankments

Slopes of *embankments* should be dictated by normal engineering practice for small dams. Details at fringes should be designed for preventing ingress of vegetation. Capital investment on weed control and prevention of wave erosion, by stone pitching or using soil-cement on the pond verges, may well be repaid by saving in maintenance.

FACULTATIVE STABILIZATION PONDS

The design for this type of system treating raw or primary treated domestic wastes has been fully covered in CSIR Research Report No. 189 (SHAW et al., 1962), from which the essential points are given below.

General

The first consideration which affects the size and arrangement of a facultative pond system is that a nuisance-free operation is governed by the size of the *primary* pond. The second consideration, that of effluent quality, governs the size and arrangement of the *subsequent* ponds.

Loading of Primary Pond

Anaerobic conditions in the surface layers of these ponds result from over-loading, which causes the oxygen demand to exceed the reoxygenation capacity.

Overloading, absence of dissolved oxygen, and odor production are, therefore, mutually associated, and the first condition can be inferred from one or both of the other two manifestations.

For domestic sewage, as well as for stronger and weaker effluents such as those from aqua privies, septic tanks and settlement tanks (see below), the following procedure is suggested for estimating the minimum detention time in the primary pond.

Concentration of BOD in the raw sewage influent (MARAIS, 1963) to the first pond is given by:

$$P_o = \left(\frac{b}{g}\right) 10^5$$

where P_o = BOD concentration in the influent to the pond in mg/l;
b = BOD contribution per person per day in lb;
g = effluent flow per person per day in gallons.

The minimum detention time in the primary pond

$$R = \left(\frac{P_o}{P} - 1\right) \times \frac{1}{C}$$

where R = the detention period in days;
C = constant dependent on temperature;
P = maximum concentration of BOD in the pond consistent with aerobic conditions.

As an acceptable value of P, the following empirical formula is given:

$$P = \frac{600}{(0.6d + 8)}$$

where d = the depth of the pond in ft.

Empirical values for C for use in South Africa and South West Africa are suggested in Table 3.

As a general guide a loading of approximately 120 lbs BOD per acre/day can be adopted for domestic raw sewage in a four-foot deep pond.

Table 3. C values for different climatic regions

Average temp. during coldest month (°C)	Below 5°C	Above 5°C
Geographic region	N.W. Districts, High Veld S.W. and N.E. Free State	Rest of interior and coastal region
C value	0.14	0.17

Pretreatment of Sewage

The advantage of pretreating effluents before discharge to a system cannot be overemphasized. As a rule of thumb, it can be taken that the reduction of BOD in a septic tank or aqua privy of one or more days retention is of the order of 40%, which obviously enables the designer to decrease likewise the size of the primary facultative pond. For small and isolated communities or in instances where less sophisticated modes of sanitation would be acceptable, the above system could be of great economic advantage. The inherent advantages of aqua privies (VINCENT et al.) are well worth considering.

The use of anaerobic ponds preceding facultative ponds are described further on.

Another advantage offered by anaerobic pretreatment of raw sewage before discharge into a facultative pond is that of aesthetics, since the floating layer of scum which periodically appears on these ponds is seldom found if pretreatment is practiced.

Sizing and Arrangement of Subsequent Ponds

The sizing of the subsequent ponds (i.e., 2nd, 3rd, 4th and 5th pond) is based principally on detention time. A vital feature for efficient reduction of fecal bacteria especially is that the ponds should be arranged in series as demonstrated above (see subsection on Sizing and Arrangment of Maturation Ponds). It has also been shown that nitrogen reduction is better in a tertiary pond than in a secondary pond, suggesting that nitrogen removals improve with increased overall detention times. It is recommended that a total of at least twenty-five days detention, based on the flow into the primary pond, should be provided in the subsequent ponds.

The first of the secondary ponds should have ten days detention, while subsequent ponds in the series (third, fourth and fifth) should have five days detention each. Further subdivision of the fifth pond should have a further beneficial effect on the bacteriological quality of the final effluent. It should be noted that the *E. coli* I count in raw sewage could be of the order of 3×10^8 per 100 ml, and that this fact should be taken into account in designing a system of ponds.

Depth of Ponds

The permissible surface loading of the primary pond increases only slightly with increased pond depths. There seems, therefore, to be very little practical advantage in constructing ponds deeper than six feet.

In localities where, by virtue of the topography, a deeper pond, or a pond which is deeper in parts, may be cheaper to construct, it should be taken into account that the ability of the pond to reduce the virus content will be impaired.

Primary ponds shallower than three feet will be unduly affected by sludge deposition, and these as well as secondary ponds would possibly also be affected by vegetation growing in such ponds.

Pond Appurtenances

The *inlet* to the primary pond may require special features to prevent undue accumulation of sludge at one spot. Therefore, features such as multiple inlets to bring about some sludge distribution in the pond may be desirable. Discharge should be below the water level but care should be taken that an accumulation of coarse material does not choke the inlet pipes. In all other respects, the positioning of inlets and outlets should be governed by the same considerations as apply for maturation ponds.

Pond bottoms may be level or graded to suit topographical features in the best possible way.

Pond embankments should be built in accordance with the earlier paragraph on embankments.

Measuring Devices

A flow-measuring or recording device should be installed ahead of the primary pond. Besides a check on pond loading, flow measurement will furnish valuable data for use when the pond system requires extending.

Screens and Detritus Channels

To maintain an aesthetically pleasing effect of the ponds, screens and detritus channels correctly sized are usually installed prior to discharge to the primary pond. They may, however, constitute a nuisance, and the outlay on continuous maintenance over a period of years would more than cancel the cost of removing accumulated detritus once in five or ten years or to allow for such accumulation* when designing the size of pond. A depression in the pond bottom around and below the inlet to accommodate the accumulated detritus would be an advantage. All screenings and detritus should be safely buried to avoid underground pollution, or composted if possible.

FACULTATIVE STABILIZATION PONDS WITH RECIRCULATION

These ponds can be considered intermediate between facultative ponds without recirculation and facultative ponds preceded by an anaerobic pond.

The performance of a facultative pond is considered satisfactory as long as the upper layer of the liquid in the pond remains aerobic for the greatest part of the day. Thus, photosynthetic activity in the upper layers must not be overwhelmed by anaerobic conditions proceeding upward from the bottom, where active anaerobic fermentation is taking place in the sludge layer. It is therefore of importance that if effluent from a second pond is recirculated and admixed with the raw sewage influent to the primary pond, the loading as calculated on the overall area can be increased considerably without creating anaerobic conditions (Abbott, 1963).

Loading

According to Abbott (1963), the BOD load applied to the recirculation pond system (which includes the primary and recirculation pond) can be as high as 250 lbs/acre/day without a nuisance being caused by anaerobic conditions. Considerable overloads can even be withstood by this system for short periods. Until more general information is available, a maximum loading of the primary-

---

* Bantu sewage usually yields a high grit load because of sand used for cleaning utensils—as high as 1 cu.yd. per million gallons, whereas the sewage from White areas may contain one sixth of this amount. Screenings would on an average amount to 8 cu.ft. per million gallons treated.

cum-recirculation pond of 200 lbs/acre/day is recommended. Recirculation from a secondary pond could be used as a relief measure during periods of overloading of a normal facultative stabilization pond.

Recirculation Rate

At the above loading, the minimum recirculation rate for satisfactory performance seems to be 1:1. Provision should, however, be made for higher recirculation rates up to 2:1 when required.

Detention Time

A detention period of 18 days is recommended by Abbott for a recirculation pond system (primary and secondary ponds combined) treating domestic sewage of average strength.

The recommended sizing of the pond system would be as follows:

Recirculation pond system	Primary pond detention (based on incoming flow)	— 8 days
	Secondary pond detention	— 10 days
Subsequent ponds	Third pond detention	— 5 days
	Fourth pond detention	— 5 days
	Fifth pond detention	— 5 days

Pond Depth

Pond depths are as described previously.

Sludge Build-up in the Primary Pond

It is conceivable that sludge accumulation in the primary pond of the recirculation system will be more rapid than for the normal facultative pond system, so that removal of the residual or nondegraded sludge from the primary pond of the former system may be required more frequently. If the system is not a temporary scheme, being used while a full-scale sewage works is being planned or is under construction, it may be desirable to provide for duplicate primary ponds in parallel so that cleaning operations can be carried out with greater facility. A primary pond with increased depth (say six feet), without reduced surface area, would have obvious advantages.

ANAEROBIC-AEROBIC STABILIZATION POND SYSTEM

When anaerobic ponds are followed by a facultative pond from which oxygenated water is recirculated to the raw sewage entering the anaerobic ponds, the system is referred to as an *anaerobic-aerobic stabilization pond system* (An-Ae system) (VAN ECK and SIMPSON, 1966). This system is considered as a primary unit in a series of ponds.

In some instances it may be advisable, for aesthetic reasons, to discharge only screened detritus-free sewage into these ponds.

A diagrammatic layout of an An-Ae system is given in Figure 3. The system consists of three anaerobic ponds, A, B_1 and B_2, and one large facultative pond, C, with aerobic surface layers. A pump recirculates water from pond C into the raw sewage entering pond A at a recirculation rate of 25 % of the raw sewage flow.

As in the case of the single facultative primary pond, the An-Ae system is followed by aerobic ponds (usually four) in series in order to obtain a final effluent of high quality.

Pond A should operate as an anaerobic digester in which active fermentation is established in the sludge layer. As a result of the waste stabilization processes, methane, carbon dioxide and sometimes nitrogen gases are produced. Ponds B_1 and B_2, which are operated alternately in series with Pond A, remove suspended solids carried over by Pond A effluent, thus obviating unnecessary loading on Pond C. Only two anaerobic ponds are operated at any one time (see Figure 3).

Pond Design and Loading of the An-Ae System

It should be noted that these design criteria are tentative and may be altered in the light of further experience. Ponds A, B_1 and B_2 should be of equal area and 8 to 12 feet deep. Pond C, which is much larger than the anaerobic ponds, should be 4 to 6 feet deep.

The daily BOD poundage of the raw sewage will determine the pond sizes of the An-Ae system. The volume of Pond A should be calculated on a maximum loading of 0.025 lb BOD/cu. ft/day or a minimum detention of 12 hours, whichever is applicable. Ponds B_1 and B_2 should be the same size as Pond A.

In determining the size of Pond C, it can be assumed that the anaerobic section of the An-Ae system will remove on average 60 % of the BOD load of raw sewage.

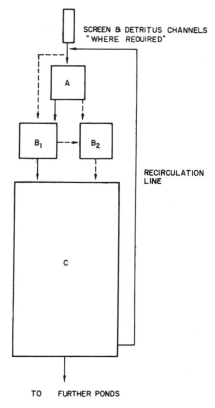

SCREEN & DETRITUS CHANNELS
"WHERE REQUIRED"

A

B₁   B₂

RECIRCULATION
LINE

C

TO   FURTHER PONDS

Figure 3
Schematic flow diagram of the An-Ae
system

The size of Pond C is based on an area loading. Pond C should not receive a loading greater than 120 lb BOD/acre/day.

The An-Ae system should be followed by not less than three 'polishing' ponds, sized according to the previous description.

Sludge Accumulation

From an anaerobic pond, sludge may have to be removed once every year. For this reason triplicate anaerobic ponds are recommended, so that the effluent may all be diverted to one set of ponds while sludge is being removed from the third pond. Accordingly, the ponds may be operated according to the following system:

Run 1: For 6 months, raw sewage to A $\longrightarrow$ B$_1$ $\longrightarrow$ C.

Run 2: Succeeding 6 months, raw sewage to A $\longrightarrow$ B$_2$ $\longrightarrow$ C, Pond B$_1$ to be desludged in interim.

Run 3: Following 6 months, raw sewage to A $\longrightarrow$ B$_1$ $\longrightarrow$ C, runs 1, 2 and 3 to be repeated until it becomes necessary to desludge Pond A (usually 2 to 4 years).

Run 4: Raw sewage to B$_1$ $\longrightarrow$ B$_2$ $\longrightarrow$ C, while Pond A is desludged.

Fly-Breeding

Anaerobic ponds are usually covered by a layer of scum in summer. This scum may offer a breeding place for flies. Fly traps containing poison placed at very frequent intervals round the perimeter of these ponds would only partly remedy the situation. It is for this reason that anaerobic ponds should be placed at least half a mile away from the nearest habitation.

Future Application

Although this system is of great technical interest, it is not recommended for general use in South Africa until more knowledge becomes available.

MECHANICALLY AERATED STABILIZATION PONDS

Advantages of Mechanical Aeration

In facultative stabilization ponds, the desirable aerobic conditions in the surface layers are largely brought about by the photosynthetic activity of green algae. If, however, the biochemical dissolved oxygen uptake, as in the case of an overloaded pond, exceeds the photosynthetic reoxygenation capacity, the critical balance would be upset and the pond would turn anaerobic, ousting the algae.

An apparent balance between biochemical dissolved oxygen requirement and photosynthetic reoxygenation capacity of the water in a pond may, however, be upset for reasons other than an increase in pond loading. A drop in temperature, or a large and sudden reduction of the algae concentration brought about by an extremely rapid increase in numbers of predator organisms such as daphnia and moina, could well be the cause of such drop in pond performance.

The lack of uniformity of oxygen concentration through all water layers contributes further to the inefficiency of algae as an oxygen producer.

To make a pond less reliant on the photosynthetic reoxygenation activity of algae, mechanical aeration of the pond contents could be resorted to. In the United States of America it has, for instance, been shown (OLSON, 1966) that at loadings of 400 lb BOD per acre per day, an overall efficiency of about 90% BOD reduction could be achieved even while the ponds were covered with ice.

Odor problems may in some instances be the most urgent reason for conversion to a mechanically aerated pond. However, the following factors are also in favor of the aerated pond over a straight facultative stabilization pond:
(1) Better land utilization through higher possible loadings in terms of persons per acre.
(2) Improved sustained quality of the effluent during winter and spring months.
(3) Less cost in sealing of ponds in porous soil on account of the smaller surface area.

Depth of Pond

In the case of a straight facultative stabilization pond without aeration, the surface area exposed to solar radiation is the critical parameter, and treatment capacity cannot be substantially increased by merely deepening the pond. This does not apply to mechanically aerated ponds in which case depths of 10 feet have been successfully employed (OLSON, 1966), since the additional depth facilitates the introduction of certain aerator mechanisms which would otherwise not have been possible.

Sludge Deposit

The aerated pond is not an activated sludge system (HINDE, 1965). Whereas turbulence and mixing are desirable in an activated sludge tank in order that mixed-liquor activated sludge be kept in suspension, this procedure is detrimental to the operation of an aerated pond. Slow circulation in the aeration cells permits settling of solids and sludge on the bottom of the pond for anaerobic digestion.

Aeration Facilities

The aerators or diffusers should be placed in such a way that the sludge layer is not disturbed. If a diffuser system is used, the diffusers should be mounted clear of this deposit to avoid turbulence.

The aeration facilities should be readily removable to allow overhaul and facilitate sludge removal, should this become necessary after a few years of operation.

To minimize turbulence and obtain highest efficiency, coarse bubble aeration should be avoided if possible.

Horsepower Requirements

The control of bubble size, rise rate and laminar flow conditions will result in efficient utilization of horsepower: the air supplied is then employed for oxygenation of wastes rather than for rapid turnover of water to keep sludge in suspension. The horsepower requirements for aerating a mechanically aerated pond have been estimated at less than 0.006 h.p. per person. At 1 cent* per kWh, the operating cost would be 48 cents per person per year.

Secondary Ponds

Secondary ponds following a mechanically aerated primary pond should be designed in the normal way.

HEALTH ASPECTS

Impact on Environmental Health

The higher building and maintenance costs of conventional sewage purification plants and the highly skilled supervising staff required, as well as the labor problem which follows in its wake, more often than not deter small municipalities and other communal authorities from installing a sewage reticulation system. If the economy resulting from the use of stabilization ponds could therefore be a factor in enabling a town to install water-borne sanitation at a much

---

* 100 cents = 1 rand.

earlier stage than would otherwise be possible, environmental health would have benefitted. It has, for instance, been shown that septic tanks and french drains in an area where the top soil is shallow leads to a deterioration of streams flowing through these areas.

It has already been indicated that the contents of a primary stabilization pond are of a similar bacteriological quality to those of humus tank effluent. If, therefore, the introduction of a stabilization pond system brings about the disappearance of a large number of individual pit latrines, or septic tanks, or the trenching of night-soil and the associated regular and unhygienic removal of sanitary pails, then these facilities would have been exchanged for something infinitely more acceptable.

The same argument is put forward with reference to the aqua privy which, if functioning properly, has many attractive features and advantages such as economy, low water consumption, hygienic operation and simplicity of use, but which fell into disrepute for reasons described elsewhere (VINCENT et al.). However, these units have been put to good use in combination with stabilization ponds to provide sanitary facilities for unsophisticated communities.

It is of interest that after a stabilization pond has been put into operation, the time required to fill the pond ensures that no effluent is discharged until such time as the biological associations have been well established and a good quality effluent has been ensured.

As far as virus removal is concerned, stabilization and maturation ponds seem to be vastly superior to conventional works, provided both systems are loaded only to design capacity. MALHERBE and STRICKLAND-CHOLMLEY (1965a, b) established that reovirus and enterovirus were not significantly affected by the conventional purification processes including primary and secondary treatment, but in contrast only occasional low-level reovirus and enterovirus isolations were made from maturation pond effluents. This may be of importance in view of the conflicting findings which have been reported on the efficacy of virus destruction in effluents by means of chlorination (CARSTENS et al., 1965; WEIDENKOPF, 1958; MARAIS et al., 1967).

The Role of Birds

Mechanical transmission of bacterial pathogens: It is conceivable that birds exposed to human fecal contamination might transport human pathogens mechanically to an impoundment reservoir, but it is considered that the danger to human health would be slight because the water would provide an imperfect medium for bacterial growth. In this regard, ponds present no greater source of contamination than would irrigation lands receiving sewage effluent or would biological filters, garbage heaps, etc., to which birds may be attracted.

Arthropod-borne viruses (arboviruses): Birds can act as reservoirs for arthropod-borne viruses which may be conveyed to man by mosquito vectors. It should be noted that the arboviruses are entirely distinct from the enteric viruses occurring in sewage, and are only transmitted to man by mosquitoes which have fed on infected birds. Birds attracted to bodies of water of any kind can act as arbovirus reservoirs, and the practical solution to this problem therefore lies in mosquito control.

Mosquito Control

Apart from constituting a health hazard, though perhaps remote in South Africa, mosquitoes have a tremendous nuisance value and should not be allowed to breed freely in ponds.

Oil should not be poured on the surface of a pond as it would interfere with the transfer of oxygen from the atmosphere. However, in an emergency an insecticide could be sprayed in normal quantities around the perimeter of a pond without any serious deleterious effect.

The best control measure is the prevention of breeding. This can best be achieved by keeping the pond clear of emergent and peripheral vegetation. Various investigators (BEADIE and ROWE, 1960; MYKLEBUST and HARMSTON, 1962; SCOVILL, 1963; LOEDOLFF, 1963) have found that under such circumstances no significant mosquito-breeding can take place. Emergent vegetation normally presents no problem in ponds of four feet or greater depth.

Bilharzia

HODGSON (1961) investigated the snail vectors of *Schistosomiasis* in a pond in Rhodesia and found that the environment in an oxidation pond is not conducive to their propagation.

Parasites

The specific gravity of ova and cysts is approximately 1.1 (LIEBMANN, 1964), and it seems therefore that the long detention times in stabilization ponds cause their settlement. Over a year of observation on a pond series at Lusaka (MARAIS, in press), no helminths, cysts or ova were found in the effluent from a series of stabilization ponds. Observations in Durban, Pretoria and Windhoek confirmed this.

Effect on the Receiving Water

The purification of raw sewage in stabilization ponds is not dependent on mechanical aids such as pumps and distributors, and is consequently not affected by corrosion, mechanical faults and power failures. Shock loadings are absorbed much more effectively than in a conventional sewage purification plant. Using a MPN of fecal *E. coli* I as a yardstick, the bacteriological purification of a primary stabilization pond is of the same order as that obtained in a conventional sewage purification plant. As it is also possible to place the design of the secondary ponds on a rational basis and to calculate the number of ponds and the detention time in each necessary to produce an effluent of a reliable high quality, a stabilization pond system can be designed to achieve the same bacteriological purification obtainable in a conventional sewage works-maturation pond combination.

Although a fecal *E. coli* I count of nil per 100 ml cannot usually be obtained in maturation ponds, *the degree of safety* (as indicated by *E. coli* I count) that can be obtained is comparable with that attainable in practice where sand-filtered effluent is chlorinated (STANDER and MEIRING, 1963). As a final safety barrier, maturation ponds offer better security. It is emphasized, however, that these results are unlikely to be attained unless the design requirements contained in this document have been met and the ponds are satisfactorily maintained at all times.

Various workers have reported that in cases where *Mycobacterium tuberculosis* was present in the raw sewage inflow, they were unable to isolate this bacterium from a secondary stabilization or maturation pond (NIWR, 1965) effluent, in the latter case even when 10-liter quantities were flocculated and the sediment investigated.

It seems reasonable that purified effluent destined for various purposes should comply with *E. coli* I limits related to these purposes. In this regard, it is necessary to take cognisance of the extent to which all natural watercourses in Natal are polluted (KEMP et al., 1966). Such background information places the upper $97\frac{1}{2}\%$ confidence limit of 1,000 *E. coli* I per 100 ml in its true perspective.

KEMP et al. (1966) took 50 *E. coli* I/100 ml and a total plate count of 5,000 per ml (5 days at 32°C) as the upper limits of a Class I water which, with only simple disinfection, should be suitable for drinking. It appears that only in the upper reaches of the Tugela River (near the Amphitheatre in Drakensberg) is a water to be found which qualifies bacteriologically as a Class I water. It is also indicated that even if all known sources of pollution were eliminated, no additional rivers would be placed in Class I. In general, the rivers draining the rural areas of Natal qualify for Class II, i.e., these waters do not contain more than 1,500 E. coli I per 100 ml and are suitable for domestic purposes after conventional treatment.

CLIMATIC EFFECT

In the functioning of stabilization ponds, two mechanisms involving biological activity are at work. The primary one is that of bacterial metabolism and the degradation of organic matter with the release of gas and mineral elements. The second mechanism is that of algal metabolism, producing sufficient oxygen to prevent anaerobic conditions of the entire body of water and thus restricting organic degradation. The process of oxygen production, through photosynthesis by algae, is dependent on the availability of carbon dioxide and the essential mineral elements and on sufficiently high temperatures to allow prolific algal growth.

Light intensities are relatively high in South Africa, even during the winter season, and provided that algae were present in sufficient numbers, photosynthetic activity in stabilization ponds would be maintained. The exception might be the Western Cape, where overcast weather can persist for several days at a time. Cold weather conditions, however, slow down algal development and in this way limit the permissible loading per unit of primary pond surface area.

Critical conditions also obtain in early spring when warmer weather sets in. Bacterial activity is accelerated and unstabilized sludge, which had collected on the pond bottom during the preceding winter, becomes subjected to more rapid degradation, thus increasing the demand placed on reoxygenation at a time when algal densities may still be low.

If pond loadings are such that algal development and the resultant photosynthetic activity can maintain aerobic surface conditions in a primary pond, then effluent stabilization is still quite effective even in winter. The amount of stabilization achieved in winter during experiments at Pretoria, using two ponds in series, is reflected by filtered BOD values in Table 4. The primary pond loading during these experiments was 145 lbs BOD/acre/day.

Table 4. BOD and nitrogen analysis of pond effluents (according to SHAW et al. 1962) (all figures are in mg/l)

Year 1961	Total BOD			Filtered BOD			Total nitrogen as N			NH₃-nitrogen as N			Filtered Kjeldahl nitrogen as N		
	A*	B	C	A	B	C	A	B	C	A	B	C	A	B	C
January	52	19	—	33	18	—	24	11.0	—	12.7	3.2	—	16.6	7.3	—
February	67	22	18	33	16	10	28	13.2	4.1	16.1	7.6	1.7	14.7	11.1	4.1
March	36	19	12	19	5	5	26	11.0	2.8	14.7	5.0	0.8	19.0	7.9	2.1
April	59	25	13	23	13	7	26	14.4	3.0	16.4	5.9	0.9	20.3	9.9	3.0
May	54	15	7	29	12	6	35	26.6	10.6	27.0	20.7	9.5	26.6	23.4	9.6
June	55	10	4	35	8	4	43	34.1	27.9	34.3	30.8	23.4	38.5	33.2	25.0
July	75	16	9	44	11	7	48	38.1	28.4	37.5	34.0	26.6	41.7	37.8	28.1
August	56	22	5	38	15	4	48	41.8	30.8	36.9	36.8	29.1	40.6	39.0	30.6
September	55	10	14	27	4	8	43	43.4	24.3	31.7	34.2	19.5	35.5	37.9	21.3
October	66	15	13	22	10	7	35	34.0	9.0	22.3	31.4	5.6	27.6	33.2	7.4
November	57	60**	21	22	6	15	26	42.0**	11.8	15.8	15.6	8.6	19.7	19.5	11.1
December	77	46**	21	9	5	7	31	27.7**	12.5	12.8	12.1	5.2	16.3	13.6	7.1
Annual mean	59	23	14	28	11	7		28.1	15.0	23.6	19.8	10.9	26.4	22.8	12.4

* Ponds A, B and C are in series.
** Dense algal growth in Pond B.

Except for a period of approximately four months in winter when activity is at its lowest, algal activity is both directly and indirectly responsible for a number of processes apart from merely maintaining aerobic conditions. As the algae are responsible for elevating the pH, some dissipation of ammonia is brought about, and by maintaining aerobic conditions, a process of nitrification (accompanied by denitrification in the sludge layer) is encouraged. Various nutrients are embodied in the cells of the algae, and if the algae are removed, the nutrient content of the effluent will accordingly be reduced.

It therefore appears that as long as a pond remains aerobic, climatic changes have relatively little effect on effluent stabilization as measured by the filtered BOD. However, enhanced algal activity in summer, by elevating the pH, has a greatly beneficial effect on the quality of the effluent by reducing the ammonia-nitrogen contents. This also holds good for phosphates which are precipitated at elevated pH values, but may be released again in winter when the pH drops.

EFFLUENT QUALITY

The quality of final effluents from the various types of pond systems will not prevent enrichment of a natural body of water, nor will it always comply in all respects with the requirements of the General Standards promulgated under the Water Act. More important, however, from the viewpoint of environmental health is the abatement of bacterial pollution and the improvement in sanitary conditions as effected by the installation of stabilization ponds in preference to septic tanks, french drain systems and night-soil disposal practices.

Similarly, maturation ponds, which serve as a further treatment stage for effluents from a conventional sewage works, bring about biological improvement, nutrient removal and reduction of the bacterial population in an open but controlled body of water. Where maturation ponds are not used, this task remains to be handled by public waters (rivers or lakes).

Furthermore, all pond systems have an excellent buffering capacity for balancing out excessive peak flows. Variations in quality of effluent are likely to be greater for a conventional system than for stabilization pond systems.

A performance schedule for the various types of pond systems constructed in accordance with the design criteria recommended in this guide is given in Table 5.

It must be noted, however, that the schedule applies almost entirely to the treatment of domestic wastes. If any considerable quantity of industrial wastes

Table 5. Performance schedule for ponds in South Africa

Parameter (in ppm except where otherwise stated)		Effluent Composition	
		Stabilization ponds (for raw and settled sewage, septic tank and aqua-privy effluent)	Maturation ponds (for well-nitrified humus tank effluent)
Colour, taste and odor		Not objectionable	Not objectionable
pH	(range)	7.0–10.5	7.0–10.5
Temperature, °C	max.	30	30
Dissolved oxygen % sat.	min.	75	75
E.coli I	max.	1,000/100 ml (97$\frac{1}{2}$% probability)	1,000/100 ml (97$\frac{1}{2}$% probability)
Biochemical oxygen demand (BOD)	max.	20	15
BOD filtered	max.	15	10
Chemical oxygen demand (COD)	max.	250	130
COD soluble	max.	180	100
OA 4 hrs from $N/80$ K MnO$_4$ at 27°C (SABS)	max.	20	15
OA 4 hrs from $N/80$ K MnO$_4$ at 27°C (SABS) soluble	max.	10	10
Ammonia-nitrogen	max.	35	10

is taken into the pond system of a sewage works, it cannot be expected that the pond effluents will necessarily show the performance as delineated in the schedule.

ALGAE REMOVAL

Desirability of Algae Removal

Sewage stabilization and effluent maturation in algal ponds provide the public-health engineer with a low-cost and efficient means of facilitating the introduction of water-borne sanitation in many places where such a forward step to improve environmental health conditions would otherwise not have been possible. However, the presence of dense algal concentrations in pond effluents is a feature which in many instances renders the effluent unsuitable for reuse or discharge into a watercourse. In this regard, it should be noted that the General Standards promulgated under Water Act No. 54 of 1956 stipulate a maximum suspended solids concentration in an effluent of 25 mg/l.

It therefore appears that if an economically feasible means of removing algae from a pond effluent could be developed, an important advance could be made by establishing stabilization ponds as an inexpensive and generally recognized means of sewage purification. However, it should be noted that high ammonia concentrations in winter also render ponds less acceptable, since the General Standards call for a maximum ammonia-nitrogen concentration of 10 mg/l.

Pilot plant work to study the feasibility of water reclamation from sewage effluent (CILLIE et al., 1966) has demonstrated vividly the important advantages to be derived from satisfactory removal of algae from maturation pond effluents, since the conventional water-treatment process of flocculation/sedimentation followed by sand-filtration has proved quite inefficient.

The development of a successful method of algae removal would have the added advantage of providing a means for the possible harvesting of algae as a highly proteinaceous foodstuff.

Mechanism of Algae Removal

The most reliable method (VAN VUUREN et al., in press) consists in introducing small volumes of air together with the effluent at the suction side of a high-speed centrifugal pump. If, however, this procedure causes the suction on the pump to be broken, an alternative would be to insert in the rising main an air-water emulsifier in front of which air is introduced. The air emulsifier, or special-purpose pump, should be designed to produce minute air bubbles evenly diffused in the stream of water passing through. The velocity of air-water emulsion in the rising main should exceed 7 feet per second to prevent separation.

Design Criteria for Flotation Process of Algae Removal

For the most efficient utilization of aluminum sulfate or lime as flocculant, a retention period of 10 minutes is required for floc-conditioning.

The tank (VAN VUUREN et al., in press) outlined in Figure 4 incorporates a floc-conditioning/flotation compartment in the center as well as a counter-current/flotation compartment of annular design around it. The flow arrangement shown in Figure 5 incorporates an air-water emulsifier and chemical dosing apparatus.

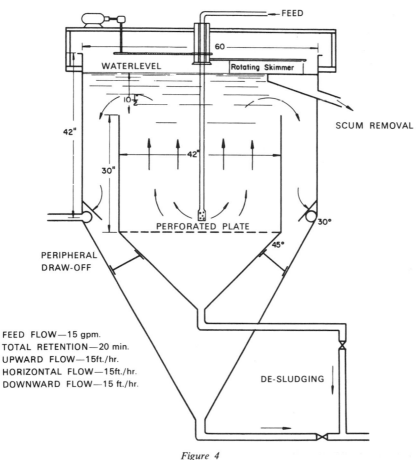

FEED FLOW—15 gpm.
TOTAL RETENTION—20 min.
UPWARD FLOW—15ft./hr.
HORIZONTAL FLOW—15ft./hr.
DOWNWARD FLOW—15 ft./hr.

Figure 4
Flotation unit for maturation pond or humus tank effluents

Cost of Flotation Process

Apart from initial costs, the flotation system designed to remove algae from maturation or stabilization pond effluents entails the following items which in turn would incur certain running expenses:

pH-correction (by introducing a mineral acid or, in special instances, carbon dioxide); addition of flocculant (aluminum sulfate or lime); electric power consumption; and supervision and maintenance.

Table 6. Typical analytical data of stabilization and maturation pond and humus tank effluents before and after flocculation treatment in a flotation unit (MYKLEBUST and HARMSTON, 1962)

Parameters mg/l	Stabilization pond effluent		Maturation pond effluent		Humus tank effluent	
	Before treatment	After treatment with 400 ppm aluminum sulfate	Before treatment	After treatment with 175 ppm aluminum sulfate	Before treatment	After treatment with 80 ppm aluminum sulfate
Total dissolved solids	500	750	500	620	500	560
Suspended solids	280	85*	55	30*	25	35*
COD (chemical oxygen demand)	515	104	104	42	65	27
OA (oxygen absorbed from $N/80$ KMnO$_4$ in 4 hrs)	48	8.0	8.4	5.2	8.4	3.4
PO$_4$ (total phosphates)	35.0	1.2	14.8	1.8	21.0	0.5
ABS (Syndets)	17.5	9.2	6.3	5.6	3.9	3.1
NH$_3$-N	20.7	16.4	4.9	4.2	12.3	9.5
Kjeldahl-N	53.8	17.1	10.8	6.7	16.7	9.1

* Floc carry-over for removal by sand-filtration.

The erection cost per capita of an algae flotation unit, complete with scum removal facilities, should be relatively small for schemes serving more than 5,000 people (less than 2 rand per person). If, however, pH correction is brought about by the introduction of carbon dioxide, relatively expensive equipment would be required. pH-correction by means of carbon dioxide would normally, however, not be justified in small schemes of this nature, but only in large schemes where water reclamation is practiced.

The cost of sulfuric acid (to obtain optimum pH) and aluminum sulfate (as flocculant) or lime (as flocculant) and sulfuric acid (for pH correction) would bring about a running expenditure of 5 to 7 cents per 1,000 gallons of effluent treated. The cost of power would be small.

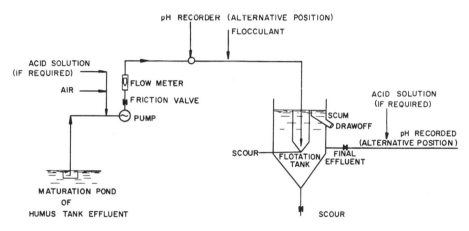

Figure 5
Flow diagram for flotation of maturation pond or humus tank effluents

Maintenance by a part-time specialist to ensure satisfactory performance by the automatic pH controller, alum or lime feeder and system as a whole would add to the running costs of a scheme serving 5,000 people to the extent of approximately 3 cents per 1,000 gallons of effluent treated. Provision for labor requirements should be small since the same people employed on the upkeep of the stabilization ponds could be required to maintain and operate the sludge drying beds, etc.

Effluent Quality Improvement Resulting from Flotation Process

The improvement of stabilization pond and humus tank effluents by means of the flotation process is illustrated in Table 6.

REFERENCES

ABBOTT, A.L. (1963): "Oxidation ponds," *Proc. Diamond Jubilee Conf.*, S.A. Inst. Civ. Engrs.

BEADIE, L.D. and ROWE, J.A. (1960): "Sewage lagoons and mosquito problems," *Proc. Symposium on Waste Stabilization lagoons,* Kansas City, Missouri.

BOLITHO, V.N. (1964): "Some economic aspects of wastewater purification in South Africa," *J. Proc. Inst. Sew. Purif.*, Part 3.

CALIFORNIA STATE WATER POLLUTION CONTROL BOARD, *Report on Study of Wastewater Reclamation and Utilization,* Publication No. 15.

CALIFORNIA STATE WATER POLLUTION CONTROL BOARD, *Report on Study of Wastewater Reclamation and Utilization,* Publication No. 18.

CARSTENS, E.M.J., COETZEE, O.J., MALHERBE, H.H. and HARWIN, R.M. (1965): "Bacteriophage of *Serratia Marcescens* as an index of human virus survival during sewage purification," *CSIR Research Rep. 241*, Pretoria.

CILLIE, G.G., VAN VUUREN, L.R.J., STANDER, G.J. and KOLBE, F.F. (1966): "The reclamation of sewage effluents for domestic use," Paper presented at Third International Conference on Water Pollution Research, Munich.

DREWS, R.J.L.C. (1966): "Field studies of large-scale maturation ponds with respect to their purification efficiency," *J. Proc. Inst. Sew. Purif.*, Part 3.

GAILLARD, J. and CRAWFORD, J. (1964): "The performance of algae ponds in Durban," *J. Proc. Inst. Sew. Purif.*, Part 3.

HINDE, J.N. (1965): "Design considerations for aerated sewage lagoons in northern climates," *Official Bulletin, North Dakota Water and Sewage Works Conference*, Vol. 32, No. 7/8.

HODGSON, H.T. (1961): "Stabilization ponds for a small African urban area," *J. Wat. Pollut. Control Fed.*, Vol. 36, p. 603.

KEMP, P.H., BRAND, P.A.J. and PRETORIUS, S.J. (1966): "Classification of the Natal Rivers according to water quality," Paper presented to the Institute of Sewage Purification (S.A. Branch), Pretoria.

LIEBMANN, H. (1964): "Parasites in sewage and the possibilities of their extinction," Paper presented at Second International Conference on Water Pollution Research, Tokyo.

LOEDOLOFF, C.J. (1963): "The mosquito problem in oxidation ponds," *J. Proc. Inst. Sew. Purif.*, Part 5.

MALAN, W.M. (1962): "The pollution of groundwater," *CSIR Special Report No. 15*, Pretoria.

MALHERBE, H.H. and COETZEE, O.J. (1965): "The survival of Type '2' poliovirus in a model system of stabilization ponds," *CSIR Research Report No. 242*, Pretoria.

MALHERBE, H.H. and STRICKLAND-CHOLMLEY, M. (1965a): "The survival of viruses in the presence of algae," *Symp. on the Transmission of Viruses by the Water Route,* Cincinnati.

MALHERBE, H.H. and STRICKLAND-CHOLMLEY, M. (1965b): "Quantitative studies on virus survival in sewage purification processes," *Symp. on Transmission of Viruses by the Water Route,* Cincinnati.

MARAIS, A.F., NUPEN, E.M. and HOFFMAN, J.R.H. (1967): "A comparison of the inactivation of *Escherichia coli* I and poliovirus in polluted and unpolluted waters by chlorination," Paper presented at the International Conference on Water for Peace, Washington, D.C.

MARAIS, G.v.R.: "New factors in the design, operation and performance of waste stabilization ponds with special reference to health," *WHO Expert Committee Meeting on Environmental Change and Resulting Impact on Health.*

MARAIS, G.v.R. (1963): "A design chart for a series of oxidation ponds treating raw sewage and some remarks on the depth of the first pond," *Civ. Engr. S. Afr.,* Vol. 5, No. 9.

MARAIS, G.v.R. (1963): "Statistical distribution of the faecal bacteria in the effluents from stabilization ponds and some considerations in the framing of a standard for the bacterial quality of the effluent," *Proceedings of the Central African Scientific and Medical Congress,* Pergamon Press, London.

MARAIS, G.v.R. and SHAW, V.A. (1961): "A rational theory for the design of sewage stabilization ponds in Central and Southern Africa," *Civ. Engr. S. Afr.,* Vol. 3, No. 11.

MYKLEBUST, R.J. and HARMSTON, F.C. (1962): "Mosquito production in stabilization ponds," *J. Wat. Pollut. Control Fed.,* Vol. 34, No. 3, p. 302.

NEEL, J.K. and HOPKINS, G.J. (1956): "Experimental lagooning of raw sewage," *Sew. and Ind. Wastes,* Vol. 28, No. 11, p. 1326.

NIWR CONTRACT REPORT CWAT 4. (1965): "Reclamation of purified sewage effluent for augmentation of domestic water supply of Windhoek," Pretoria.

OLSON, O.O. (1966): "Aerated lagoon system for Harvey, North Dakota," *Official Bulletin North Dakota Water and Sewage Works Conference,* Vol. 33, No. 7/8, 1966.

Private communication by the Chief Chemist, Windhoek Municipality.

SCOVILL, R.P. (1963): "Mosquito control in an industrial waste lagoon," *J. Wat. Pollut. Control Fed.,* Vol. 35, No. 5, p. 663.

SHAW, V.A. (1962): "An assessment of the probable influence of evaporation and seepage on oxidation pond design and construction," *J. 2 Proc. Inst. S.P.,* Part 4.

SHAW, V.A. (1963): "A system for the treatment of night-soil and conserving tank effluent in stabilization ponds," *Publ. Hlth. Johannesburg,* Vol. 63, No. 2.

SHAW, V.A., MEIRING, P.G.J. and VAN ECK, H. (1962): "Preliminary results of research on raw sewage stabilization ponds," *CSIR Special Rep. No. 189,* Pretoria.

STANDER, G.J. (1955): "Preliminary results of experiments on the further biological purification of sewage effluents," *A.J. Inst. mun. Engrs. S. Afr. Distr.*

STANDER, G.J. and MEIRING, P.G.J. (1963): "Health aspects of maturation and stabilization ponds," *Publ. Hlth. Johannesburg,* Vol. 63, No. 2, p. 5.

STANDER, G.J. and MEIRING, P.G.J. (1965): "Employing oxidation ponds for low-cost sanitation," *J. Wat. Pollut. Control Fed.,* Vol. 37, No. 7, pp. 1025–1033.

VAN ECK, H. and SIMPSON, D.E. (1966): "The anaerobic digestion pond system," *J. Proc. Inst. Sew. Purif.,* Part 3.

VAN VUUREN, L.R.J., MEIRING, P.G.J. and VAN BLERK, S.H.V. (in press): "A flotation process for water reclamation."

VINCENT, C.J., ALGIE, W.E. and MARAIS, G.v.R. "A system of sanitation for low-cost, high-density housing," *CCTA Publ. 84.*

VINCENT, C.J., ALGIE, W.E. and MARAIS, G.v.R. (1962): "A system of sanitation for low-cost, high-density housing," *WHO Symposium on New Developments in Sewage Treatment, Cincinnati.*

VOIGHTS, D. (1955): "Lagooning and spray disposal of neutral sulphite semi-chemical pulp mill liquors," *Proc. 10th Ind. Waste Conference,* Purdue Univ. Ext. Ser. 89, p. 497.

WEIDENKOPF, S.J. (1958): "Inactivation of Type 1 poliomyelitis virus with chlorine," *Virology,* No. 5, p. 59.

Removal of Nitrogen by Ammonia

Emission from Water Surfaces

A. Melamed and C. Saliternik

INTRODUCTION

Removal of mineral nutrients in wastewater treatment processes is of paramount importance in practically all systems where effluent is not disposed of through ocean outfalls. Phosphorus removal may be the chief objective in abatement of algal bloom, where effluent is discharged into inland water bodies. Removal of nitrogen may be aimed at, not only in disposal into surface water bodies, but also in groundwater recharge, where high concentrations of nitrates are undesirable.

The first step in the process of biological stabilization of organic nitrogenous compounds of sewage origin, is transformation from organic nitrogen to ammonia, via aerobic or anaerobic fermentation. This may be followed by oxidation of ammonia into nitrite and finally into nitrate, by nitrification bacteria, under favorable environmental conditions. Ammonia is also taken up by microorganisms and resynthesized into nitrogenous organic compounds.

NITROGENOUS COMPOUNDS IN EFFLUENT OF BIOLOGICAL WASTEWATER TREATMENT PROCESSES

Various biological processes of wastewater treatment differ with respect to the ratio of the various nitrogen forms in the effluent.

In anaerobic fermentation biological synthesis is rather low. This was shown by McCARTY (1964) on the basis of energy output. The same results are arrived at when the rate of synthesis is evaluated on the basis of yield factors, in kinetics of biological growth and BOD removal (AGARDY et al., 1963). Thus, ammonium nitrogen, rather than cellular organic nitrogen, predominates in the effluent of anaerobic wastewater treatment units (STEWART, 1958; SCHROEPFER and ZIEMKE, 1959; PARKER et al., 1959; PARKER, 1962).

In aerobic bacterial processes biological synthesis takes place at a far higher rate than in anaerobic ones (McCARTY, 1964; AGARDY et al., 1963). Operational conditions enhancing synthesis of biological mass, e.g., high-rate activated sludge or biological filters, are not favorable for nitrification (DOWNING et al., 1964; BARTH et al., 1965). Therefore, in high-rate processes, organic nitrogen (in the sludge) and ammonia (in the effluent) prevail.

On the other hand, in low-rate processes, little biological mass is produced, and nitrification takes place (DOWNING et al., 1964; BARTH et al., 1965). Thus, nitrates comprise the major nitrogenous constituent in the effluent of low-rate aerobic bacterial processes.

In stabilization ponds, under facultative aerobic conditions, algae predominate in the biological mass. The main nitrogenous forms are ammonia and organic cellular nitrogen (BEREND, 1965; MERON et al., 1965).

Normally, ammonia is present in oxidation ponds, and nitrogen is not the limiting factor in growth of algae.

PROCESSES FOR NITROGEN REMOVAL

A major effort by many workers was directed in recent years towards developing effective methods for removal of nitrogen.

Nitrates may be removed by biological denitrification (WUHRMAN, 1962; JOHNSON and SCHROEPFER, 1964). Little progress was made in chemical removal of nitrates (ENGINEERING SCIENCE, 1963).

Organic nitrogen, the product of biological growth, may be removed by various means. Nevertheless, in most processes only a fraction of the total nitrogen present in a system is removable as organic nitrogen. Only in high-rate algae ponds may a high efficiency of nitrogen removal be achieved (OSWALD, 1963) by harvesting of organic nitrogen.

Ammonia, the most common nitrogen compound in wastewater treatment systems, may be removed by chemical and physical methods. Ammonia may be extracted by ion exchange (ENGINEERING SCIENCE, 1963). It is naturally fixed on clays (NOMMIK, 1957) and organic matter (NOMMIK and NILSSON, 1963b) in the soil; however, in biologically active aerobic soils, ammonia is soon nitrified and leached by the downward movement of water.

The most effective method for removal of ammonia has been by ammonium gas desorption. Packed columns were developed and applied in removing ammonium from treated wastewater.

This method is rather costly on account of the high investment in desorption towers and the high aeration rate required (SLECHTA, 1966; KUHN, M.S. Thesis).

It was therefore desirable to seek other ways of extracting ammonia by gas emission.

AMMONIA EMISSION FROM WATER SURFACES

Theory

In an aqueous solution of ammonia:

$$NH_3 + H_2O \leftrightarrows NH_4OH \tag{1}$$

$$NH_4OH \leftrightarrows NH_4^+ + OH^- \tag{2}$$

Only the undissociated ammonia is volatile, and its concentration may be increased by raising the pH of the solution, as shown in Figure 1.

The mass transfer coefficient for ammonia desorption is of a very high magnitude. Thus, air bubbled through an aqueous ammonia solution is very close to reaching equilibrium with the undissociated ammonia in solution (REPORT OF DIRECTOR, 1963). Therefore, the rate of desorption of ammonia from an aqueous solution is directly related to the flux of air in contact with it. It is in fact independent of the time of contact or length of travel of air bubbles through solution, as expressed in equation (3).

$$\frac{dC}{dt} = -f \cdot \rho \cdot \frac{F}{V} \cdot H \tag{3}$$

where C = concentration of volatile ammonia form
    t = time
    f = constant
    ρ = density of gaseous ammonia
    H = Henry's constant
    F = flow rate of air
    V = volume of solution

The above holds, assuming there is no concentration gradient of ammonia in solution. This assumption is valid for wastewater ponds (BEREND, 1965).

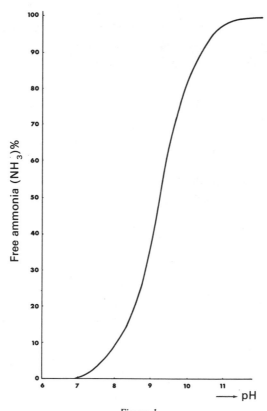

Figure 1
Percentage of free ammonia vs. pH

Solution of equation (3) for batch operation results in

$$\ln \frac{C_t}{C_o} = f \cdot \rho \cdot \frac{F}{V} \cdot H \cdot t \qquad (4)$$

where C_o = initial concentration of ammonia in solution
$\quad\;\; C_t$ = concentration of ammonia at time t

also:

$$C_t = C_o \cdot e^{-f \cdot \rho \cdot (F/V) \cdot H \cdot t} \qquad (5)$$

Let

$$K = f \cdot \rho \cdot \frac{F}{V} \cdot H \qquad (6)$$

then

$$C_t = C_o \cdot e^{-Kt} \qquad (7)$$

For the continuous flow of ammonia solution through a mixed reactor or pond

$$\frac{dC}{dt} = Q(C_o - C) - KCV \qquad (8)$$

where C = concentration of ammonia leaving mixed reactor
$\quad\;\; Q$ = flow rate of ammonia solution at steady state conditions

$$\frac{dC}{dt} = Q(C_o - C) - KCV = 0 \qquad (9)$$

Hence

$$C = \frac{C_o}{1 + K \dfrac{V}{Q}} \qquad (10)$$

but

$$Q = \frac{V}{T} \qquad (11)$$

where T = hydraulic detention time in reactor or pond

Then

$$C = \frac{C_o}{1 + KT} \tag{12}$$

Experimental Results

Ammonia emission experiments were carried out in the laboratory. Rate of emission was determined as a function of: (1) detention time; (2) pH; (3) temperature.

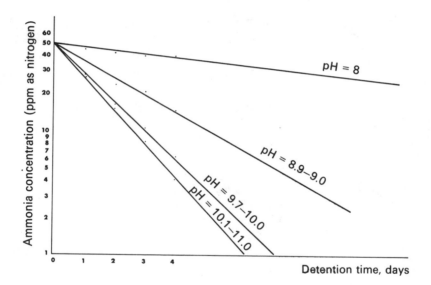

Figure 2
Volatization of ammonia as a function of pH level
and detention time, temperature 20°C

Experiments were carried out indoors in beakers (diameter 15 cm, height 30 cm) filled with a well-buffered ammonium chloride solution, at a constant pH level. Temperature was controlled by thermostats.

Results of experimental runs are presented in Figures 2 and 3.

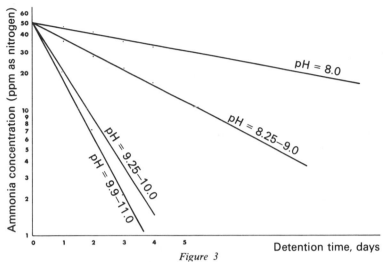

Figure 3
Volatization of ammonia as a function of pH level
and detention time, temperature 30°C

CONCLUSIONS

Experimental results agree with theory.

It was proved that high efficiencies of ammonia removal (70–90%) may be achieved in detention periods of two to four days. These ammonia removal rates, which were obtained indoors, in relatively quiescent air, may be regarded as minimum rates. In field conditions, with prevailing wind velocities, substantially higher removal rates are expected, (K of Eqn. 6 being directly related to wind velocity).

In natural waters, without the addition of buffers, the pH may drop in the course of ammonia emission. This may be advantageous in that it eliminates the need to recarbonate the effluent prior to its disposal in order to obtain the desired pH level.

Detention of effluent in open ponds was proved to be an efficient means of removing ammonia nitrogen. This method may be cheaper than forced aeration in absorption towers or similar devices. It is particularly suitable in areas where earth stabilization ponds are in common use, and where climatic conditions are favorable.

This method may be useful for nitrogen removal, particularly in Israel.

REFERENCES

AGARDY, F.G., COLE, R.D. and PEARSON, E.A. (1963): "Kinetic and activity parameters of anaerobic fermentation systems," First Annual Report, Berkeley, SERL, University of California.

BARTH, E.F., MULBARGER, M., SALOTTO, B.V. and ETTINGER, M.B. (1965): "Removal of nitrogen by municipal wastewater treatment plants," 38th Annual Conference, Water Pollution Control Federation, Atlantic City, New Jersey.

BEREND, J.E. (1965): "Performance and efficiency of deep stabilization ponds," M.Sc. Thesis, Technion–Israel Institute of Technology, Haifa, Israel (in Hebrew).

DOWNING, A.L. et al. (1964): "Nitrification in the activated sludge process," The Institute of Sewage Purification.

ENGINEERING SCIENCE, INC. (1963): "Protection of water resources of Lake Tahoe Basin through controlled waste disposal."

JOHNSON, W.K. and SCHROEPFER, G.J. (1964): "Nitrogen removal by nitrification and denitrification," W.P.F.C. Journal, Vol. 36, No. 8, p. 1015.

KUHN, P.A.: "Removal of ammonium nitrogen from sewage effluent," M. Sc. Thesis, University of Wisconsin.

McCARTY, P.L. (1964): "Thermodynamics of biological synthesis and growth," Second International Conference on Water Pollution Research, Tokyo.

MERON, A., REBHUN, M. and SLESS, B. (1965): "Quality change as a function of detention time in wastewater stabilization ponds," J. Wat. Pollut. Control Fed., Vol. 37, No. 12, pp. 1657–1670.

NOMMIK, H. (1957): "Fixation and defixation of ammonium in soils," Acta. Agric. Scand., 7:395–436.

NOMMIK, H. and NILSSON, K.O. (1963): "Fixation of ammonia by the organic fraction of the soil," Acta. Agric. Scand., 13:371–390.

OSWALD, W.J. (1963): "The high rate pond in waste disposal," Development in Indust. Microbiol. AIBS, Vol. 4.

PARKER, C.D. (1962): "Microbiological aspects of lagoon treatment," J. Wat. Pollut. Contl. Fed., 34, 149.

PARKER, C.D. et al. (1959): "Performance of large sewage lagoons at Melbourne, Australia," Sew. and Ind. Wastes, 31, 133.

Report of the Director. (1963): Water Pollution Research, p. 69

SCHROEPFER, G.J. and ZIEME, N.R. (1959): "Development of the anaerobic contact process," Sew. and Ind. Wastes, 31, 164.

SLECHTA, A.F. (1966): "Phosphorus and nitrogen removal at the South Tahoe Public Utility District."

STEWART, M.J. (1958): "Reaction kinetics and operational parameters of continuous flow anaerobic fermentation processes," Report No. 4, I.E.R. Series No. 90, Berkeley, SERL, Univ. of California.

WUHRMAN, K. (1962): "Nitrogen removal in sewage treatment processes," 15th International Congress of Limnology Abstracts, University of Wisconsin.

Utilization of Thermal Water From

Nuclear Power Plants

George Kligfield

INTRODUCTION

While fossil fuel power stations have been gradually growing in size and output, and efficiencies optimized, they still put over half of the plant energy output back into the cooling water source as waste heat. There have been minor local complaints about the detrimental effects of this warming-up condition, but some waterways received benefits from this heat. As the trend in recent years has been toward larger stations, 1,000 megawatts and above, and the use of nuclear fuels is under consideration, the new watchword for every technical publication, most technical people, the press, and the public is—Pollution—Thermal Pollution. Without discussing the correctness of this emphasis, something must be done to prevent pollution and incorporate waste heat utilization into our technical progress to meet power demands and social development in the next decades. I will review in detail an approach to the utilization of warm wastewaters of approximately 115°F for agricultural benefits, and demonstrate the concept of thermal *enrichment* as opposed to thermal *pollution*.

Concerned atomic energy groups in their respective countries are setting rigid regulations for containment, radioactive monitoring of plant releases, and waste management. Let us view progress in our nuclear power development as a stimulus for the utilization of warm-water effluent from the conventional end of the turbo-generator plant—the turbine condenser cooling water.

The Eugene Water and Electric Board demonstration project for warm-water utilization can be considered a pilot program for a nuclear power station away from the shoreline, away from the big metropolis—the load demand center, moved to a new area where a new complex for residential housing, industrial park, recreation, and an agricultural area can blossom.

EARLY STUDIES

Early studies in the utilization of thermal effluents from power stations were directed toward plant economics rather than anti-thermal pollution programs. Consideration was given to heat recovery for plant heating by directing effluents

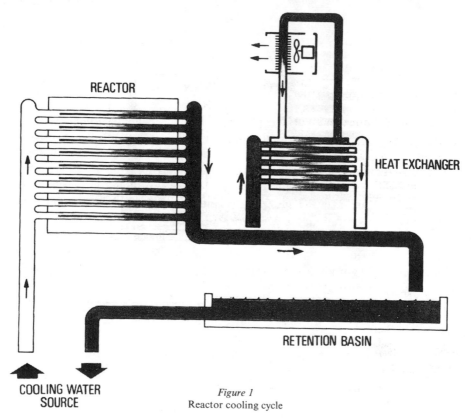

Figure 1
Reactor cooling cycle

from once-through production-type reactors through heat exchangers (see Figure 1). Equipment sizes, high costs, and seasonal demands for heat made this concept uneconomical.

Recently, this problem was again investigated. A study was made of conversion of waste heat to power using new fluorocarbons as the primary fluid, operating similar to a huge refrigeration cycle to generate sufficient power to make the cost-benefit ratio attractive and to effect some cooling of the effluent before its return to the river. Again, because of the large sizes required for the turbines, pumps and heat exchangers, low efficiencies—*10 to 14%*, and minor reduction in net temperature of the return waters, this concept proved unfeasible. Figure 2 depicts the basic heat cycle, which is theoretically favorable, but not economically practical at this time.

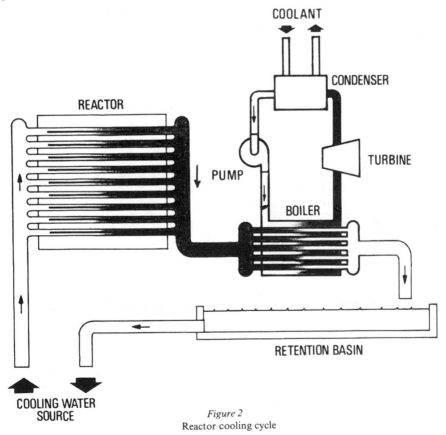

Figure 2
Reactor cooling cycle

As emotional pressures mount to prevent thermal pollution (often considered the root of biological pollution) of streams, waterways and estuaries, economics must become secondary, for water purity has become a vital issue.

Experiments have been conducted using long canals cut parallel to the Columbia River bank for several miles to effect cooling from evaporation prior to re-entry of the water to the river. Such canals had to be large and long, and were only partially effective in approaching even the natural low-flow, late-summer river water temperature of 68°F.

In another study the warm effluent was diverted into an arid area away from the river. The Columbia River Basin is an arid region with an average yearly precipitation of 6–8″. The water was allowed to percolate into the ground and enter the groundwater, eventually flowing to the river. Test wells in the general vicinity indicated a strange phenomenon: the water table in the area rose slowly at first, and the groundwater temperature also started to increase; soon it was evident that the ground was acting as a huge hot-water storage basin. Eventually, small streams ran off to the river bank. These streams, too, started cooler than the effluent, but soon the temperature rose. This indicated that the ground is not a good heat sink, and that the loss of temperature through surface evaporation is still the most effective method of cooling warm water.

Current plans for nuclear power plants in the 1,000-megawatt range include cooling towers for 500,000 gpm, where the effluent heat is transferred to the atmosphere. Drawbacks are present in the formation of fog banks in the vicinity of such towers during cool climatic conditions. In some cooling towers, air enters the bottom and the water is sprayed into the tower as a mist, causing rapid evaporation and a resultant cooling of the effluent by 20–25°F. The cooled water collects at the bottom and can be recirculated to the condensers or directed to the waterway. Such towers have high initial costs—up to $8,000,000 plus up to 10% annual operating costs—with 10,000 to 25,000 gpm makeup required for a 1,000-megawatt plant.

PRESENT CONSIDERATIONS

The demonstration project to be discussed here utilizes warm water for agriculture during three phases of the growing season: early spring to prevent freeze-killing of fruit buds, blossoms, and early fruit; normal ground crop irrigation; and fruit-burn prevention during hot dry periods. This project can be expanded to provide controlled-temperature feed to fish-rearing ponds and to hothouse horticulture (for greenhouse heating).

As the demand for electric power increases in Oregon's Willamette Valley, the Eugene Water and Electric Board, a municipal utility, has been forced to consider fossil or nuclear plants, since water potential for hydroelectric plants is no longer available in this Northwestern area. In fact, the mighty Columbia River will soon be a slack-water navigable stream from the Pacific Ocean almost to the Canadian border, through the locks of the many dams now in operation and others to be completed in the near future.

A nuclear plant has been selected, and tentatively sited, as the most economical in this area (fossil fuels not being locally available). This means that large quantities of warm effluent will eventually be released to natural streams. Discharging warm water into these streams is socially and legally unacceptable, as evidenced by recent state and federal regulations. Eugene Water and Electric Board responded to the challenge and conceived a demonstration project to show the benefits to be reaped by agriculture from use of such supplies of warm water.

A PLAN IS EVOLVED

Hanford Engineering Services, a division of Vitro Corporation of America, having designed nuclear projects for the past quarter century, was engaged to investigate the suitability of using the industrial warm water (now being discharged from the Weyerhaeuser Paper and Pulp plant to the McKenzie River) and the proposed site from an engineering and agricultural standpoint. The results were positive.

Seven farmers, owning approximately 170 acres of orchard and ground crops in this general area, jointly offered their farms and orchards for this demonstration program. The Weyerhaeuser Paper and Pulp Company agreed to make available warm water effluent (approximately 115°F) which they had been discharging to the river two miles upstream of the farm area.

With financing from Eugene Water and Electric Board, we completed the engineering and design, and then coordinated construction. Supervision of the total farm management is by our horticultural group.

Thus, Eugene Water and Electric Board is providing power and system maintenance; Weyerhaeuser, the warm water; and the seven owner-farmers the farm plots on their properties, operating under supervision and within the prescribed plan of the demonstration.

Many groups representing industry, agriculture, fisheries, state and federal agencies, also have interests in the project and all must be considered.

IRRIGATION SUPPLY &
DISTRIBUTION SYSTEM

The project operates under a Board of Review headed by the sponsor, the Eugene Water and Electric Board, and is composed of:

Pacific Power and Light Company
Portland General Electric Company   Adjacent area
Idaho Power Company   utility companies

Weyerhaeuser Paper and Pulp Company—Industry representative and supplier of warm water

Oregon State University—School of Agriculture

The Federal Water Pollution Control Administration

The United States Department of Agriculture—Soil Conservation Service

A spokesman for the project farmers

Vitro Corporation of America—engineers, project managers, and farm operation supervisor

This Board acts in a review and consulting capacity, reviewing all programs and budgets; mediating any major problems of project partners; and reviewing public information dissemination.

The project manager has set up the farm program, is working in the field with the farmers, and will coordinate all future demonstration units requested by state and federal agencies and the University of Oregon.

He will also prepare, for the Review Board, quarterly reports on all planned and forecasted activities and results of demonstrations as evidenced.

WORK PLAN

This is a three-year program, now demonstrating the effects of heat energy contained in the irrigation waters to ascertain if warm water has a more beneficial effect on air temperature, humidity, and soil temperature than does the application of normal (cool) river or well water. In the application of warm irrigation water, an educational program is incorporated and directed toward improving:

> effective use of irrigation water
> efficiency of irrigation farm management
> diversity of crops.

Federal Water Pollution Control Administration personnel, working closely with the project manager, will participate in the initial planning and sponsorship of later investigations related to the National Thermal Pollution Research Program.

Agreements have been drawn up with the farmers for the use of their land for the full three years of the project.

WHAT IS HAPPENING NOW (MAY, 1969)

The crops which had been planned were growing by the summer of 1969, and include strawberries, blueberries, beans, squash, corn, tomatoes, cabbage, peppers, and cauliflower. The established orchards are of apples, peaches, pears, cherries, filberts, walnuts, and multiple nursery stock such as pines and decorative

Later in the summer, determinations will be made to demonstrate the feasibility of a double crop.

To date, effective overhead sprinkling of warm water over early buds, blossoms, and young fruit for frost protection has been completed. As the 1969 season progresses, the program will include:

Reduction of temperature at crop level during the periods when atmospheric temperatures exceeds 83°F

Irrigation (sprinkle for cooling) of berries, fruit and row crops

Evaluation of characteristics of water runoff (temperature, fertilizer, herbicide and insecticide analysis); monitoring for potential pollution

Continuous surveillance and reporting of indicated difference between normal versus warm-water irrigation.

WHAT IS PLANNED FOR 1970 AND 1971

Convincing data on crop yields, crop quality, and water pollution cannot be based on a single season's experience. The present program will therefore continue through 1971. Each year's data will be carefully analyzed and recommendations will be made to the Review Board for changes and additions to the demonstration project.

Frost protection will be continued and, based on 1969 results, refinements will be made in spray nozzle sizes, spacing, rate of rotation, and droplet sizes related to icing and growth control. Prescribed methods of protection for each type of fruit tree will be incorporated. Frost protection will be used on ground crops to protect early blossoming strawberries, early plantings of beans and corn, and again in the early fall for a late double-crop demonstration of peas and bush beans.

Plant cooling will be a continuation of the 1969 program in the fruit orchards and extended to the walnut trees, newly established peach orchards, and ground crops such as beans. As in 1969, extensive surveillance for mold, scabs, or fungi will be continued.

Irrigation will be demonstrated by rill, subsoil, and overhead sprinkling. Rill will be used on small plots to measure soil-heat retention, and comparisons will be made of the heat effect and plant response throughout the growing season. Since this project aims at determining methods of introducing heat to the soil, rill and subsurface irrigation will be coupled with surface mulching techniques to obtain optimum conditions for growth stimulation. This work will be an extension of research carried out at the agricultural college of Oregon State University in developing mulching techniques to retain radiant energy in the soil.

The irrigation season starts as cold mountain runoff and winds move into the farm areas. Warmth from water will induce early germination with accompanying rapid root formation. The rates of other biological processes tend to double with a 50° F rise in temperature. Lesser increases in soil temperature promise advantages for early establishment of plant systems. As immature plants suffer from cold shock with a greater susceptibility to invasions from pathogens, the faster-growing plant will be more resistant to attack.

Populations of fungal and bacterial pathogens will be examined in both warm- and cold-water irrigation plots. As soil microflora are responsible for major changes in crop productivity and these organisms are sensitive to temperature changes, careful evaluation of microbial populations will be made. These observations will be the principal indicators of changes between normal and warm-water irrigation.

RUNOFF FROM FARM AREAS

Studies will continue throughout the three-year program to provide a key to the control of pollution of surrounding streams. Measurements of temperature and the retention or leaching of herbicides, fertilizers, and pesticides will be refined so that their contributions to the receiving waters can be closely determined. Water quality analysis of the McKenzie River will continue both upstream and downstream of the demonstration site.

Two special collection basins will be used to monitor runoff, one for thermal irrigation and the other for normal irrigation. In addition to temperature, the chemical makeup of each will be monitored for nitrogen, nitrate, nitrite, ammonia, phosphate, sulfate, and potassium.

HEAT ENERGY CONSIDERATIONS AND
ENVIRONMENTAL EFFECTS

Warm-water irrigation, ponding of warm water during the off-irrigation season, and flushing to the river after cooling, all set in motion heat-energy influences that can change the environment. Off-site weather stations will be installed to make comparisons with the on-site stations.

Economics is a most important incentive in warm-water irrigation. It could encourage conversion of the site to raising of premium perennial crops such as asparagus, strawberries, blueberries, and added corn and bush beans. Early fruit brings premium prices; this can also be the case with end-of-season produce from double-cropping. Demonstration plots will be established for controlled stimulation of early blooming as well as to permit a more uniform timing of blooms and fruit maturation. Of course, blossom pollination in early season and other ecological activity will be taken into account.

THE SYSTEM INSTALLATION

The water from the Weyerhaeuser plant is supplied to the system pump station at a temperature varying from 95° to 117°F. The system pumps and two-mile irrigation supply line were engineered on the following basis:

An analysis of the orchard area was made, and 65 acres were fitted with solid-set sprinklers for frost protection

Sprinklers are set in a 40′ × 40′, 40′ × 30′, and 40′ × 55′ staggered pattern

Sprinkler discharge is at 1.8 gpm

Water requirement per acre is ~ 50 gpm

Initial water requirements are 3,250 gpm

Main irrigation line—10,050 feet of 16″-, 14″-, and 12″-line

The system water pumps have been sized for a 3,500 gpm capacity to handle an expanded program over the three-year period. Provisions have been included for added pumping capacity, and the line sized to handle up to 5,000 gpm. The system has 4,050 feet of main line across the farms and approximately 7,000 feet of submains installed on the farms. As the demand varies from 500 up to 3,250 gpm, controls sensitive to system-header pressure actuate the pump starters automatically to meet water demands.

Two weather stations, one off the farm site and another on-site, provide an early-warning system and also serve as data acquisition centers for recording air and soil temperatures, dewpoint, and wind direction and velocity. In 1970 two additional stations will be added to obtain wider area comparisons.

Automatic alarm devices are installed in each farmer's home to indicate when the temperature approaches frost danger at 35°F. The farmer is then on the alert to actuate the frost protection sprinklers from a local control station on his property if the temperature drops to freezing. The project manager, too, receives an early warning and participates in the spray protection operation. During extended low-temperature periods, it is imperative that spray systems be controlled to give proper plant tissue temperature and also assure continuous sprinkling to maintain ice temperature at 31°F.

The theory behind frost protection is that the spray freezes on the buds and/or blossoms which are kept at 32° to 31°F, and the heat of fusion is made available for the plant tissue. Ideal conditions have been observed when air temperatures are just below freezing, the water at the spray nozzles is about 95°F, and a mist is formed which settles over the fruit and nut trees providing frost protection without ice formation. The temperature of the falling mist has shown that, at 30°F air temperature, the mist and droplets cooled as they fell, and at the ground the temperature was close to ambient. In other instances where ice is formed, it has been on the lower, heavier branches without resultant tree damage.

FINANCIAL PLANNING

Benefits from the use of warm water, possibility of reducing thermal pollution of river waters, and control of runoff will all be related to crop production and economics in order to establish the cost-benefit ratios. These costs will be extrapolated and comparisons made with future, larger ponding systems created by effluents from nuclear power stations.

The costs for the *three-year* demonstration project are approximately as follows:

Total construction	$314,200
Technical services—initial study, engineering and demonstration supervision	525,500
Operation and maintenance	172,200
Miscellaneous—legal, administrative, and accounting	96,000
Land usage @ ~ $50 per acre	27,700
	$1,135,600

TREE AND PLANT COOLING

After frost periods are over, late in May, the high sprinklers are lowered to three feet from the ground and will be actuated in the hot, dry mid-summer periods. When the temperature reaches 83°F, these sprays, using maximum 95°F water, will be used to raise the humidity and lower the atmospheric temperature to help produce fruits and nuts that are plump, of higher grade, and burn-free. This concept of humidity control will also be used on pole beans to demonstrate increased yield by reduction of blossom drop. This will be a formal experiment, accumulating data to be used for comparisons with subsequent years, including: quantity and temperature of water at each plot; spray nozzle data (size, height, angle, and rotation speed); and hourly atmospheric conditions (temperature and humidity) to compare with off-site weather stations.

Row-crop irrigation is handled much the same way, with comparisons between normal irrigation water temperature on control plots and the warm-water plots, continuously assembling data on water quantities and temperature, atmospheric temperature and humidity, soil temperature and humidity, and, eventually, crop yield and quality.

CONCLUSION

From the above review, it can be seen that the scope of this demonstration project, using commercial rather than laboratory bench models, ranges across many areas vital to the public interest. The tying together of nuclear power and agriculture promises major economic benefits.

Today we are experiencing a rapidly expanding population—agriculture and industry must keep pace. It is necessary to investigate the potential of a planned growth pattern in Oregon and the Pacific Northwest through this engineered project which is aimed at the integration of power production and agriculture.

Between the years 1965 and 2010, the Pacific Northwest is expected to increase its irrigated area from $6\frac{1}{2}$ million to 17 million acres, while the population will increase from 5 million to 14 million. Irrigated acreage expansion in the 1970's is predicted at 175,000 acres per year. The installed power-generating capacity of the region in 1966 was 14 million kilowatts and will be doubling each decade (BONNEVILLE POWER ADMINISTRATION POWER DISTRIBUTORS, 1965 Report, p. 5). It is envisaged that this expansion will be primarily nuclear.

Each station being planned will use fresh water as a coolant. This water, if made available, would be adequate to irrigate 1,188,000 acres with four acre-feet of water per year (Figure 3).

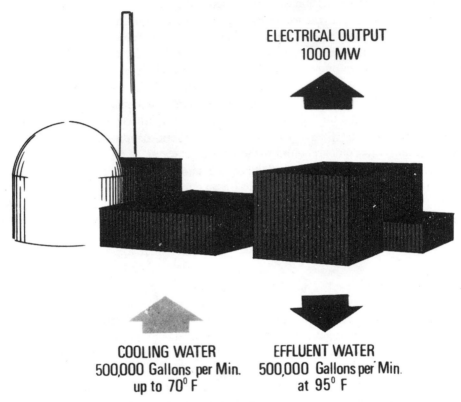

ELECTRICAL OUTPUT
1000 MW

COOLING WATER
500,000 Gallons per Min.
up to 70° F

EFFLUENT WATER
500,000 Gallons per Min.
at 95° F

Figure 3
Power reactor cooling requirements

Ponding, or a cooling lake, can be the key to the utilization of this water in the creation of new population centers, and can provide, as well, a tempered irrigation water supply (see Figure 4).

The power station no longer has to be adjacent to large bodies of water, but only ᴛo an adequate water supply available for seeding the pond and replacing amounts used in irrigation and lost by evaporation. Such cooling lakes have been designed for small plants, but a 1,000-megawatt station with a 20°F rise

Figure 4
Reactor cooling lake

in water temperature will require a pond surface of between 1,000 and 2,000 acres (CLARK, 1969), i.e., a lake approximately one mile wide by two miles long. The effluent from the plant would enter the shallow end, about 15′ deep (the bottom sloping to a depth of about 50′). The return to the power station would be drawn from the bottom third of the deep section. As the water, 500,000 gpm from the 1,000-megawatt plant, flowed through the lake, the surface evaporation would provide cooling and, by convection, the cooler water would seek the lower levels. At the pumping rate noted, the water of a lake this size would be recycled every 15 to 18 days. Such a cooling pond would require a steady inflow to replace evaporation and prevent a solids build-up.

The purpose of this lake can be manifold, as indicated in Figure 4. It could be designed to provide warm water for irrigation (taken from the shallow end during the growing season), a recreation area, an industrial area, and a suburban urban residential area. The siting of a nuclear plant no longer need be a matter of controversy between property owners and the utility company—it can be a joint plan of utility company, local citizens, and state and federal governments, with mutual benefits for all.

REFERENCE

CLARK, JOHN R. (1969): "Thermal pollution and aquatic life," *Scientific American*, Vol. 220, No. 3.

Chlorination of Sewage

Oxidation Pond Effluents*

Yehuda Kott

INTRODUCTION

In some developed countries, sewage effluents are diverted to lakes or rivers and are chlorinated before entering the natural water system. In other parts of the world treated sewage effluents are discharged to rivers without any further treatment. In localities where the seacoast is conveniently near, sewage may flow, treated or untreated, to the sea (SUNER and PINOL, 1966; SHUVAL, 1958).

In many countries oxidation of sewage by means of lagoons or sewage oxidation ponds is carried out in small communities (KOTT, 1968), but at least one case is known where this treatment is used on a large scale (PARKER et al., 1959). However, irrespective of the direction of the flow of final effluents or their ultimate use, such oxidation pond effluents are never chlorinated.

Chlorination as a means of disinfection in water and sewage is very well known (LAUBACH, 1961; ALLEN and BROOKS, 1952). The basic studies of MCKEE and others (MCKEE et al., 1960) show that disinfection of sewage, whether raw or treated, is possible and depends mainly on the amount of disinfectant used (KOTT and BEN-ARI, 1967). The disinfection of such effluents causes mass kill

* Sponsored by the Ministry of Agriculture, Israel.

of bacteria but in no case are these effluents suitable for irrigation of crops which are consumed uncooked. The oxidation pond effluents are diverted to rivers or lakes in some countries, while in others—including Israel—they are used for restricted irrigation. It is therefore of interest whether chlorination of such effluents could somewhat lower the irrigation restrictions. The chlorination of sewage oxidation pond effluents appeared to be highly unfeasible because of the preconceived notion that the chlorine demand of oxidation pond algae would be extremely high. Studies carried out on the effect of chlorine and bromine on algae (KOTT et al., 1966; KOTT and EDLIS, 1969; BETZER and KOTT, 1969) showed clearly that the action of chlorine on *Chlorella sorokiniana,* or *Cladophora* sp., is very slow and the penetration of chlorine through the cell wall takes several hours. These results indicated the feasibility of chlorination of sewage oxidation pond effluents. If chlorination of pond effluents is found to result in very low coliform counts, this could bring about the easing of some of the existing restrictions and prohibitions for irrigation with such effluents.

The purpose of this study was to determine the concentration and time needed for chlorination of oxidation pond effluents that would bring about effective kill of coliform bacteria.

MATERIALS AND METHODS

Oxidation pond effluents used in this study were taken from various sources, such as an experimental oxidation pond operated outside the laboratories at the Technion—Israel Institute of Technology, and natural ponds in the vicinity of Haifa.

A pure culture of *E. coli* B strain grown on nutrient media and *Chlorella sorokiniana* grown in the laboratories were both added to artificial effluents to simulate sewage oxidation pond effluents.

Artificial Sewage Effluents

Nutrient broth of a BOD value of 90 mg/l was used as sewage effluent, to which *E. coli* B bacteria at a concentration of 10^4 to $10^5/100$ ml. and *Chlorella sorokiniana* of a laboratory strain at a concentration of $3,000/mm^3$ were added.

Artificial Oxidation Pond Effluents

Trickling filter effluents of a BOD value of 40 to 60 mg/l were used to simulate this effluent. The order of magnitude of coliform bacteria was $10^8/100$ ml, and $3,000/mm^3$ *Chlorella sorokiniana* were added.

Experimental Oxidation Pond Effluents

Raw sewage from a residential area was brought to the laboratories and fed into a 70-liter aquarium. Detention time was five days, and the effluent was collected through an overflow system. Operation of the pond was regulated to yield an effluent having a BOD value of 10 to 50 mg/l and an algal count within the range of 100 to $10,000/mm^3$.

EXPERIMENTAL PROCEDURE

Glass beakers containing two liters of oxidation pond effluents were placed in constant-temperature water baths, and to these effluents were added 6 to 15 mg/l chlorine. Each beaker was then covered with a watch-glass, the contents were stirred with magnetic stirrers and samples were withdrawn after 0, 15, 30 and 60 minutes. Residual chlorine was determined at the end of each experiment according to Standard Methods (STANDARD METHODS FOR THE EXAMINATION OF WATER AND WASTEWATER, 1965). Coliform counts were carried out on the samples after dechlorination by addition of sodium thiosulphate. The multiple tube fermentation technique was used according to Standard Methods, employing Brilliant Green Bile 2% for the confirmed test.

RESULTS

The action of chlorine on organic matter was studied in many places and results of a number of studies show that the oxidizing mechanism of the chlorine is dependent mainly on pH, temperature, concentration and contact time. In wastewater treatment, pH values are constant and temperature changes are seasonal only; therefore the main factors are concentration versus contact time. Table 1 contains results obtained when various concentrations of chlorine were applied to oxidation pond effluents, resulting in a decrease in the number of

Table 1. Effect of various chlorine concentrations on coliform kill in oxidation ponds at 30°C

Chlorine dose applied	MPN (confirmed) per 100 ml							
	6 mg/l			8 mg/l			15 mg/l	
Source of effluent	Saar	Regba	Nutrient broth	Trickling filter effluent	Saar	Regba	Nutrient broth	Trickling filter effluent
Contact time (minutes)								
0	1.3×10^7	5.4×10^4	$1.0^* \times 10^7$	7.9×10^7	3.5×10^8	3.3×10^7	1.0×10^7	7.9×10^7
30	4.5	1.6×10^5	1.1×10^3	4	<2	2	<2	33
60	<2	5.4×10^4	—	<2	4.5	2	<2	2
Residual chlorine, mg/l	0	0	—	—	1.4	0.8	—	8.5
Initial BOD, mg/l	110	154	90	45	75	75	90	45
Initial number of algae per mm³	41	93	3000	3000	132	450	3000	3000

* Presumptive test only was carried out because a pure culture of E. coli B was employed.

coliform bacteria. The table summarizes results obtained using 6 to 15 mg/l chlorine on artificial wastewater, artificial oxidation pond effluents and natural oxidation pond effluents.

As expected, faster bacterial kill was achieved at higher concentrations. At concentrations of 6 mg/l and lower, coliform numbers remained high and almost no decrease was achieved. However, at concentrations of 8 mg/l and higher, coliform counts were low and reached levels equivalent to those found in potable waters.

Sewage oxidation pond effluents were subjected to chlorination with 8 mg/l chlorine dose at a temperature of 10°C (such temperatures are common in Israel in winter time), and for comparison sewage effluents from a trickling filter plant were used (see Table 2). Under the specific experimental conditions, it was noticed that the coliform bacteria count in the trickling filter effluent was higher than that in sewage pond effluents. However, after 30 minutes contact time, the same order of magnitude was reached in both types of effluent. No further changes were recorded after one hour contact time. It should be mentioned that at Sampling Point No. 4 of the Sewage Treatment Plant (see Table 2) much higher coliform counts were recorded. It can be seen from this table that algal numbers in sewage oxidation do not influence coliform number decrease in the effluents.

Results in Table 2 show that algal numbers in sewage pond effluents had no effect on decrease of coliform numbers after chlorination and vice versa.

Table 2. Effect of 8 mg/1 chlorine at 10°C on various effluents

Source of effluent	MPN (confirmed) per 100 ml						
	Experimental oxidation pond	Sarid	Yifat	Trickling filter		Trickling filter Sampling Point 4**	
				minimum*	maximum*	minimum*	maximum*
Contact time (minutes)							
0	1.3×10^6	7.9×10^6	2.4×10^6	1.7×10^7	7.9×10^7	1.09×10^7	1.39×10^8
15	4.0×10^2	7.9×10^3	1.1×10^4	—	—	—	—
30	6.8	64	120	30	240	200	4.9×10^6
60	1.3	2.4×10^2	130	8	50	109	1.2×10^3
Residual chlorine, mg/l	4.7	1.2	1.1	—	—	—	—
Initial BOD, mg/l	35	—	110	—	—	—	—
Initial number of algae per mm³	30	4675	2175	—	—	—	—

* Minimum and maximum values of at least six runs.
** Effluents at entrance to secondary settling basin.

Chlorine action was studied at temperatures at which its oxidizing effect is accelerated; however no such study was performed on oxidation pond effluents. Table 3 shows that chlorine action in oxidation pond effluents is dependent solely on organic matter found in the pond and temperature, but algae, which are thought to be stable organic matter, do not consume measureable amounts of chlorine, and therefore the coliform count drops more rapidly when the experiment is performed at 30°C.

Table 3. Effect of temperature on chlorination of Yifat oxidation pond effluents

Chlorination temperature	MPN (confirmed) per 100 ml after chlorination by 8 mg/1		
	10°C	20°C	30°C
Contact time (minutes):			
0	2.4×10^6	4.9×10^5	4.9×10^6
15	1.1×10^4	1.3×10^3	<2
30	1.2×10^2	—	<2
60	1.2×10^2	5.4×10^2	<2
Residual chlorine, mg/l	1.1	0.5	0.4
Initial BOD, mg/l	130	130	102
Initial number of algae/mm³	3000	2175	950

Table 4 summarizes results obtained on effluents of different ponds at a concentration of 8 mg/l chlorine at 30°C. It is seen that the smallest decrease in coliform number was achieved when nutrient broth was used as the wastewater medium. Using trickling filter effluent, fifteen minutes after injection of chlorine into the experimental vessel, a high kill of coliform was achieved, their number decreasing from 7.9×10^7/100 ml to 13/100 ml, and after an hour to less than 2 per 100 ml—irrespective of the algal concentration in the sample.

Table 4. Effect of 8 mg/1 chlorine at 30°C on coliform kill

Source of effluent	MPN (confirmed) per 100 ml								
	Nutrient broth	Trickling filter effluent*	Experim. pond	Saar	Regba	Sarid	Yifat	Mishmar Haemek	Yagur
Contact time (minutes)									
0	1.0×10^7	7.9×10^7	3.3×10^7	3.5×10^8	5.4×10^8	5.4×10^7	4.9×10^8	4.6×10^6	2.6×10^4
15	—	13	4.5	34	13	1.3×10^3	<2	22	17
30	1.1×10^3	4	<2	<2	—	11	<2	7.8	17
60	—	<2	<2	4.5	<2	<2	<2	33	49
Residual chlorine, mg/l	—	—	—	1.4	1.7	1.6	0.4	1.4	0.6
Initial BOD, mg/l	90	45	43	75	75	—	102	50	23
Initial number of algae per mm³	3000	3000	1850	135	70	1260	150	40	80

* Artificial oxidation pond effluent.

Experimental oxidation pond effluents yielded low numbers of coliform bacteria after one hour contact time. On examination of effluents from oxidation ponds from different localities, the results obtained were found to be in very good correlation with those obtained on artificial effluents, or experimental ponds, and in one hour's contact time, the coliform count frequently dropped to less than two bacteria per 100-ml sample.

Table 5 summarizes results of various experiments carried out on samples taken from an experimental oxidation pond, in which the number of algal cells ranged from as low as 100/mm³ to as high as 10,000/mm³, and the BOD of the effluent varied from 10 to 45 mg/l. It can be seen that the number of coliform bacteria dropped very rapidly and was found to range from less than 2 per 100 ml to 4.5/100 ml after one hour of contact—without any correlation with algal numbers.

Table 5. Influence of constant chlorine dose vs. changing algal numbers on coliform kill

Contact time (minutes)	MPN (confirmed) per 100 ml when number of algae/mm^3 is								
	100	130	230	320	1,850	3,000	5,000	8,880	10,000
0	1.1×10^7	1.3×10^7	2.8×10^7	2.4×10^6	3.3×10^7	1.6×10^8	3.5×10^7	1.3×10^5	7.9×10^4
15	2	—	<2	—	4.5	1.1×10^3	2	2	2
30	2	23	<2	<2	<2	<2	<2	<2	<2
60	<2	<2	<2	<2	<2	<2	<2	—	4.5
Initial BOD, mg/l	33	40	34	38	43	45	19	10	15

Experimental Conditions: Chlorine dose applied: 8 mg/l
                            Temperature: 30°C
Source of effluents: experimental oxidation pond

DISCUSSION

The mechanism of chlorine action on wastewater has been studied thoroughly and basic data enabled researchers and operators to use it for local demands. However, oxidation pond effluents were not subjected to chlorination because of the feeling that the chlorine demand of such effluents would be extremely high due to consumption of chlorine by algae.

Field practice in Israel has shown that oxidation pond effluents can be used for restricted irrigation, mainly in summer. However, in the winter season, when rain is sufficient for agricultural demands, pond effluents are not utilized and the danger exists of overflow discharges reaching and contaminating potable water supplies. In order to prevent this, excess volumes should be either diverted elsewhere, or be subjected to further treatment.

Previous research aimed at comparing the killing mechanism of bromine with that of chlorine showed that chlorine did not penetrate the algal cells within several hours of contact treatment. These results appear to indicate that, as contact time in the chlorination procedure of wastewater is short, no serious chlorine demand by the algal cell would be encountered when chlorinating oxidation pond effluents.

This study shows that oxidation pond effluents act in a manner similar to wastewater effluents coming from conventional treatment plants. Increasing chlorine concentration or temperature yielded the same results as in cases where no algae were present. Moreover, it could be seen very clearly that at the applied dosage of 8 mg/l chlorine a very low coliform count was obtained. Analysing results obtained with artificial effluents consisting of nutrient broth, trickling filter effluent, experimental pond effluents or natural oxidation pond effluents showed that whenever the BOD of such wastes was in the range of 10 to 60 mg/l, the coliform bacterial count dropped very rapidly after chlorination. Whenever the BOD was high in the same group of effluents, the chlorinated sample showed high coliform counts. This was observed again when nutrient broth of 90 mg/l BOD was used (see Table 4). Field samples of oxidation pond effluents from various localities very often gave a coliform count of less than 2/100 ml, and these results correlate very well with those for the laboratory experimental oxidation pond.

The fact that algae present in oxidation pond effluents do not consume any chlorine and are an "inert" material is emphasized best in Table 5. Greatly varying algal counts (100 to 10,000 per mm^3) did not affect chlorination and yielded equivalent results for contact times of 30 minutes and one hour.

The data obtained in this study show clearly that chlorine action is specific on decomposing organic matter found in wastewater, and that algal cells, on the other hand, are very slowly affected by chlorination. The practical value of this finding is that it may lead to a reappraisal of the possible application of chlorination to oxidation pond effluents. At the same time, suitable chlorination of oxidation pond effluents could open the way for modification of some of the restrictions now existing in connection with use of oxidation pond effluents for crop irrigation.

ACKNOWLEDGEMENT

The participation in this study of Mrs. H. Ben-Ari is gratefully acknowledged.

REFERENCES

ALLEN, L.A. and BROOKS, E. (1952): "Some factors affecting the bacterial action of chlorine," *Proc. Soc. Appl. Bacteriol.*, **15**, 155.

A.P.H.A., A.W.W.A., W.P.C.F. (1965): "Standard Methods for the Examination of Water and Wastewater," 12th Edition, American Public Health Association, New York.

BETZER, NACHUM and KOTT, YEHUDA (1969): "Effect of halogens on algae. II. *Cladophora* sp.," *Water Research*, **3**: 257–264.

KOTT, YEHUDA (1968): "Reclamation of stabilization pond effluents for wide-scale agricultural use," Research Project Report 013–262, Technion Research and Development Foundation Ltd.

KOTT, YEHUDA and BEN-ARI, HANNA (1967): "Chlorine dosage versus time in sewage purification," *Water Research*, **1**: 451–459.

KOTT, YEHUDA and EDLIS, J. (1969): "Effect of halogens on algae. I. *Chlorella sorokiniana*," *Water Research*, **3**: 251–256.

KOTT, YEHUDA, HERSKOVITZ, GALILA, SHEMTOB, A. and SLESS, J.B. (1966): "Algicidal effect of bromine and chlorine on *Chlorella pyrenoidosa*," *Appl. Microbiol.*, **14**: 8–11.

LAUBACH, EDMOND S. (1961): "Rational and accomplishment of chlorine disinfection," Rudolf's Research Conf. on Public Health Hazards of Microbial Pollution of Water, held at Rutgers State University, N. Brunswick.

McKEE, JACK A., BROKAW, CHARLES J. and McLAUGHLIN, RONALD J. (1960): "Chemical and colicidal effects of halogens in sewage," *J.W.P.C.F.*, **32**: 795–819.

PARKER, C.D., JONES, H.L. and GREEN, N.C. (1959): "Performance of large sewage lagoons at Melbourne, Australia," *Sew. and Ind. Wastes*, **31**: 133–159.

SHUVAL, H., COHEN, A. and PURER, Y. (1968): "The dispersion of bacterial pollution along the Tel-Aviv shore," *Rev. Intern. Oceanogr.*, Med. IX: 107–121.

SUNER, J. and PINOL, J. (1966): "Coliform bacteriophages and marine water contamination," *Advances in Water Pollution Research*, **3**: 105–111, W.P.C.F.

Water Quality Protection

in Streams in Mining Districts

Bobby G. Wixson

INTRODUCTION

Population growth and the rising standards of living have placed increased demands upon the water and mineral resources of the world. It is most important that water and mineral resources be efficiently utilized and safely preserved for existing and future generations. While industry is one of the brightest prospects for progress in new or underdeveloped areas, many industrial plants encounter problems of water pollution.

Since water availability and use are not uniformly distributed throughout the world, stream pollution problems will vary from place to place. One of the industries that must be concerned with the protection of water quality is the mining industry. Prior to the nineteenth century, mining districts were usually located in remote areas where their activities and related water pollution problems would largely go unnoticed. However, this no longer holds true, with increasing populations and developing countries extending into the various corners of the earth. It has been estimated that by the year 2000 the mining industry will withdraw 3.4 billion gallons of water daily and return 2.7 billion gallons, with its quality affected in some manner, daily to stream flow (WATER IN INDUSTRY, 1965). Wastes from the coal industry usually present problems associated with suspended solids and acid mine drainage. In other mining districts, milling discharges containing chemical substances added for ore concentration may cause stream pollution. Stream pollution problems within mining districts may vary from mine to mine, being dependent on the ore composition and type of mining method applied for economic removal of the sought-for mineral.

No one general stream pollution abatement program should be applied to mining operations. However, studies in developing mining areas may be used to illustrate different problems and methods which may be used to protect water quality in affected streams. A recently discovered and developing mining district in a relatively unpopulated and nonindustrialized area exists today in the United States of America and may serve as an example of modern engineering design as well as a study of stream pollution problems.

THE NEW LEAD BELT

In 1955 rich lead deposits were discovered in the southeastern part of the State of Missouri. A major portion of this find is located within the boundaries of the Clark National Forest, thus necessitating lease of the land from the US Government in order to develop the lead reserves. By 1962 the ore belt had been defined and was found to extend in a north–south direction for approximately thirty-six miles, through two sparsely populated and nonindustrialized counties. Galena (lead) was the principal ore mineral, with lesser quantities of sphalerite (zinc) and chalcopyrite (copper) recovered as by-products. The lead ore was disseminated throughout favorable rocks in the Bonneterre Formation, mostly dolomite, at depths ranging from 700 to 1,200 feet (MINERAL AND WATER RESOURCES OF MISSOURI, 1967). The name given to this new mining district was the Viburnum Trend or the "New Lead Belt."

Since the Bonneterre Formation also acts as a good aquifer, extensive pumping (5,000 to 7,000 gpm) was necessary in order to prevent flooding of most of the mines in the area. The mining companies developing the area also decided to treat the wastewater of their ore-concentration process by holding the tailings in settling ponds before discharging the overflow effluent into local streams.

At the present time the United States ranks among the leading lead-producing nations of the world. In that country, the State of Missouri heads the list, with an annual production of 210,800 short tons of lead metal in 1968. The significance of the new mining district was reflected in the US Bureau of Mines report (ARUNDALE, 1968) that the "New Lead Belt" will be capable of producing over 350,000 short tons of lead metal annually. The expansion of existing facilities and present development of new mines have given the area international significance, since these will make southeastern Missouri the leading lead-producing district in the world. The new mining development is located eighty miles southwest of St. Louis, Missouri, in the southeastern part of the state.

Stream water quality standards in the "New Lead Belt" were established in 1966 by the Missouri Department of Conservation Water Quality Criteria for the Black River Drainage Basin. In 1967 the first mine and mill started production. By the summer of 1969 one lead smelter and four mines will be in production, with one additional new mine under construction.

Together with the natural enthusiasm for the forthcoming industrialization, a widespread concern for the future of the local streams developed. Similar problems encountered in other mining districts had demonstrated that pollution by lead and other heavy metals may have serious consequences upon the water quality and ecology of streams receiving mining wastes. In addition, it was anticipated that milling and flotation operations would contribute other chemicals, some of which may have unknown toxic properties.

The streams affected by the new mining district are all within the Black River drainage basin where the rolling Ozark landscape is composed of forests and farms. Limited agricultural usage and the sparse population have helped to keep the streams relatively unpolluted. Except for the cleared areas around the mines, small towns and scattered farms, the country is densely covered with forests of oak and short-leaf pine. Annual precipitation ranges from 40–44 inches and the climate of the area is moderate, with mild winters and humid summers.

STREAM POLLUTION EVALUATION PROGRAM

The complexity of the mining district required that stream pollution evaluations be approached from as many aspects as possible. In order to evaluate stream pollution, it was necessary to know the natural background concentrations of the investigated constituents. In most areas natural background conditions rarely exist today because of heavy industrialization or increased populations. Prior determinations are often unreliable, and only recently have analytical procedures been sufficiently improved for accurate analysis. In developing new areas, valid natural background determinations are important prior to the inception of mining operations. In the "New Lead Belt" background sampling was carried out and natural baselines established in order to determine pollution effects in receiving streams (Wixson and Bolter, 1969). A study of the unusual topography of the new mining district indicated that the waste-waters from each mine would be channeled into separate stream tributaries. By careful planning, this unusual drainage pattern was found to be advantageous for establishing a series of pollution sampling stations below mines in the "New Lead Belt." It was also found to be possible to set up, in the same area, control sampling sites on unpolluted streams that were not affected by population increases or industrial development. By use of the selected sites, pollution effects fron individual mines and cumulative effects in the larger streams could be studied. The unique stream drainage pattern, location of mines and sampling sites is shown in Figure 1.

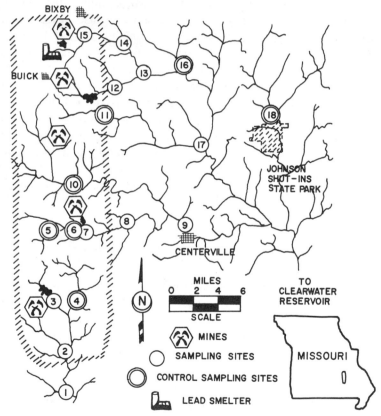

Figure 1
Location of sampling stations in the "New Lead Belt" of southeast Missouri

The Missouri Water Pollution Board and Missouri Department of Conservation have both assisted in the stream pollution survey carried out in the "New Lead Belt." Meetings have been held with both agencies to discuss research findings and projected water quality problems. Over 1,000 blue-gill sunfish were furnished by the Missouri Department of Conservation, Division of Fisheries, for laboratory bioassay studies on the toxicity of heavy metals.

Major lead companies developing mines and mills in the "New Lead Belt" have rendered valuable assistance in preliminary and continued research by allowing mine and plant visitations, meetings with key personnel, and making available pertinent information most vital to this study. One plant (Fletcher Mine, St. Joseph Lead Company) has assisted the reported research study by providing samples and amounts of reagents used at their facility for separating and concentrating the lead, zinc and copper by the flotation process. This made possible the development of research techniques for specific compounds and decomposition products which have caused pollution problems in streams receiving mining wastewater.

CHEMICAL AND BIOLOGICAL DETERMINATIONS

Chemical and biological determinations were carried out to measure the impact of the developing mining district on streams in the affected area. Bee Fork Creek, one of the first streams to receive tailings from the new lead mining district, was selected for intensive study. A Perkin-Elmer model 303 atomic absorption spectrophotometer was used to determine concentrations of lead, zinc and copper found in mines' wastewater and area streams. Nonpolluted values were also determined for streams not affected by the mining development. Lead, zinc and copper concentrations were found to be below normal instrumental detection limits using standard methods. It was therefore necessary to develop improved methods of analysis with sufficient sensitivity to detect low concentrations of heavy metals.

Copper was determined by a combination of solvent extraction with the APDC/MIBK method and atomic absorption. Lead and zinc were determined directly using the newly developed "Sampling Boat" technique.

Heavy metal studies indicated that the range of values for copper, lead and zinc were from 1–20 ppb (parts per billion). The most frequently occurring values for all 3 elements were from 4–6 ppb, and this parameter was used as the normal unpolluted stream background value for the three studied heavy metals (TIBBS,

1969). It was found that contaminating heavy metal concentrations entering the stream below Fletcher Mine were, on the average, two to three times higher than background values (Table 1). Any future increase in the concentration may be used to detect contamination and to warn the mining company that their ore concentration process is not functioning properly.

Table 1. Heavy metal analysis (in parts per billion) for
Bee Fork Creek

	Sampling Station			
	Six (control)	Seven	Eight	Nine
		below mine discharge		
Lead	5.8	15.3	9.1	6.2
Zinc	7.3	15.9	14.1	6.1
Copper	6.4	17.4	7.4	7.0

Field and laboratory studies were also conducted with concentrations of heavy metals similar to and greater than those found in mining wastewaters, to determine the TLm (median tolerance limit) and toxic concentrations for blue-gill sunfish *Lepomis macrochirus,* representative fish in the streams affected by the mining district (PFLIEGER, 1966). The effects of the heavy metals were investigated through postmortem examination of the experimental fish. Gills were removed from control fish and test fish exposed to heavy metals, prepared and embedded in paraffin for sectioning. Gill tissue sections were then cut, mounted and stained (GLICK, 1949) to make the heavy metals show up in the tissue. Color photomicrographs were taken to compare nonexposed gill tissue with similar tissues from fish exposed to lead and copper.

In laboratory tests using the threshold approach advocated by ABRAM (1967), lead, zinc and copper were found to precipitate rapidly in the slightly basic (pH 7.6–8.2) water from streams in the "New Lead Belt." However, if the water was made slightly acidic (pH 6.0), the heavy metals remained in solution and were found to penetrate the gill tissue and destroy the membrane capability for oxygen transfer (WIXSON and HANDLER, 1969). These findings were in agreement with prior research into the effects of heavy metals on fish (LLOYD, 1965; MOUNT, 1966).

The concentrations of lead, zinc and copper now present in the tailing discharge at Fletcher Mine were not found to approach the limits of acute toxicity to blue-gill sunfish under existing water quality conditions (HANDLER, 1969). However, additional long-term studies are being carried out to determine cumulative effects of the heavy metals.

Important chemical parameters were measured and evaluated in order to characterize the major water quality constituents of streams in the mining district (STANDARD METHODS, 1965). No significant changes in water quality were found for dissolved oxygen, alkalinity, hardness or stream temperature; however, fluoride concentrations in the mine water (1 ppm) was found to differ from those normally found in surface streams (0.15 ppm).

Biological samples were collected at the stream sampling sites along with water quality samples. Biological evaluations included studies on the effects of mining pollution on bacteria, algae and fish.

POLLUTION PROBLEMS IDENTIFIED

At the Fletcher mine, underground water is pumped to the surface at a rate of 4,000 to 7,000 gpm. Part of this water (1,600 gpm) is diverted through the milling flotation process where several reagents are added. The automated flotation process is controlled by a computer which continuously receives analytical information from an X-ray monitoring unit. The following reagents are used in the lead-zinc flotation process (courtesy of St. Joseph Lead Company): 343, sodium isopropyl xanthate; Z-200 diethyl dithiocarbamate; Frother 71, mixed alcohols; zinc sulfate, $ZnSO_4$; sodium cyanide, $NaCN$; copper sulfate, $CuSO_4 \cdot 5H_2O$; sodium dichromate, $Na_2Cr_2O_7 \cdot 2H_2O$. The flotation effluents are then channeled, together with the rest of the undergound water, into three settling ponds in series. The total area of the three settling ponds is approximately 50 acres, and all three ponds discharge over the top of a spillway arrangement into Bee Fork Creek (Figure 2). The mine water discharge from the settling ponds is approximately three times the volume of the receiving stream.

A stream pollution problem was found to exist just below the point where the mine and mill water entered Bee Fork Creek. A thick mat-like symbiotic growth of bacteria and filamentous algae covered the stream bottom and destroyed the benthic aquatic organisms.

Biochemical Oxygen Demand (BOD) and Chemical Oxygen Demand (COD) determinations, useful evaluations for most pollution surveys, did not indicate that a significant quantity of oxidizable compounds was present in the water. Since bacteria play an important role as decomposers in stream environments,

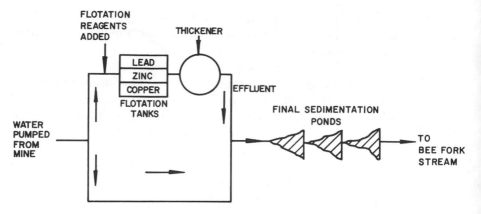

Figure 2
Flow diagram of mine water at Fletcher plant

Standard Plate Counts at 20°C were made to enumerate the numbers of bacterial colonies and compare population differences between unpolluted and polluted streams. Filamentous algae were collected and sent to the laboratory for identification (PALMER, 1962) and further study. Nonfilamentous algae collected with the water samples were counted by means of the transparent millipore filter technique (McNABB, 1960). Confirmatory photomicrographs were taken for comparison of both types of algae in polluted and unpolluted streams. Tests were carried out to determine what mining reagents or decomposition products were contributing to the undesirable biological growth in the stream receiving the mine wastewater.

Through field and laboratory studies the pollution problem was traced to a monomolecular surface film composed of flotation reagents formed in the settling ponds. This film was not sufficiently detained in the settling ponds for biological decomposition to occur, but moved rapidly across the surface of all three ponds due to the spillway discharge arrangement. This surface film of flotation reagents was found to cause stream pollution by the growth of bacteria and filamentous mats of blue-green algae *Oscillatoria* in the stream receiving the settling pond effluent. Present studies have indicated that bacteria in the streams are able to metabolize the xanthates for growth (Figure 3).

The small area being polluted at present serves as an indicator of future environmental changes that may occur with the development of additional mines. Milling reagents used by different mining companies may vary, but the effects on the water quality and stream biota may be similar.

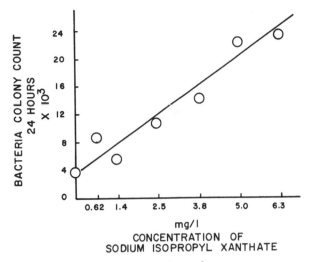

Figure 3
Growth of bacteria using sodium isopropyl xanthate
as food source

POLLUTION ABATEMENT RECOMMENDATIONS

During the next few years greater volumes of milling operations wastewaters, along with increased amounts of groundwater from mine expansion, will be discharged into the streams of the "New Lead Belt." The evaluations of which organic or inorganic compounds affect the water quality and ecological systems will furnish much valuable information on means of protecting other streams and rivers from future lead-zinc mining pollution. This knowledge may also contribute to the substitution of flotation reagents, more efficient wastewater treatment of tailings and the development of improved pollution abatement programs in mining districts.

On the basis of knowledge gained through this research, the following applied stream pollution abatement recommendations (WIXSON et. al., 1969) were made for the mining district in the "New Lead Belt": (1) that the mine water should be separated from the flotation process wastewater containing chemicals and tailings; (2) that the flotation process effluent be detained until the chemical reagents are biologically degraded; (3) that baffling or below-surface discharge of the flotation effluent be employed to retain the surface film of alcohols;

(4) that trees and thick underbrush be removed from mine settling ponds to decrease excess organic matter and increase efficiency of wind action; and (5) that research be continued to improve treatment of mining wastewaters to prevent possible future stream pollution.

Industry, state and government agencies can all work together to protect water quality in undeveloped areas. Developing countries may benefit by the past experiences gained through research in mining districts. Adequate planning is very necessary in order to establish realistic criteria and standards to protect public health and water quality in new mining districts. Good instrumentation is needed to detect and measure pollutants. Monitoring should be employed to provide information for pollution assessment and control. Good planning is the key to success and wise water quality protection, conservation and management are the rudder by which nations must guide their ship of progress.

ACKNOWLEDGMENTS

This study was funded in part by the U.S. Department of the Interior, Office of Water Resources Research (A-021-MO). Sincere thanks are due to the St. Joseph Lead Company, the Missouri Lead Operating Company, the Missouri Department of Conservation, the Missouri Water Pollution Control Board, and the Clark National Forest for their most welcome help and assistance. Most especially, I want to acknowledge the assistance of the US Department of the Interior, Office of Water Resources Research, and the University of Missouri-Rolla, who are deeply involved in Water Quality research.

REFERENCES

ABRAM, F.S.H. (1967): "The definition and measurement of fish toxicity thresholds," *Advances in Water Pollution Research, Proceedings 3rd Intl, Conf. Water Poll. Res.*, Vol. I, Water Pollution Control Federation, Washington, D.C. 75.

ARUNDALE, J.C. (1968): "The mineral industry of Missouri in 1968," U.S. Department of the Interior, Bureau of Mines, Mineral Industry Survey, Report BOMR-222.

GLICK, D. (1949): *Techniques of Histo- and Cytochemistry,* Interscience Publishers, New York, 23.

HANDLER, A.R. (1969): "Some effects of lead-zinc mining wastewater on a stream environment," M. Sc. Thesis, The University of Missouri-Rolla, Rolla, Missouri.

LLOYD, R. (1965): "Factors that affect the tolerance of fish to heavy metals poisoning," Biological Problems in Water Pollution, 3rd Seminar, 1962, U.S. Public Health Service, Cincinnati, Ohio, 181.

MCNABB, C.D. (1960): "Enumeration of freshwater phytoplankton concentrated on the membrane filter," *Limnology and Oceanography,* 5 (2), 57.

"Mineral and water resources of Missouri," (1967): Report of the U.S.G.S. and Mo. Div. of Geol. Survey and Water Resources. Vol. XLIII, Second Series.

MOUNT, D.I. (1966): "The effect of total hardness and pH on the acute toxicity of zinc to fish," *Air and Water Poll. Intl. Journal,* 10, 49.

PALMER, C.M. (1962): "Algae in water supplies," *U.S. Public Health Service Publication No. 657,* U.S. Government Printing Office, Washington, D.C.

PFLIEGER, W.L. (1966): "A check list of fishes of Missouri with keys for identification," Missouri Department of Conservation, Jefferson City, Missouri, D-J Series No. 3, Project F-1-R,

Standard Methods for the Examination of Water and Wastewater (1965); 12th edition, American Public Health Association, New York.

TIBBS, N.H. (1969): "The background concentrations of copper, lead and zinc in streams of the New Lead Belt, Missouri," M.S. Thesis, The University of Missouri-Rolla, Rolla, Missouri.

Water in Industry (1965): National Association of Manufacturers Publication, New York.

WIXSON, B.G. and BOLTER, E.A. (1969): "Missouri stream studies relating to the New Lead Belt," Presented at the Mining Environmental Conference, The University of Missouri-Rolla, Rolla, Missouri, and published in the proceedings.

WIXSON, B.G., BOLTER, E.A., TIBBS, N.H. and HANDLER, A.R. (1969): "Pollution from mines in the New Lead Belt of Southeastern Missouri," Presented at the 24th Purdue Industrial Waste Conference, Lafayette, Indiana; and published in the proceedings.

WIXSON, B.G. and HANDLER, A.R. (1969): "Some effects of lead-zinc mining wastewaters on blue-gill sunfish *Lepomis macrochirus,*" Presented at the Missouri Academy of Science Annual Meeting, St. Louis, Missouri.

Wastewater Nutrients

and Algae Growth Potential

G. Shelef and R. Halperin

INTRODUCTION

Nutrients found in wastewater can support considerable algal biomass production. The discharge of wastewater, after various degrees of treatment, into a receiving body of water can trigger algal blooms and accelerate problems of eutrophication. The proportion of wastewater in the receiving waters which supports an appreciable algal growth is important in order to determine the dilution and the permissible discharge of wastewater effluents to receiving bodies of water.

Determination of nutrients which might constitute the limiting factors to algal growth is essential in order to remove those nutrients from wastewater effluents by biological and/or chemical means.

A major effort has been invested in order to assay algal growth with respect to nutrient sources. Most of the research, notably that of SKULBERG (1967), OSWALD and GOLUEKE (1966), BARTSCH (1967) and GOLDMAN and CARTER (1965) has concentrated on the receiving bodies of water rather than on the wastewater effluents which might constitute a principal source of nutrients. Assaying the wastewater effluents might be of much practical value in assessing their role as nutrient contributors and in finding means of removing the nutrients.

In addition, as shown by GOTAAS et al. (1954), OSWALD and GOTAAS (1957),

GOLUEKE et al. (1967) and others, algal waste-treatment methods such as stabilization ponds and aerobic ponds depend to a great extent on algal biomass production which is directly related to the rate of photosynthetic oxygenation of the organic matter. Furthermore, growth and production of the algal biomass is directly related to removal of nutrients by assimilative incorporation into algal cellular material. Therefore, the elucidation of the relationship between the various nutrients found in wastewater effluents and algal growth potential is necessary for the design and evaluation of algal waste-treatment processes.

This paper describes three independent experiments in which various types of wastewater effluents, at various dilutions, served as media for two species of algae, namely *Selenastrum gracile* and *Chlorella pyrenoidosa*. Both batch and continuous-culture techniques were employed, and a special emphasis was placed on discerning the nutrients which constitute the determining factors of algal growth and production.

All three experiments were performed at the Sanitary Engineering Research Laboratory (SERL) of the University of California, Berkeley.

MATERIALS AND METHODS

Experiment 1

Cultures of *Selenastrum gracile* were inoculated into multiple series of 250-ml flasks with 150 ml of wastewater effluents of different degrees of treatment and at various dilutions with distilled water. As was shown in experiments at Lake Tahoe (ALETI, 1968), *Selenastrum gracile* constitutes a proper indicator organism for assay purposes because of its following characteristics:
  broad nutrient response;
  adaptation to laboratory conditions;
  distinctive shape, uniform size and clear division which facilitate quantitative
    evaluation;
  nonattachment to glass;
  ubiquity in natural bodies of water.
The initial concentration of algae was approximately 50 cells/mm^3 (50,000/ml) and the carry-over of nutrients by the inoculum was minimized by careful washing and resuspension of the algae.
  Four types of wastewaters were tested:
  a) Raw sewage from a typical residential area.

b) Primary effluent after approximately 2 hours of primary sedimentation in a settling tank.
c) Secondary effluent from an activated sludge plant (standard rate).
d) Alum-treated secondary effluent, in which a 25 mg/l dose of alum was employed for the coagulation and flocculation of the effluent.

All the wastewater effluents were obtained from the experimental sewage treatment plant at the Richmond Field Station of the University of California at Berkeley.

The nitrogen and phosphorus contents of the various wastewaters are given in Table 1.

Table 1. Nitrogen and phosphorus content of various wastewater effluents used in experiment 1

Type of effluent	Concentration, mg/l total	
	Nitrogen	Phosphorus
Raw sewage	29.7	14.6
Primary effluent	31.4	9.6
Secondary effluent	23.4	9.0
Alum-treated secondary effluent	22.8	6.0

The first three effluents listed in this table were made up in three dilutions: 0.1%, 1% and 10%; the alum-treated effluent was diluted at 1%, 10% and 50%.

The dilution water was enriched with mineral nutrients, excluding nitrogen and phosphorus, as described in Tables 2 and 3.

Three experimental runs were performed, each with 72 flasks. The flasks were shaken continuously at about 100 oscillations per minute and were continuously illuminated with fluorescent light at light intensity levels of 350–400 foot-candles. Some of the control flasks contained dilution water alone, while others contained the wastewater effluent, dilution water and inoculum but were darkened to prevent any photosynthetic growth.

Algal growth and production were measured by cell count, total suspended solids and volatile suspended solids determinations (STANDARD METHODS FOR EXAMINATION OF WATER AND WASTEWATER, 1965) every two days (up to six days after the inoculation).

Table2. Composition of nutrient
compounds in dilution water

Compound	Concentration mg/l
MgSO$_4$	18
CaCl$_2$	6
Fe (EDTA)	0.05
NaCl	6
KCl	6
Trace-elements solution*	1 ml/l

* See Table 3 for composition of
trace-element solution.

Table 3. Composition of
trace-elements solution (ARNON, 1938)

Compound	Concentration mg/l
H$_3$BO$_3$	2.86
MnCl$_2 \cdot 4$H$_2$O	1.81
ZnSO$_4 \cdot 7$H$_2$O	0.22
CuSO$_4 \cdot 5$H$_2$O	0.08
MoO$_3$	0.015
CoCl$_2 \cdot 6$H$_2$O	0.04

Experiment 2

Cultures of *Chlorella pyrenoidosa* (thermotolerant strain TX 71105) were grown in six growth units described by OSWALD (1963). Each unit consisted of a one-liter cylindrical pyrex culture tube equipped with ports for the injection of a CO_2-air mixture and each illuminated with four 30-watt "Optima" fluorescent lamps. Light intensity incident on the culture surface was approximately 1,000 foot-candles, while the temperature of the culture was maintained at 35°C ($\pm$ 1°C).

Activated sludge effluent obtained from a pilot plant at the Richmond Field Station of the University of California served as the basic medium. The composition of the activated sludge effluent is given in Table 4.

The activated sludge effluent, used as the basic medium in the experiments, was enriched with various nutrients to determine which nutrient could be responsible for accelerating algal growth. The composition of the various media thus formed are given in Table 5. Compounds used in the preparation of the media were identical with those used routinely at the Sanitary Engineering Research Laboratory (SERL) to prepare the Urea Medium given in Tables 6 and 7. SERL Urea Medium (at half strength) constituted the experimental control. All media were filtered twice through glass wool before use. After inoculation, the culture was maintained under continuous illumination until two days after attainment of maximum algal concentration. Algal biomass was measured by volatile suspended solids.

Table 4. Composition of activated sludge effluents

Characteristic	Range	Average
Total suspended solids, mg/l	5–35	15
Volatile suspended solids, mg/l	5–30	12
BOD (5-day, 20°C mg/l)	10–25	20
COD, mg/l	20–40	35
Total hardness, mg/l as $CaCO_3$	110–170	156
Total alkalinity, mg/l as $CaCO_3$	60–120	100
pH	7.0–7.7	7.5
NH_3-N, mg/l		0.5
NO_3-N, mg/l	15–25	20
Total phosphorus, mg/l	8–11	9
Organic P, mg/l	0	0
Inorganic P, mg/l	8–11	9
LAS,* mg/l		0.5
Chlorides, mg/l	65–110	80
Sulfate, mg/l	90–100	92

* Linear Alkyl Sulfonate.

Experiment 3

Cultures of *Chlorella pyrenoidosa* were grown under steady-state conditions in a 9.7-liter chemostatic spin-type growth unit (the "Algatron"). A detailed de-

Table 5. Composition of activated sludge effluent media used in the experiments (ml/l)

Component	Media No. 1	Media No. 2	Media No. 3	Media No. 4	Media No. 5	Media No. 6	Media No. 7*
Activated sludge effluent	980	980	980	980	980	980	—
Urea (1.0 M)	—	12.5	12.5	12.5	12.5	12.5	12.5
$MgSO_4$ (1.0 M)	—	—	—	—	—	5.0	5.0
Iron solution	—	—	—	0.9	0.9	0.9	0.9
Trace elements (see Table 7)	—	—	0.5	—	0.5	0.5	0.5
$CaCl_2$ (0.1 M)	—	—	—	—	—	0.5	0.5
KH_2PO_4 (1.0 M)	—	—	—	—	—	—	3.0
K_2HPO_4 (1.0 M)	—	—	—	—	—	—	1.5
Distilled water	20	7.5	7.0	6.6	6.1	0.6	976

* SERL Urea Medium ($\frac{1}{2}$ strength).

Table 6. Composition of SERL Urea Medium

Nutrient	Molar concentration in media (ml/l)
Urea	2.5×10^{-2}
KH_2PO_4	0.6×10^{-2}
K_2HPO_4	0.3×10^{-2}
$MgSO_4 \cdot 7H_2O$	1.0×10^{-2}
Fe Versenol 120	1.74×10^{-4}
Micronutrients	(See Table 7)
$CaCl_2$	1.0×10^{-4}

scription of the "Algatron" growth unit is given by OSWALD et al. (1965) and SHELEF (1968). The temperature of the culture was maintained at 27°C ($\pm$ 1°C), and an air + CO_2 mixture was added continuously.

The following light sources were used in this experiment:

a) Two 500-watt iodine-quartz lamps enclosed in a water jacket which provided an irradiance of 0.171 cal/cm²-min incident on the culture surface at the center of the culture drum.

b) One 400-watt sodium vapor arc lamp (Lucalox) that provided an irradiance

Table 7. Modified Arnon's micronutrient formula

Nutrient	Molar concentration in media (ml/l)
H_3BO_3	4.6×10^{-5}
$MnCl_2 \cdot 4H_2O$	9.2×10^{-7}
$ZnSO_4 \cdot 7H_2O$	7.7×10^{-7}
$CuSO_4 \cdot 5H_2O$	3.2×10^{-7}
MoO_3 (99.5%)	1.0×10^{-7}
$CoCl_2 \cdot 6H_2O$	1.7×10^{-7}

of 0.290 cal/cm^2-min incident on the culture surface at the center of the culture drum.

The following media were used in the experiment:

1) Settled domestic sewage from Richmond, California. The composition of the settled sewage used in the experiment is given in Table 8.

Table 8. Composition of settled sewage used in the experiment

Characteristics	Range	Average
Total solids, mg/l	804–1306	1116
Total suspended solids, mg/l	81–121	112
Volatile suspended solids, mg/l	44–82	71
BOD (5 days), mg/l	115–175	123
COD, mg/l	225–312	258
Total hardness, mg/l as $CaCO_3$	125–202	156
Total alkalinity, mg/l as $CaCO_3$	145–212	167
pH	6.8–7.6	7.3
Total nitrogen, mg/l	37–45	41
organic–N, mg/l	8–25	16
NH_3-N, mg/l	14–26	25
NO_2-N, mg/l	0–0.6	0.2
NO_3-N, mg/l	0.4–3.4	1.7
Total phosphorus, mg/l	10–14	11.0
organic P, mg/l	0.3–1.0	0.5
inorganic P, mg/l	9–13.0	10.5
LAS*	4.0–11.0	7.0
Chlorides, mg/l	65–110	80
Sulfate, mg/l	90–100	92

* Linear Alkyl Sulfonate.

2) Nitrogen-enriched settled sewage to which urea was added to form a 0.025 M concentration.

3) SERL Urea Medium (Tables 6 and 7) served as control medium.

Various dilution rate levels were maintained in the culture unit, and the algal concentration and algal biomass production were allowed to reach steady-state conditions.

The concentration of the algal biomass in the "Algatron" reactor and the daily algal biomass production were measured by the total suspended solids after subtracting the bacterial biomass which was calculated using parameters of bacterial growth kinetics and BOD removal as reported by ECHOFF and JENKINS (1967).

RESULTS AND DISCUSSION

Experiment 1

The production of algal biomass grown on various wastewater effluents, diluted to 10 % with distilled water, is given in Figure 1. It shows a marked reduction in algal production after six days of growth for secondary and alum-treated effluents as compared to raw wastewater and primary treated effluents. Several possible explanations offered for this phenomenon are as follows:

a) Algal growth was related to the level of total nitrogen in solution (see Table 1). Since the raw wastewater and primary effluent contained more nitrogen than the secondary and alum-treated effluents, a higher level of algal biomass was supported with these effluents.

b) Although not shown in Table 1, secondary, conventional, activated sludge effluents contain nitrogen in the oxidized form of nitrate-nitrogen, while raw wastewater and primary effluents contain it in the reduced forms of organic-nitrogen and ammonia-nitrogen. Because more energy is required for algae to assimilate nitrate-nitrogen as compared to ammonia-nitrogen, algae utilize the reduced forms of nitrogen most readily.

c) The secondary and alum-treated effluents may have been lacking in certain necessary nutrients such as iron, manganese and/or other trace elements easily precipitated out of solution or adsorbed on settlable materials. Precipitation could have resulted from the high oxygen levels found in the aeration tanks, which oxidized these heavy metals to insoluble forms.

An interesting point concerning the effect of phosphorus on algal growth is that, although there is a considerable discrepancy in phosphorus levels of the

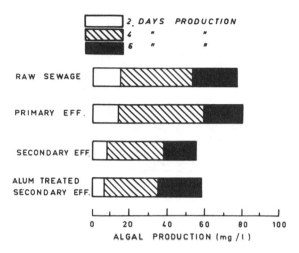

Figure 1
Production of *Selenastrum gracile* fed by 10% dilutions
of various wastewater effluents

secondary and alum-treated effluents, there was very little difference in algal growth with these two effluents. This would point to the fact that phosphorus was not a growth-limiting factor in this case.

The increase in algal concentration for the six-day period of the experiment (in two-day intervals) for each type of effluent, at their respective dilutions, is shown in Figure 2.

Both the 0.1% and 1% dilutions supported a minimum algal population regardless of the type of effluent used. This was undoubtedly due to the fact that the nitrogen level in both cases was extremely low. For the 0.1% dilution it was less than 0.03 mg/l and for the 1.0% dilution it was less than 0.3 mg/l.

The maximum growth rate for the 10% dilutions occurred between the second and the fourth day after the test began and then proceeded to level off. In the 50% dilution for the alum-treated water, however, the maximum rate of growth occurred between the fourth and sixth day.

Thus, the effect of initial nutrient concentration on the peaking-out time for algal growth is an important consideration in attempting to develop a convenient point at which to terminate an algal bioassay test. It becomes apparent that it is extremely important to carry a test to a point where no further growth is observed for a period of time, say two days. This assures that the full algal growth potential of the water was measured.

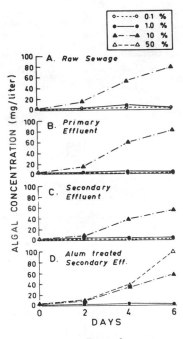

Figure 2
Production of *Selenastrum gracile*
vs. time when various wastewater
effluents served as growth media

The effect of dilution on the concentration of algae, as expressed by cell-count, is also given in Figure 3. The small algal production which occurred when the dilution of the wastewater effluents remained below one percent, gives some indication of the permissible dilution of wastewaters in receiving bodies of water with regard to the prevention of algal blooms.

Experiment 2

The maximum concentration of algal biomass reached with activated sludge effluent and its various enrichments as compared with SERL Inorganic Medium is given in Figure 4.

The addition of nitrogen in the form of urea increased the maximum concentration more than twofold. The addition of micronutrients (the composition of trace elements is specified in Table 7) gave rise to a further increase. Iron also

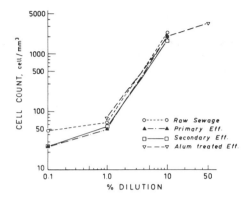

Figure 3
The effect of the dilution of various sewage
effluents on *Selenastrum gracile* counts
at *t* = 6 days

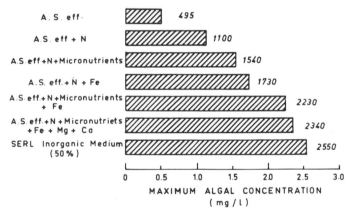

Figure 4
Maximum concentration of *Chlorella pyrenoidosa* when activated
sludge effluent with various nutrient enrichments served as growth
media, as compared with inorganic algal media

caused a significant increase. The addition of both iron and micronutrients
brought the maximum concentration to a level which is double that of activated
sludge enriched with nitrogen only.

The synergistic effect observed on addition of both iron and the micronutrients

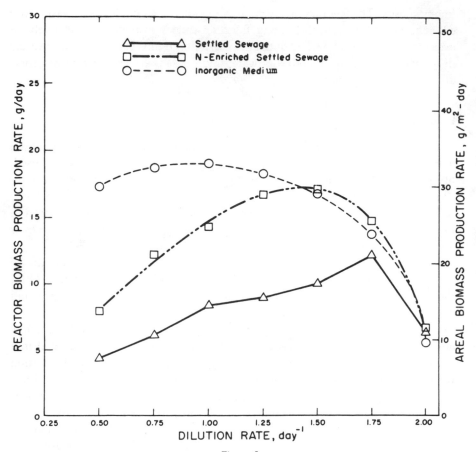

Figure 5
Algal biomass production rates (total and areal) as a function of applied dilution rate in
experiments in which settled sewage served as the medium and iodine-quartz lamps
as the major light source

solution might be explained by the role of iron and the other trace elements,
notably manganese, in the production and formation of chlorophyll (BROWN et al.,
1958; WIESSNER, 1962).

When activated sludge effluent enriched with nitrogen, iron and micronutrients
served as the growth medium, the maximum concentration of algae was approximately the same as when inorganic media were used. Thus, it was clear the
phosphorus did not constitute a growth-limiting factor with the given levels of

light intensity. The fact that nitrogen, iron and micronutrient levels in wastewater effluents constitute growth-limiting factors, while phosphorus is relatively in excess, is important in dealing with eutrophication trends caused by wastewaters discharged into receiving bodies of water and for sanitary engineering considerations of nutrient removal.

Experiment 3

The relationship between the applied dilution rate and algal biomass production when settled sewage, N-enriched settled sewage and inorganic medium were used, are given in Figure 5 for the iodine-quartz light source and in Figure 7 for the "Lucalox" light source.

The effect of the applied dilution rate on the resulting algal concentration in the reactor for the various media and for the aforementioned light sources is given in Figures 6 and 8.

It should be emphasized that experiments with continuous cultures can be most practical when considering bodies of water with low residence-times. Thus, the parameter of the applied dilution rate and its effect on algal production and concentration can be of great value.

From the experimental results with both light sources it appears that for low and intermediate levels of dilution rates, enrichment with nitrogen resulted in a significant increase in algal production and concentration. With high dilution rates, which in general are accompanied by relatively low algal concentrations, the algal production rates were almost independent of the degree of enrichment of the media, and light probably became the sole growth-limiting factor.

Comparing the various media for supporting algal production and concentration, it is clear that enrichment with nitrogen alone, although increasing the production, was not enough to bring the production levels to those accomplished with the inorganic medium. This is in line with the conclusions drawn in Experiment 2 where activated sludge effluent constituted the basic medium.

The differences in algal production and concentration, as observed with the various media, reached their maximum mainly at the optimal dilution rates (between 0.8 and 1.2 day^{-1}) at which the production levels reached their peak. At very low dilution rates (i. e., 0.5 day^{-1}), the enrichment of nitrogen was less marked; this might be due to the relatively high concentration of algae existing in the reactor under low dilution rates at which effects of "crowdedness" interfered by reducing the algal production, accompanied by the effect of nitrogen starvation.

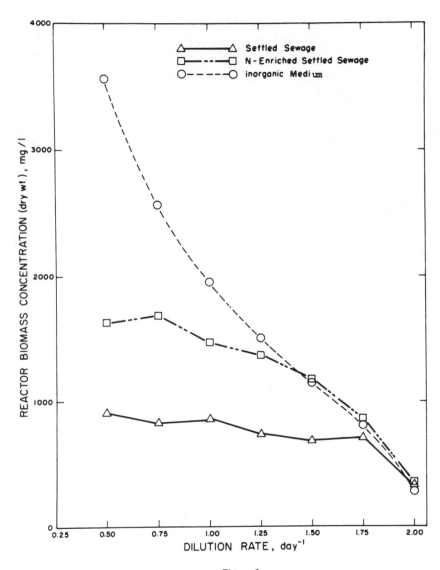

Figure 6
Algal biomass concentration as a function of applied dilution rate in experiments in
which sewage served as the medium and iodine-quartz lamps as the major light source

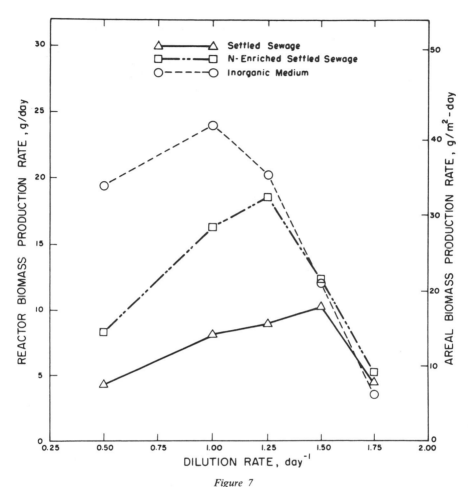

Figure 7

Algal biomass production rates (total and areal) as a function of applied dilution rate in experiments in which sewage served as the medium and a "Lucalox" lamp as the light source

CONCLUSIONS

From the results of these experiments it can be concluded that with the wastewater effluents tested, dilutions greater than 1% had a significant effect on algal production. Thus, it appears that it is possible to use the bioassay method to determine the assimilative capacity of a receiving body of water. The method appears to

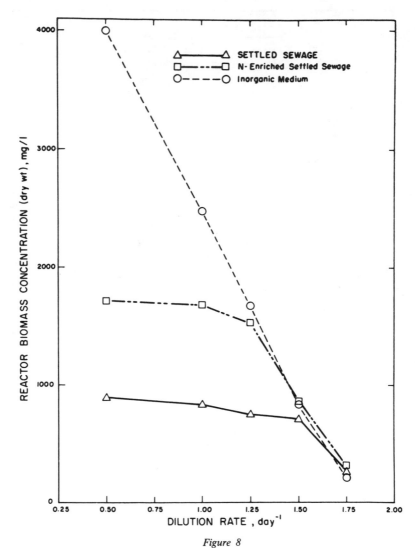

Figure 8

Algal biomass concentration as a function of applied dilution rate at which
sewage served as the medium and a "Lucalox" lamp as the major light source

be a promising way to determine, in the laboratory, nutrient responses at varying concentrations possible in a natural receiving body. From the information obtained in this experiment, permissible dilution ratios for wastewater discharges into receiving bodies can be formulated.

Similarly, the need to carry these bioassays past the point of peak production was demonstrated, since the initial nutrient level determines the time for peaking-out.

Nitrogen appeared to be the most significant growth-limiting macronutrient, while phosphorus was in considerable excess. Iron also appeared to play a significant role as a growth-limiting nutrient.

Similarly, the applied dilution rate had a marked effect on determining the role played by nutrients of a given concentration as growth-limiting factors. At high dilution rates (short detention periods), the effect of a given nutrient level was much less pronounced than at a low dilution rate (long detention period). The application of this phenomenon to studying eutrophication problems in natural water systems is obvious. For bodies of water such as streams, tidal estuaries and other water systems with short retention times, higher nutrient levels may be permissible than in long-retention systems such as lakes and large, slow-moving rivers.

Thus, the use of the bioassay technique, both in batch and continuous cultures, can be an important tool in trying to assess the effect of a wastewater discharge on a receiving body of water.

ACKNOWLEDGEMENTS

The experiments summarized in this paper were made under the guidance of Professors W. J. Oswald and W. J. Kaufman of the Sanitary Engineering Research Laboratory at the University of California.

The authors are also in debt to M. Zabat, Dr. E. J. Middlebrook and H. K. Gee who helped conduct this research.

REFERENCES

ALETI, A. (1968): "Lake Tahoe Research Laboratory on Eutrophication of Surface Water" (private communication).

ARNON, D.I. (1938): "Micro-elements in culture solution experiments with higher plants," *Am. J. Bot.*, **25**: 322–325.

BARTSCH, A.F. (1967): "An algal growth potential (AGP) test—a bioassay," Joint Industry-Government Task Force on Eutrophication (preliminary report).

BROWN, T.E., EYSTER, H.C. and TANNER, H.A. (1958): "Physiological effects of manganese deficiency," in Lamb, Bentley and Beattie (eds). *Trace Elements*, Ch. 10, pp. 135–155. Academic Press, N.Y.

ECKHOFF, D.W. and JENKINS, D. (1967): "Activated sludge systems—kinetics of the steady and transient states," *Sanitary Eng. Res. Lab. Report No. 67*–12, Univ. of Calif. (Berkeley).

GOLDMAN, C.R. and CARTER, R.C. (1965): "An investigation by rapid C^{14} bioassay of factors affecting the cultural eutrophication of Lake Tahoe, Calif.," *J. Wat. Pollut. Control Fed.*, **37**: 1044–1063.

GOLUEKE, C.G., OSWALD, W.J. and GEE, H.K. (1967): "Effect of nitrogen additives on algal yield," *J. Wat. Pollut. Control Fed.*, **39**: 823–834.

GOTAAS, H.B., OSWALD, W.J. and LUDWIG, H.F. (1954): "Photosynthetic reclamation of organic wastes," *The Scientific Monthly*, **79**: 369–378.

OSWALD, W.J. (1963): "Light conversion efficiency of algae grown in sewage," *Trans. Am. Soc. Civil Eng.*, **128**: 47–83.

OSWALD, W.J. and GOLUEKE, C.G. (1966): "Eutrophication trends in the U.S.—a problem," *J. Wat. Pollut. Control Fed.*, **38**: 964–971.

OSWALD, W.J., GOLUEKE, C.G. and HORNING, D.O. (1965): "Closed ecological systems," *Proc. Am. Soc. Civil Eng., J. SED.*, **91**: 23–46.

OSWALD, W.J. and GOTAAS, H.B. (1957): "Photosynthesis in sewage treatment," *Trans. Am. Soc. Civil Eng.*, **122**: 73–105.

SHELEF, G. (1968): "Kinetics of algal biomass production with respect to light intensity and nitrogen concentration," PhD. Thesis, Univ. of Calif. (Berkeley).

SKULBERG, O. (1967): "Algal cultures as a means to assess the fertilizing influence of pollution," *Advances in Water Pollution Research*, Vol. 1, Pergamon Press, Washington, D.C.

Standard Methods for Examination of Water and Wastewater (1965): Amer. Public Health Assoc., 12th Ed.

WIESSNER, W. (1962): "Inorganic micronutrients," Ch. 17, pp. 267–286, in Lewin (ed.), *Physiology and Biochemistry of Algae*, Academic Press, N.Y.

Regional Wastewater

Management Systems

R. J. Giglio, D. D. Adrian,

F. C. Kaminsky, R. F. Rikkers

INTRODUCTION

The public has been demanding and governmental decision-makers have been undertaking plans to maintain and upgrade water quality standards in streams. Vocalization of the desire for enhancing standards has occurred at the same time that significantly improved technology for treating wastes has been developed. As a result, a number of communities simultaneously face the problem of planning additions to existing facilities and constructing several types of new plants. Sewage collection systems have to be expanded to serve these plants and improvements are needed to reduce infiltration and to reduce the reliance on combined sewers.

Two basic approaches are available to communities faced with the problem of upgrading sewerage systems. Each community can operate as an independent decision-making unit, or groups of communities can combine resources to provide a regional waste treatment system. For many communities the costs of individually providing the necessary improvements are prohibitive, and if lower costs can be achieved by the formation of a regional system, the latter approach provides an attractive alternative. Further cost-sharing incentives for the regional

229

approach may be provided by the policies of governmental agencies which in many cases support investment by individual communities in treatment facilities. For example, in the United States these agencies may require that communities, prior to funding, submit plans for investment in treatment facilities which are compatible with the long-range plans of recognized regional planning agencies.

The on-going research described in this paper is directed towards the development of a methodology and mathematical/computer models which can aid planning agencies to make decisions concerning the development of regional plans. Specifically, the models will help guide the form and growth of a wastewater system by answering, for several time periods, such interrelated questions as:

What types and capacities of treatment plants are required?
Which sewage sources are to be served by the same treatment complex?
Where should treatment facilities be located?
Where should the effluent be discharged into the river?

Some preliminary economic studies have documented the incentives for regionalization. For example, under certain conditions the discounted savings accruing for combining three small plants (three million gallons per day) into one facility are more than enough to pay the increased cost of building lengthy (up to twenty miles) interceptors.

MATHEMATICAL MODELS AND PLANNING CONCEPTS

At present, most planning studies start with individual plant demands as given and then proceed to plant configurations and design specifications and, finally, working drawings. The regional planning concept states that planning should and can start at a higher level, that of regional needs and restrictions. Quantitative models are helpful and possibly necessary for this type of planning.

Anyone formulating plans must, at the very least, have a conceptual description—or model—of the environment and the system under consideration. A systems engineering or operation research approach systematizes and extends a conceptual model by quantifying as many factors as possible and by utilizing mathematical/computer techniques. The practical effect of the availability of these techniques is that planners are able to take into consideration more intra-system interactions and deal with problems of larger scope. With a quantitative model, a planner can examine with relative ease the consequences of many different investment and operating strategies and select those which are the most efficient. For a large problem such a procedure would be impossible without mathematical/computer tools.

Even the most sophisticated analysis techniques, however, cannot completely solve a complex problem. There are two reasons for this: factors which are presently impossible to quantify, and limitations in the techniques themselves. Because it is not possible to quantify many factors (e.g., the value to the public of improving river quality by a specified amount), analyses must be in a form such that decision-makers can use them in conjunction with their judgment. For example, a regional planning model can calculate the cost of maintaining several stream quality levels. This information is then utilized by the decision-maker in order to select the best quality-cost combination.

Limitations in analysis techniques generally result in a hierarchy of models. A regional system which can include several plants becomes prohibitively unwieldy if each possible plant is modeled in great detail. Therefore, gross system characteristics such as size and location of facilities are first chosen with the aid of a model which includes only the major cost and physical variables of individual facilities. The regional plan then serves as the framework for more detailed plant design criteria which, in turn, ultimately result in detailed engineering specifications.

Industry has long recognized regional planning concepts and the usefulness of mathematical models. Fortunately, a great deal of industrial experience is relevant to the present problem because the planning of waste treatment plants bears a remarkable similarity to the planning of manufacturing facilities—in particular, chemical and refining facilities. In both cases, large quantities of "raw material" are transported to plants requiring a high capital investment and exhibiting economies of scale. In the plant the raw material is continuously transformed to a finished product which must then be distributed. The industrial studies have demonstrated the economies of regional planning, and it would be ludicrous for, say an oil company, to be guided by local political boundaries and build a refinery in each city or town. However, in the past, political considerations have largely ruled waste-treatment plant locations. While in some cases this might be an optimal policy, there is no reason to believe that this is always so.

DESCRIPTION OF THE WASTEWATER MANAGEMENT SYSTEM

The manner in which the physical waste treatment system is viewed by the research team provides a preliminary gross model which indicates the extent to which reality is abstracted. This model serves a useful function in providing a mechanism for the introduction and definition of terminology which will be used repeatedly in subsequent discussion. It also identifies those subsystems, within the total system under consideration, which must be understood. Understanding, from the point of view of the research team, is synonymous with modeling and, consequently, models of subsystems will have to be developed. The work completed to date on the modeling of these subsystems represents a major portion of the current research effort. Figure 1 pictorially describes a waste treatment system.

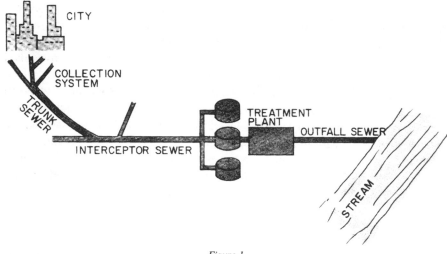

Figure 1
Waste treatment system

The total system under study is viewed as a set of subsystems which have unique characteristics and are amenable to quantitative analysis. The most basic subsystem, representing a location from which wastewater is generated, is called a sewage source. A sewage source may originate in a political community, a part of a political community, a residential development, an industrial plant, etc., and, of course, the total system will contain several sources.

Sewage flows are the input "driving forces" to the system. Changes through time in sewage flow and quality determine the changes which must be made to facilities if standards are to be met. In order to describe the flow of wastewater through the system, each sewage source will have associated with it a list of characteristics. This list is called a stream vector (SMITH, 1968a). The characteristics included in the stream vector are the flow rate and the concentrations of all contaminants for which standards are set, such as BOD, suspended solids, nitrates and phosphates.

The treatment plants in the wastewater system represent the second type of subsystem. Primary, secondary and several types of tertiary plants will be considered as possible methods of treatment. Treatment plants and sewage sources are connected by a series of interceptors which are also considered to be a subsystem. The series of interceptors connecting the treatment plants and the sewage sources will be called the system network.

Although little practical experience is available on the use of storage in a wastewater system, the feasibility of utilizing storage will be investigated as part of the research. Thus, these facilities, which can be placed both prior to and subsequent to the treatment, form another subsystem. The final subsystem is the river which receives effluent from the treatment plants.

The manner in which the elements of the stream vector change from the input of a subsystem to the output of that subsystem is of paramount importance. Major emphasis is being given to the analytical description of these transformations which are called transfer functions. For example, the transfer function associated with a primary treatment plant analytically describes the change that occurs in the wastewater from a point immediately prior to the treatment to a point immediately after treatment as a function of design parameters.

When the transfer functions for all components are known, the stream vector at any point in the system can be calculated. It is a function of the stream vectors at the source points and the upstream transformations which these source vectors undergo in transport, storage and treatment. Such calculations are required in order to determine if a particular regional plan will satisfy the imposed standards.

RESEARCH AND ANALYSIS

The necessary ingredients for developing and ultimately using a general model are drawn from diverse disciplines and include the following:

a) economics of constructing and operating facilities;
b) quantitative description and analysis of the physical mechanisms of the subsystems of plants, transport networks and water bodies;
c) analysis tools which can accommodate full-size problems;
d) a pilot region to test the methodology.

This wide range of demands, which is discussed in more detail below, can be satisfied only by assembling a project team with a varied background. Present members have expertise in environmental engineering, optimization techniques, stochastic processes and computer methods. The team's burden is somewhat eased by the fact that the members can utilize many existing techniques and data sources. However, because of the scope of this project some original work must be done in the fields of Environmental Engineering and Operations Research.

Economic Data

A regional planning study requires reliable data on construction and operating costs for the major waste treatment facilities. Actual costs vary by location and time and are difficult to obtain because firms most skilled in cost estimating are unwilling to divulge their proprietary information for general consumption. These observations may seem formidable obstacles to developing a general methodology. Since the purpose of the research is to develop a planning methodology applicable to any region of the country, however, precise numerical values of cost parameters are not of primary concern. Only the functional form of these costs must be known.

In general, the cost functions reflect the existence of economies of scale. By economies of scale we mean that unit costs are decreasing functions of capacity. The existence of economies of scale is, in fact, one of the prime motivations for regional planning. To develop a methodology it would be sufficient to know, for example, that the investment cost of a primary settler was of the form $C_0 + C_1 A + C_2 A^\alpha$, where A is a measure of the settler's capacity and C_0, C_1, C_2 and $\alpha (0 < \alpha < 1)$ are empirically determined parameters. Cost functions for different locations or points in time will have varying values of the C's and α's, and the help of a consultant or contractor normally will be required to supply engineering-economic data for an actual application. However, the model and computer programs can be designed to accept a wide range of parameter values. To run specific cases, the user need supply only basic data for calculation of particular parameter values.

Some of the information required on cost relationships and transfer functions is available in the literature (e.g., SMITH (1968a, b) and SWANSON (1968)). This information, however, is usually not presented in a form which is directly suitable for a regional planning model. Thus, a substantial effort is currently in progress to accumulate and analyze the available information and to determine gaps in current knowledge.

Analysis of Subsystems

In a regional planning model, the costs and transfer functions of each sub-system must be known as a function of its design and operating parameters. For example, the purpose of a primary sedimentation tank is to remove suspended solids from the wastewater, thereby reducing the BOD. Thus, the flow rate, suspended solids and BOD components of the influent stream vector are transformed by the primary settler. A basic design variable affecting both solids removal and construction costs is the surface area of the sedimentation basin; therefore, the transfer function of the primary settler has as its parameter the overflow rate.

The relationships between river quality and the stream vectors at points of discharge into the river have been modeled. The Camp-Dobbins equations and the work of LOUCKS et al. (1967) are providing the basic approach. For this subsystem, a study of the cost and effectiveness of using storage to achieve low flow augmentation may be fruitful, and results from such a study could be incorporated in a planning model. Studies related to this problem have been reported in the literature (LIEBMAN and LYNN, 1966; LOUCKS, 1966; MONTGOMERY and LYNN, 1964).

Interceptor lines are major components of a regional system and are not well understood (i.e., have not been modeled) from the point of view of input-output quality analysis. Is there a significant change in wastewater quality? Are the Streeter-Phelps equations applicable to these confined systems? Can the reaeration and oxidation parameters be reliably estimated? Such questions are being studied and must be answered in order to describe the interaction between an interceptor and other subsystems.

In the analysis of subsystems, a parallel effort is being directed to the optimization of a treatment plant complex. This is complicated by the fact that it is not possible to plan subsystems without regard to the entire problem, because regional considerations influence the stream vector experienced by any plant. However, for any given stream vector only one of the possibly infinite number of feasible configurations is optimal. Thus, it is possible to find the "optimal envelope" of plant construction costs as a function of the influent and effluent stream vectors (see Figure 2). Only plants whose costs are on the minimum cost envelope need be considered in the regional model. Furthermore, although each point on the envelope probably represents a different plant configuration, only the cost curve itself need be included in the regional model, drastically reducing its complexity.

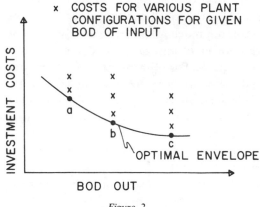

Figure 2
Investment optimal envelope

Suppose, for example, it is desired to decrease BOD to a degree which requires both primary and secondary treatment. Since the effluent from a primary facility is the influent to the secondary, the design parameters for the two facilities are interrelated. As a result, a degree of freedom may exist in the design of this particular treatment complex. As the capacity of the primary facility is increased, the required capacity of the secondary may decrease. The basic question is which alternative (or set of alternatives) is optimal for the stated purpose.

A study is in progress to develop an optimization procedure which will determine the minimum-cost primary and secondary designs for any combination of influent and effluent stream vectors. A family of cost functions (optimal envelopes) for the optimal treatment complexes will then be generated and subsequently used in the regional model. This optimization problem is not linear and it is expected that non-linear programming techniques will be utilized. The primary and secondary facilities are serially connected in the sense that the effluent from the primary settler is the input to the secondary facilities. This serial relationship suggests that a dynamic programming approach may also be useful.

The Regional Model

A feasible approach to the regional planning problem is to select a small number of regional plans which appear to be both economical and feasible. Results of the work on subsystem analysis would allow one to determine which alternatives meet the river standards and, for those which are feasible, determine the associated cost. If only a small number of alternatives exist, or the planning horizon is short, this approach would be reasonable. In a system encompassing a relatively large number of sewage sources, however, the number of possible regional plans is large. In fact, the number of alternative plans increases exponentially with the number of sewage sources and the length of the planning horizon. Thus, an efficient method is needed which will generate and evaluate a huge number of regional plans. Ideally, the technique would search the alternative plans in such a manner that each succeeding alternative meets the imposed river standards at a lower total cost until the optimal solution is found. The complexity of the present problem indicates that common algorithms, such as linear programming, will not be suitable for this purpose. Reasons for this order of complexity are given below.

This regional planning problem, like most others, is dynamic in two basic "dimensions." One dimension regards the interaction between location and capacity decisions within a given time period. For example, a decision to invest in a treatment facility of a given design capacity at a given location cannot be made independent of decisions regarding which sewage sources will be served by this facility, the location and capacity of an interceptor system leading from the sources to the facility and, of course, an equivalent set of decisions related to other treatment facilities in the system. In this dimension, there are two dominant economic forces in opposition. One force arises from the concept of economies of scale and argues for a single, large treatment plant for the entire system. The second force recognizes that interceptor lines are expensive and argues for a separate small treatment plant for each of the sewage sources. An optimal single time period (i.e., static) wastewater system would find the optimal balance between these two economic forces.

The second dynamic dimension is, of course, the time dimension. If, for example, we restrict our attention to a particular treatment plant location, a decision concerning investment in capacity at that plant in a given time period cannot be made independent of future requirements and calls for decisions concerning expansion in the future. Once again, two opposing economic forces are present. Given that either new or additional capacity is required, one force argues for large, initial preinvestment to meet requirements in the distant future. This force derives from the fact that typical expansion costs include a large fixed cost. Thus, it is cheaper to incur this fixed cost only once. This is an economies-of-scale concept. The other economic force arises from a recognition of the time value of money. In present-day dollars, it is cheaper to postpone any investments until they are absolutely required. This force argues for expansion investment in each time period if capacity requirements are monotonically increasing.

It is the dependent nature of decisions both within each dynamic dimension and, especially, between the two dimensions which make regional planning problems difficult. Techniques are available for selecting optimal investment strategies for a single facility through time (GIGLIO, 1966). Also, in some cases, single time period, multi-facility planning problems can be solved (EFROYMSON and RAY, 1966). (But these are not as complex as the single period wastewater treatment system planning problem.) Practical techniques for solving large planning problems which are both multi-period and multi-facility do not yet exist.

Work to date suggests that the problem can be decomposed geographically, such that service zones will be defined for each treatment facility. As a second step investment timing will be determined. Although this is an approximation, we expect this method's accuracy to equal that of the input data. Another approach which holds promise is a heuristic with a "man in the loop." This approach would utilize a large time-sharing computer with "instantaneous" display devices such as a cathode ray tube. This would enable an experienced planner to modify computer-generated solutions and quickly see the results. The computer carries out the extensive calculations, while the human uses his judgment. Thus, man and machine each do that task for which they are most suited.

Model Validation

To help insure the validity of the models, a region in Massachusetts has been selected for a pilot application. This region contains several communities in south and central portions of the State which utilize the Connecticut River for effluent disposal. It is well suited to serve as a test case, and the collection of data on the region's characteristics is underway.

ACKNOWLEDGMENTS

The writers acknowledge with thanks the assistance of their colleagues Professors Bernard B. Berger and John H. Nebiker; Philip A. Lutin, Research Associate; Ronald Deacon, Peter Meier, Donald Ray and Gerald Trane, Research Assistants. Financial support was provided by OWRR grant WR-BOll-

Mass. Thanks are also extended to the American Water Resources Association for permiting the authors to reprint this article which was presented in modified form at the Fourth AWRA conference, November 1968.

REFERENCES

EFROYMSON, M.A. and RAY, T.L. (1966): "A branch-bound algorithm for plant location," *Operations Research*, Vol. 14, No. 3.

GIGLIO, R.J. (1966): "Optimal capacity expansion," Technical Report No. 16, Graduate School of Business, Stanford University.

LIEBMAN, J.C. and LYNN, W.R. (1966): "Optimal allocations of stream dissolved oxygen," *Water Resources Research*.

LOUCKS, D.P. (1966): "A probabilistic approach to stream standards," *Proceedings of the Fifteenth Southern Water Resources and Pollution Control Conferences*, North Carolina State University.

LOUCKS, D.P., REVELLE, C.S. and LYNN, W.R. (1967): "Linear programming models for water pollution control," *Management Science*, Vol. 14, No. 4.

MONTGOMERY, M.M. and LYNN. W.R. (1964): "Analysis of sewage treatment systems of simulation," *Journal of the Sanitary Engineering Division, Proceedings of the American Society of Civil Engineers*, Vol. 90, No. SA 2.

SMITH, R. (1968a): "Preliminary design and simulation of conventional wastewater renovation systems using the digital computer," *Water Pollution Control Research Series*, WP–20–9, U.S. Department of the Interior, Federal Water Pollution Control Administration.

SMITH, R. (1968b): "Cost of conventional and advanced treatment of wastewaters," *J. Wat. Pollut. Control Fed.*, Vol. 40, No. 9.

SWANSON, C.L. (1968): "Unit process operating and maintenance costs for conventional waste treatment plants," Presented at Ohio Water Pollution Control Federation Meeting, Dayton, Ohio.

Diffusion of Odors from

Stabilization Ponds in Arid Zones

J. Kendler and A. Donagi

INTRODUCTION

The available data on odor nuisances from stabilization ponds in arid zones are quite limited. The climatological conditions, including specific temperatures and intensive solar radiation of the arid zones, are factors which may greatly increase the inconvenience caused by odor nuisances.

This general lack of data gives added importance to any scientific information on the specific problems of these areas. The present investigation on odor diffusion from the stabilization ponds of Eilat, even though it is of a limited nature, may enhance our knowledge in this field.

The town of Eilat is one of the most important ports and tourist resorts of Israel. It is, therefore, obvious that either air pollution or odor nuisances will strongly affect this site and has to be prevented.

Since 1960, sporadic complaints on unpleasant odors affecting the commercial center, and especially the hotels, were received by the District Health Office, their number increasing in recent years.

A preliminary inspection was carried out by the local health officials in order to assess the potential sources of pollution. Their conclusions were that the source of the odor may be traced to the following:

a) The municipal stabilization ponds which release odorous gases, mostly hydrogen sulfide, whenever their operation is faulty. This pollutant is swept by the wind towards the hotels in the resort area.

b) The sprinkler system used for irrigation of date plantations with the wastewater of the ponds.

Following the inspection, a limited-scale air pollution survey was carried out in August 1967 by the Central Laboratory for Air Pollution and Radiation Hazard Control of the Israel Ministry of Health. The purpose of the survey was to determine the following points:

1) The level of air pollution due to hydrogen sulfide, around the hotels at a distance of about 1,700 meters from the ponds.

2) The various factors and mechanisms responsible for the release of the hydrogen sulfide.

3) The potential solution to the problem.

Parallel with the air pollution survey, measurements of the wastewater in the ponds were also performed. A complimentary survey was carried out by the Sanitary Engineering Laboratories of the Technion–Israel Institute of Technology in 1968. Following these surveys, a more complete understanding of the efficiency of operation of the ponds was gained and appropriate prevention measures were taken.

THE OPERATION OF OXIDATION PONDS

Oxidation ponds (also called stabilization ponds or sewage lagoons) are one of the common methods for stabilizing domestic and industrial wastes. They are used widely in many countries and in Israel they have become one of the most commonly accepted solutions for treatment of wastes of small and medium-sized communities. A large-scale project, the "Recovery of the Dan Region Wastewater", is underway in Israel.

This method is based on the degradation of the organic material by the activities of microorganisms such as algae, bacteria and *Actinomycetes,* which consume complex organic matter and produce intermediate substances as a part of their metabolic process.

The literature contains numerous data on the quality of liquid discharges from these ponds (CALDWELL, 1946; PARKES et al., 1959; SAMSONOV, 1965; LAGOONS AS A METHOD OF SEWAGE STABILIZATION, 1961), but information on gaseous emissions is lacking.

In addition to oxygen, which is formed throughout the operation of the ponds, algae, bacteria, sulfur oxides, nitrogen oxides, ammonia, methane, hydrocarbons and hydrogen sulfide are among the airborne products that may be emitted from the ponds. Increase of the pollution load of the sewage treatment plant may well contribute to the overall atmospheric contamination due to gaseous emissions of biologically degraded products. In addition, oxidation ponds may be the source of naturally occurring hazes and malodorous smells (NELSON and LEDBETTER, 1962).

One of the hydrocarbons of importance is methane, which was reported to be produced at a rate of about 10 cubic feet of gas per kilogram of BOD destroyed (OSWALD, 1960).

LUDZACK et al. (1961) reported on the loss of ammonia to the atmosphere, but were unable to calculate a balance of the nitrogen. Along the same lines, HERMANN (1957) reported that nitrogen (50–73 %) and phosphorus (up to 13 %) as hydrogen phosphide could possibly be lost to the atmosphere. Increase in total nitrogen in the effluent compared to the influent has also been reported (HERMANN, 1957; U. S. PUBLIC HEALTH SERVICE, 1957). Fixation of nitrogen in ponds was mentioned (POST, 1960) and would seem to indicate that, under certain operating conditions, nitrogen can be fixed from the air.

Among the microorganisms found in water, algae are of importance as far as taste and odor are concerned. Even if they are not the direct cause of the problem, they may provide the food necessary for *Actinomycetes* which, in turn, will produce odorous metabolic products.

Algae are found in surface water exposed to sunlight, and oxygen, which is their by-product, is of importance to the overall ecosystem by preventing foul or septic conditions from developing and by stimulating the growth of aerobic rather than anaerobic bacteria.

The most important algae from the viewpoint of odor production are certain diatoms, blue-green algae and pigmented flagellates. Most notorious are the blue-green algae, but green algae, too, are associated with odors. Some of these algae which have been identified as agents of odor are *Hydrodictyon, Stranastrum* and *Mitrella*. Other associated genera are: *Dinobryon, Uroglenopsis, Peridinium, Mallomonas, Pandorina, Volvox, Ceratium, Asterionella, Synedra, Tabellaria, Anabaena, Microcystis, Coelosphaerium,* and *Aphanizomenon* (PALMER and TARZWELL, 1955).

According to MALONEY (1963), the decomposition of dead algal material is the prime agent in producing algal odor. He reported that little odor was noted during active and stationary phases but, after the beginning of the autolysis, there was a reported increase in odor. This rise was explained in two ways:

a) Odoriferous material was kept in the cells and not released until autolysis.

b) These materials were not produced until late in the growth cycle. Temperature and pH changes both affected the intensity of the odor.

Water ponds with the proper nutrients will harbor high concentrations of *Actinomycetes,* organisms closely related to bacteria and fungi. These microorganisms as well as their metabolic by-products, such as aromatic amines, ketones, aldehydes, saturated fatty acids and unsaturated aromatics, are considered to be sources of taste and odor in water.

THE SURVEY SITE AND PREVAILING WINDS

Hydrogen sulfide measurements were performed at the end of August 1967 at two sites in the Eilat resort area. The first, where the existing hotels are located, is about 1,700 meters from the lagoons. The second site was chosen because of its importance as an area where the construction of new hotels was planned.

Other sampling sites were the date plantations and the vicinity of the ponds (about 15 meters in the direction of the prevailing winds). The pond water and soil were also analyzed.

The prevailing winds in Eilat are unique because their direction is, most of the time, from north to south, with only slight fluctuations from this direction. The wind velocity is usually low, especially at night, and throughout the measurement period did not exceed 8 m/sec. These peculiar meteorological conditions create a funneling effect by which the offensive odors from the ponds are transferred into the hotel area.

METHODS

Apparatus

The sampling train, composed of a series of three impingers, a "Gelman" flow meter and a vacuum pump, was used for hydrogen sulfide sampling. The air was sampled at a rate of 2–3 liters/minute for 20 to 40 minutes. The sampling solution was ammonium molybdate. A "Staplex" Battery Sampler was used wherever power connections were unavailable.

pH meter: The "Metrohm" Model E 444 with an expanded scale was used for the pH measurements.

Base Reagent

This reagent was prepared by dissolution of 17 g of ammonium molybdate $(NH_4)_6Mo_7O_{24} \cdot 4H_2O$ in 900 ml of distilled water. After adjustment of the pH to 1.5 ± 0.2 by dropwise addition of 2 N HCl, the solution was transferred to a one-liter volumetric flask and filled to the mark with distilled water.

Analytical Method

A new Molybdenum-Blue Spectrophotometric Method, developed at the Central Laboratory for Prevention of Air Pollution and Radiation Hazards, was employed (DONAGI et al., 1967). By this direct method the blue color is developed during the sampling and is measured spectrophotometrically at 710 mμ. The concentration is determined by comparison with a calibration curve previously prepared using sodium sulfide.

The same method may also be employed for the determination of the sulfide content of water, as was practised in this survey. By this method, 60–70 ml are introduced into 100-ml volumetric flasks. The pH is adjusted to 1.5 ± 0.2, and 20 ml of the ammonium molybdate reagent are added. The flask is filled to the mark with distilled water. The spectrophotometric measurements are performed as described above for the air samples.

RESULTS AND DISCUSSION

The hydrogen sulfide measurements are summarized in Table 1. It may be seen from the results that the pollution level at the hotel site constitutes a serious health nuisance, verging on a potential health hazard to tourists and personnel.

The hydrogen sulfide concentration is as high as 0.36 ppm 1,700 meters from the ponds and attains 0.56 ppm at a distance of 1,300 meters. Unusual peak concentrations of 7.0 to 9.0 ppm were found 15 meters from the ponds. It will be of interest to compare these high concentrations with the various air pollution standards.

The proposed Israel Air Quality Standards for this pollutant are 0.007 ppm for a 24-hour average, and 0.1 ppm for any single measurement. The U.S. Air Quality Criteria are less stringent and amount to 0.05 and 0.12, respectively (A. P. C. D. RULES AND REGULATIONS). The odor threshold of hydrogen sulfide is 0.13–1.0 ppm (WEISBURD and GRISWOLD, 1962). This figure clearly indicates that

Table 1. Hydrogen sulfide concentration in atmospheric samples
(Eilat, August 22–24, 1967)

Date of sampling	Hour of the day	Volume of air (liters)	H_2S cone (ppm)	Wind direction	Wind speed (m/sec)
\multicolumn{6}{c}{Hotel area (1,700 m from the ponds)}					
22.8	19.30	30	0.05	SW–NE	2
22.8	20.00	40	0.23	N–S	5
22.8	20.45	40	0.17	N–S	5
22.8	22.20	80	0.07	N–S	8
22.8	23.20	60	0.32	N–S	2
23.8	16.20	80	0.00	NW–SE	3
23.8	17.20	90	0.01	NW–SE	3
23.8	18.10	90	0.22	N–S	1
23.8	18.50	60	0.06	N–S	2
24.8	05.10	60	0.36	N–S	2
24.8	05.50	60	0.24	N–S	2
24.8	06.35	50	0.11	NE–SW	4
24.8	07.15	50	0.00	NE–SW	8
24.8	08.35	50	0.06	NE–SW	8
24.8	09.55	40	0.21	NE–SW	3
24.8	10.25	60	0.00	NE–SW	4
\multicolumn{6}{c}{Planned area (1,300 m from the ponds)}					
23.8	15.10	60	0.13	NE–SW	6
23.8	21.20	60	0.56	N–S	3
\multicolumn{6}{c}{Arbitrary site (15 m from the ponds)}					
23.8	09.00	30	8.80	N–S	2
23.8	10.10	30	6.70	N–S	5

a serious odor nuisance will undoubtedly exist in Eilat due to the high H_2S concentrations. The corrosive power of this pollutant which, in addition, causes economic damage should also be noted.

High sulfide concentrations were found in the wastewaters of the oxidation ponds. The results are given in Table 2. The sulfide concentration was as high as 18.2 mg/l in the first pond and 10.7 mg/l in the third.

Since the sprinklers (located at about 1,300 meters from the ponds) use the effluent from the third pond for irrigation, the high residual concentration of sulfides in this pond hints that irrigation may be considered as a contributor to the overall hydrogen sulfide pollution.

Along these lines, it may be deduced from the sulfide concentration gradient

Table 2. Chemical analysis of oxidation ponds' water

Pond No.	Sulfide concentration (mg/l)		Turbidity (OD)		pH	Organic material (g/l)	Inorganic material (g/l)
	Filtered	Unfiltered	Filtered	Unfiltered			
1	18.2	24.8	0.420	0.960	7.5	0.516	2.083
2	16.0	18.7	0.640	0.800	8.0	0.721	2.114
3	10.7	13.9	0.420	0.560	8.5	0.832	2.078

and from the fact that in the third pond the sulfide concentration is still high, that the oxidation ponds are not functioning properly.

Table 2 also gives the results of some turbidity and pH measurements of the wastewaters in the ponds. The slight, gradual increase of pH from the first to the third pond shows that it is the latter which is most efficient. This increase in pH compares favorably with the decrease in sulfide concentration (see same table). Nevertheless, the relatively high turbidity of the wastewater in all three ponds hints that decomposed algal matter, which is a prime agent of algal odors, is present. This conclusion is substantiated by the measurements of total solids and organic matter in the ponds, which are also summarized in Table 2. There is practically no change in the total-solids content, whereas the organic-matter content increases from the first to the third pond, a phenomenon that may indicate decomposition of algal matter.

CONCLUSIONS

1. The present survey has shown that the oxidation ponds of Eilat were not functioning properly, and emitted hydrogen sulfide which was measured at the downwind sampling stations. The hydrogen sulfide concentration measured was higher by more than one order of magnitude than that of the US Air Quality Criteria (AQC) and even higher by the standards of the Israel AQC.

2. The high hydrogen sulfide concentrations create an odor nuisance in the resort zone (located about 1,700 meters from the ponds) and the new area allocated for construction of new hotels (about 1,300 meters from the ponds). The wastewater irrigation of the date plantation using sprinklers further increases this nuisance.

3. The measurements of sulfides, pH, turbidity and total solids of the wastewater validate the fact that the oxidation ponds do not operate properly and thus support the conclusions derived from the atmospheric measurements of H_2S.

4. Various measurements of the chloride content of the oxidation ponds (DATA OF THE MINISTRY OF AGRICULTURE AND MINISTRY OF HEALTH, 1966–67) have shown high levels of 2,900–7,600 mg/l. These high chloride concentrations may be attributed to the diffusion of underground brackish water into the ponds. This may be an additional reason for the improper working conditions of the ponds.

5. It appears that measurements of air pollution levels around the ponds, in the direction of the prevailing winds, may serve as a means of assessing improper function of stabilization ponds. This is especially true when no other sources of hydrogen sulfide emissions are present in the surroundings.

COMPLEMENTARY ANALYSIS

The results of the investigation were submitted to the responsible sanitary authorities. As a consequence of this study, the Department of Sanitary Engineering at the Technion-Israel Institute of Technology was asked to verify the above-mentioned conclusions. A complementary survey was undertaken by the Technion (SLESS and REBHUN, 1968) at the beginning of 1968. The main conclusions of that survey were as follows:

1. The stabilization ponds do not operate properly. This statement was supported by the low dissolved oxygen levels in the ponds found during this survey. A possible explanation for the high sulfide concentration of the settling pond (No. 1) may be the large diameter of the inlet pipe (32"), which permits a relatively slow flow of the wastes.

2. Proliferation of sulfur-reducing microorganisms in the ponds increases the amount of sulfides created in the ponds. The fact that the ponds had not been cleaned for a number of years enhanced the proliferation of these organisms.

3. Reduction of the wind velocity to about 10 km/hr or less seems to give rise to a relatively high concentration of hydrogen sulfide in the hotel resort area. It appears that the slow winds are strong enough to pick up the odors from the ponds but not to bring about sufficient atmospheric diffusion and dilution.

4. High organic load (40 kg of BOD/1,000 m^2/day) and short detention periods (5–7 days) are factors which disturb the growth of algae (such as *Euglena* and *Chlorella*) and do not permit the production of sufficient oxygen necessary for the oxidation of the sulfide formed.

5. The chloride content of the wastewater was found to be higher than usual. This confirms the idea that penetration of underground water having high chloride

content does occur. It is known that the high chloride content of stabilization ponds affects their proper operation (ABBOT, 1962; PARKER, unpublished data), owing to the action of chlorides on the microorganisms.

In conclusion, it may be indicated that in arid zones, where stabilization ponds are utilized for waste treatment, measurements of the hydrogen sulfide level in the atmosphere, as well as the sulfide content determination of the wastewater in the pond, will be an effective means for assessing proper operation.

REFERENCES

ABBOTT, A.L. (1962): "The Wynberg-Muizenberg sewage treatment scheme," *J. Inst. Sewage Purification,* pt. 3, pp. 224–33.

A.P.C.D. Rules and Regulations, Ch. 2 and 3, Div. 20, California State Health and Safety Code.

CALDWELL, D.H. (1946): "Sewage oxidation ponds—performance, operation and design," *J.S.I.W.* **18**, 433.

Data of the Ministry of Agriculture and Ministry of Health (1966–67).

DONAGI, A., KENDLER, J. and DAVIDSON, M. (1967): "The direct ultramicrodetermination of hydrogen sulfide in the atmosphere by the molybdenum blue method," *Israel J. of Chem.,* **5**, 152.

HERMANN, E.R. (1957): "Development of design criteria for waste stabilization ponds," Ph.D. Dissertation, The Univ. of Texas.

"Lagoons as a method of sewage stabilization," (1961): Summary of a lecture at the Israeli Assoc. of Water. Eng., Tel Aviv.

LUDZACK, R.B. et al. (1961): *J. Wat. Pollut. Control Fed.,* **33**, 492.

MALONEY, T.E. (1963): "Research on algae odor," *J.A.W.W.A.,* **55**, 4.

NELSON, R.Y. and LEDBETTER, J.O. (1962): *J. Air Pollut. Control Assoc.,* **12**, 29.

OSWALD, W.J. (1960): *Proc. Symp. on Waste Stab. Lagoons, Water Supply and Pollution Contr. Activ.,* Region VI, USPHS.

PALMER, C.M. and TARZWELL, C.M. (1955): "Algae of importance in water supplies," *Public Works Mag.,* **88**, 6.

PARKER, C.D.: Unpublished data, cited in SLESS and REBHUN, 1968.

PARKES, C.D., Jones, H.L. and GRENE, N.C. (1959): "Performance of large sewage lagoons at Melbourne, Australia," *J.S.I.W.* **31**, 2.

POST, N. (1960): "The odor phase of waste disposal," *Water and Sewage Works Reference No. 1,* pp. R-377-79.

SAMSONOV, B. (1965): "Maximum permissible loading on a sewage stabilization pond," M.Sc. Thesis, Technion—Israel Inst. of Technology, Haifa, Israel.

SLESS, J.B. and REBHUN, M. (1968): "Investigation of the efficiency of operation of the oxidation ponds in Eilat," Technion–Israel Inst. of Technology, Haifa, Israel.

U.S. PUBLIC HEALTH SERVICE (1957): "Sewage stabilization ponds in the Dakotas," **1**:28–29. Joint Rep. with N. and S. Dakota's Dept. of Health, Cincinnati, Ohio, R. A. Taft Sanit. Eng. Center.

WEISBURD, M.I. and GRISWOLD, S.S. (1962): *Air Pollution Control, Field Operation Manual,* U.S. Dept. of Health, Educ. and Welfare, Washington, D.C.

Irrigation with Reclaimed Wastewater

Lawrence Hirsch

INTRODUCTION

With the increased evident need to conserve water supply, there must be intensified future utilization of reclaimed wastewater. A recent study (WATER SUB-COMMITTEE REPORT, 1968) by leading water experts for the Los Angeles Chamber of Commerce predicts a deficiency of water supply for Southern California beginning in about thirty years, based on the projected development of all "new" water supplies currently available. The imbalance is projected to increase, notwithstanding the anticipated 1500% increase in the use of reclaimed water and the development of de-salted ocean water from the proposed Bolsa Island salt-water conversion plant.

The resultant consumer-cost effect is shown in Figure 1 as the projected rates for potable water in San Diego County. This figure shows a projected water rate increase from $36 per acre-foot (current cost) to nearly twice this rate within less than ten years.

The projected trend in San Diego County agriculture is towards:
1. A gradual shift to inland locations.
2. Less dry farming.
3. More irrigation farming.
4. More intensive land use.

251

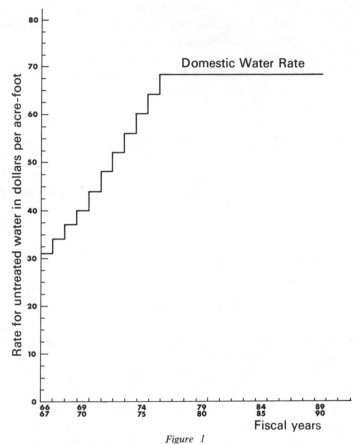

Figure 1

Projected rates for untreated potable water, San Diego County

5. Fewer farms.
6. Larger farms.
7. Application of advanced technology in production.

This trend has universal overtones and leads towards a new outlook on irrigation with wastewater.

A review of the technical literature indicates that wastewater irrigation was practiced in the early nineteenth century as a means of both sewage treatment and disposal. The development of technical knowledge has led, in recent years, to a re-examination of the possibilities of treatment and disposal of certain types of industrial wastes through application of irrigation techniques. In this respect, irrigation has been used for the disposal of effluents from frozen food processing canneries, dairies, paper mills and pharmaceutical laboratories.

However, irrigation with wastewater is not a panacea for either balancing a critical water supply or for the economical treatment and disposal of all sewage and industrial wastes in all locales. The practice of "water management," as it has evolved, requires a balanced and sound consideration of sanitary, aesthetic, economic and other practical factors governing the use and re-use of water.

Irrigation with reclaimed water constitutes a major element of total water management and presents the same general management problems involving the interrelationship of water, soil and plants that are inherent in the successful application of potable water to irrigation. Each of the related factors is important.

DETRIMENTAL CHEMICAL FACTORS

Some constituent elements of wastewater are known to have serious detrimental effects upon the growth of certain plants if present in critical or greater concentrations. Salinity, boron, lithium and sodium constituents are specific indicators of irrigation water quality. The allowable concentrations are determined by many factors, the more significant of which include soil permeability, irrigation practices and plant selectivity.

The suitability of the available raw sewage as a supply source for reclaimed irrigation water is influenced by plant water consumption requirements with respect to evapotranspiration and soil leaching needs, and the tolerance of ground covers, shrubs and trees to the critical elements that may be contained in reclaimed wastewater.

A meaningful discussion of wastewater irrigation must first consider the general agricultural objective, the two categories of which we define as (1) landscape-horticulture and (2) commercial agriculture. The first includes grass, turf, shrubs, trees and flowers for recreation and aesthetic enjoyment such as golf courses, sport fields, parks and highways or "green belt" landscaping. The second category may include the same species of turf, plants, shrubs and trees, but also food crops, animal silage and grazing.

The latter category strives for optimum yield and quality to meet competitive market conditions, while the former is much less restrictive. These basic agricultural objectives hence largely determine, together with (1) soil physiochemical properties and (2) applied practices of water management, the suitability of wastewater as an irrigation supply.

WILCOX (1963) groups the characteristics of a water determining its quality for irrigation use under four headings:

(1) Total concentration of dissolved solids (TDS);

(2) Sodium-adsorption-ratio (SAR);

(3) Concentration of HCO_3;

(4) Concentration of boron and other toxic substances.

Total concentration of dissolved solids is the most important single criterion because of its relationship to the availability of the water to plants. When irrigation water is applied to the soil, the TDS increases due to plant transpiration and to evaporation.

TDS is usually measured in terms of electrical conductivity (EC $\times 10^6$ @ 25°C), but can be expressed in total meq./l of cations or in ppm TDS. Most irrigation waters range in EC $\times 10^6$ up to 5,000 (3,200 ppm TDS).

Sodium is unique among the cations in its effect on the soil. Sodium from the irrigation water is adsorbed or fixed, in an exchangeable form, on the surface of the clay particles. After long continued use of the irrigation water, the soluble sodium of the irrigation water and the exchangeable sodium of the soil come into a mass-action type of "steady state" relationship. Very adverse physical conditions develop in most soils if the exchangeable sodium exceeds 10–15% of the total exchangeable cations of the soil. Such soils, when wet, are plastic and sticky and only slowly permeable to air and water. They shrink and crack, when dry, and form hard clods that are difficult to work into a seed bed.

The hazard in connection with the use of high-sodium irrigation waters can be evaluated in terms of the sodium-adsorption-ratio (SAR), which is defined as:

$$SAR = \frac{Na}{\sqrt{\dfrac{Ca + Mg}{2}}}$$

where the concentrations of the ions are in meq./l. Knowing the SAR of the irrigation water, it is possible to estimate the exchangeable-sodium-percentage (ESP) of the soil that is at, or might come to, equilibrium with the water. Irrigation waters should not have SAR values much above 8 to 10.

Bicarbonate and Ca ions in water can, under certain conditions, precipitate as $CaCO_3$. This reaction can take place when an irrigation water is applied to a soil. As the irrigation water is concentrated in the soil, the Ca is precipitated, but the sodium remains in solution. This results in an increase in the SAR and in the related sodium hazard. The difficulty can be controlled, in many instances, by the use of soil additives.

Boron is the characteristic element of such well-known substances as boric acid and borax. It is essential to normal plant growth, but concentrations only slightly above optimum are toxic to the more boron-sensitive plants. Boron is present in all irrigation waters of the Western United States. Only a few surface waters carry concentrations that are toxic to plants, but many groundwaters are high in boron. As little as 1 ppm of B in irrigation water is roughly the upper limit for use on sensitive plants, while 4 ppm of B is approximately the maximum for even the more tolerant crop plants.

Very few substances other than B occur in toxic concentrations in natural waters. However, many of the constituents of municipal wastes are probably toxic to plants to varying degrees, for example As, Cu and Li.

PUBLIC HEALTH SIGNIFICANCE

The amount of treatment required for protection of health when crops are irrigated with sewage is typified by requirements of the California Administrative Code, Title 17, Public Health. This code requires that: Effluent from a primary sewage treatment plant that is undisinfected may be used on nursery stock, cotton, and such field crops as hay, grain, rice, alfalfa, sugar beets, fodder corn, cow beets, and fodder carrots, provided that dairy cows are not pastured on the land while it is moist from effluent irrigation and do not have access to ditches carrying sewage or effluent from the sewage treatment plant. This type of effluent cannot be used on any growing vegetables, truck crops, berries, vineyards, or low-growing fruits and orchard crops during season when the fruit may be in contact with the ground. However, these restrictions do not apply to the use of well-oxidized, non-putrescible and reliably disinfected or filtered effluents which meet certain strict bacteriological standards. These standards correspond approximately to those of the United States Public Health Service Drinking Water Standards.

PLANT NUTRIENT VALUE

One of the attributes of reclaimed water is the generally higher level of plant nutrient value. Reclaimed water of sewage origin contains significant amounts of nitrogen, phosphorous and potassium which are of value as plant food. Normal food requirements of turfs, shrubs and trees can be met by reclaimed water with minimum supplemental fertilization. At current retail prices of ammonium nitrate, triple superphosphate and potassium chloride, the nitrogen, phosphorous and potassium in a typical San Diego municipal wastewater, Table 1, would be worth about $10, $5, and $3 per acre-foot, respectively, or a total of $18 per acre-foot. There would be no need for the application of additional chemicals when utilizing this reclaimed water for landscape-horticulture, with the exception of the use of supplemental nitrogen for turf areas during rainy seasons when reclaimed water may not be used for a period of two months or longer.

The availability of nutrient-fertilizer in domestic sewage in Israel has been reported on by HERSHKOVITZ and FEINMESSER (1967); this sewage contains an

Table 1. San Diego water reclamation study

Sampling Point 2—Rose Canyon (results in mg/l except where noted)			
	9/17/62	9/19/62	9/21/62
Calcium (Ca)	107	112	90
Magnesium (Mg)	22	25	38
Sodium (Na)	240	215	215
Potassium (K)	18.5	17	18
Iron (Fe)	0.3	0.27	0.23
Manganese (Mn)	0.0	0.0	0.0
Ammonia (N)	32.5	35	36.2
Chloride (Cl)	188	192	204
Sulfate (SO_4)	390	365	340
Bicarbonate (HCO_3)	317	317	336
Carbonate (CO_3)	0	0	0
Phosphate (PO_4)	27	20	19
Boron (B)	1.4	0.9	1.3
ABS	4.6	4.0	4.0
Dissolved solids	1108	1124	1100
Total hardness ($CaCO_3$)	360	384	380
Total alkalinity ($CaCO_3$)	260	260	276
pH	7.3	7.6	7.4
EC micromhos/cm at 25°C	1875	1920	1780
BOD, 5 day 20°C	258	203	240
Suspended solids, total	330	317	276
Suspended solids, volatile	246	240	208

average of 5.5–6.6 lb nitrogen (N), 1.7–2.2 lb phosphorous (P_2O_5), 2.9–3.5 lb potassium (K_2O), and 22–26.4 lb organic matter per capita per annum.

SUMMARY

Both domestic and irrigation waters should be low in total salt content.

Domestic waters should be low in hardness, i.e., should be "soft" waters, while irrigation waters should be hard waters. In this connection, SCOFIELD and HEADLEY (1921) summarized the results of a series of reclamation experiments in the frequently quoted statement: "Hard water makes soft land and soft water makes hard land."

Bicarbonate is undesirable in both domestic and irrigation waters. Problems of scaling or corrosion may develop in connection with the use of domestic waters, depending on the relative concentrations of Ca and HCO_3. The loss of Ca from irrigation waters, as a result of the reaction with HCO_3, increases the sodium hazard.

Many of the substances that are listed as toxic in the Drinking Water Standards are also toxic to plants. Exceptions are Fe, Pb, and F which are less toxic to plants. A number of the heavy metals, that are toxic in domestic water, are precipitated or adsorbed by the soil and are thus less of a hazard. Boron is an element that is much more toxic to plants than to humans, a fact that is often overlooked.

While removal of nutrients in sewage is one of the chief problematic aspects of wastewater renovation, the presence of the selfsame nutrients becomes an attribute in water intended for irrigation. Normal fertilizer requirements of turfs, shrubs and trees can be met by reclaimed water with minimum supplemental fertilization. The total value of nitrogen, phosphorous and potassium found in reclaimed effluent, valued at current retail prices for common fertilizers, amounts to a total of about $18 per acre-foot.

REFERENCES

HERSHKOVITZ, S.Z. and FEINMESSER, A. (1967): "Utilization of sewage for agricultural purposes," Water and Sewage Works.

SCOFIELD, C.S. and HEADLEY, F.B. (1921): "Quality of irrigation water in relation to land reclamation," *Jour. Agr. Res.,* **21**:265–278.

WATER SUBCOMMITTEE REPORT. Los Angeles Area, Chamber of Commerce, 1968.

WILCOX, L.V. (1959): "Effect of industrial wastes for irrigation use." *Spec. Tech. Publ. 273*, pp. 58–64. Amer. Soc. for Testing Materials.

WILCOX, L.V. (1963): "Urban v.s. rural water quality," Conference on Practical Solutions to the Water Quality Equation, Anaheim, California (conducted by the Santa Ana River Basin Water Pollution Control Board).

The Use of Reverse Osmosis in the

Treatment of Industrial Effluents

H. Cohen

INTRODUCTION

In recent years increasing attention has been given to the continual contamination of both surface runoff and underground water resources. They are being contaminated by industry, agriculture and municipalities to such an extent at times that water sources have to be abandoned.

Much effort is being made, especially by large industries in the United States and at considerable expense, to limit this problem as far as possible. The prime moving force for this effort is local, state and federal government pressures.

In the past few years, a new tool has been developed that shows excellent promise not only of producing reusable potable water from industrial wastes but also of recovering chemicals that ordinarily are lost in industrial effluents spilled into the streams, rivers and oceans.

This process is called reverse osmosis or hyperfiltration. At present it is also being developed in Israel at the Negev Institute in Beer-Sheva, for the production of drinking water from brackish water. A desalination plant of this type, with an ultimate capacity of 50,000 gallons per day, has been erected at Kibbutz Yotvatah. It is expected to reach full production in August, 1969 (LOEB and COHEN, 1969).

PRINCIPLE OF REVERSE OSMOSIS

I would like first to discuss the principle of reverse osmosis as applicable to recovery of water and/or chemicals from industrial and municipal effluents, and from contaminated rivers or wells. Data from several pilot plants operated in the United States will then be presented.

Basically, reverse osmosis is a membrane separation process that utilizes a membrane that has the ability to allow water to pass through it, leaving the solute behind. The membrane most widely used today is that of cellulose acetate, developed by Drs. Loeb and Sourirajan at U.C.L.A. in the early 1960's and known as the Loeb-type membrane. Its structure is such that it has a very thin, dense layer approximately 0.25 μ in thickness. The rest of the membrane, approximately 0.1–0.2 mm thick, is a porous substrate. It is the "skin" that is the active surface and "performs" the separation.

It is well known that the osmotic process is much utilized in nature, in the human animal and plant systems. The principle can be explained most simply, I think, with the following description of the process.

Let us take a vessel that is divided into two closed compartments, the barrier between them being an osmotic membrane. In one compartment we have distilled water with a continuous water source to keep it filled. The second compartment, also closed, but with a long standpipe connected to the top, is filled with saline solution.

Because of the differences in concentration of the solutions and the properties of the osmotic membrane, distilled water will permeate the membrane into the saline solution, thus diluting it. This permeation will continue until the diluted salt solution rising in the standpipe will reach a certain level at which the permeation of distilled water will stop. The column height attained represents a pressure on the saline side and is known as the osmotic equilibrium pressure of the system.

If we apply a pressure on the diluted solution exceeding that of the osmotic equilibrium pressure, we would obtain a flow of distilled water across the membrane in the opposite direction, thus in effect returning the saline solution to its original concentration or even increasing the latter, depending on the pressure that is applied. This process involving the use of pressure is called reverse osmosis or hyperfiltration. In actual fact, a small percent of the solutes will permeate with the distilled water. This effect is attributed to the imperfections of the membrane.

In practice there are three basic geometries now in use in pilot plants: the single tube or tube bundle, spiral wound and filament-type systems. Generally, cellulose acetate is the membrane used, and the principle of permeation of water is identical for all cases. Each geometry has its own advantages and disadvantages but a discussion of these does not fall within the framework of this paper.

APPLICATIONS IN ISRAEL

The Negev Institute chose what is felt to be the most simple geometry for development, the single tube. It may be described as a high-pressure tubular assembly containing the cellulose acetate membrane in the form of a thin-walled tube wrapped with a fine-mesh nylon cloth and inserted into a metal or plastic pressure support pipe that contains small, 1–2 mm perforations, spaced some 70 to 80 mm apart, along its entire length.

The nylon and the perforations serve to collect the clean water permeating the membrane.

In a working plant these tubular assemblies may be connected in series or parallel. The raw feed is pumped through the system under hydraulic pressure, forcing the clean water to permeate the membranes. The feed continues downstream and becomes continuously more and more concentrated until rejected from the last assembly in the train. Each assembly produces clean water which is collected in a common manifold.

In order to show, in practical terms, what can be expected from the system just described, I think it best to cite some data from the plant we now have in operation at Kibbutz Yotvatah. The plant is operating at 50 atmospheres pressure, inlet water temperature between 26 and 30°C, using Composite Tubular Assemblies 57 mm in diameter and 6 m long. Each assembly produces an average of 800 to 900 liters per day and represents 1 m² of membrane surface area.

Table 1. Typical data, reverse osmosis desalination plant, Yotvatah

	TDS	Cl⁻	SO₄⁻	HCO₃	Ca	Mg	Na + K
Feed ppm	2284	513	823	275	131	250	292
Product ppm	208	80	36	24	8	19	41
Desalination ratio	11.0	6.5	22.8	11.4	16.4	13.2	7.2

It should be noted that cellulose acetate membranes have a much higher rejection capability for divalent ions than monovalent ions, as can be seen in

Table 1 above. Furthermore, bacteria, viruses, and most organic compounds are almost completely rejected as long as they do not act as a solvent to the cellulose acetate. This is a very important factor when considering the requirement that the recovered water is to be used for domestic purposes. The membrane may be used at temperatures up to $\sim 45°C$ and has an effective operating range between a pH of 3 and 8.

TREATMENT OF INDUSTRIAL WASTES

In the industrial waste field, reverse osmosis can play a major role in both the recovery of water for reuse by industry and in the recovery of chemicals that at present are dumped into our rivers and streams. The process can be used to concentrate undesirable dissolved solids to a concentration that becomes amenable to decomposition by combustion, or, if desirable, to further chemical processing for recovery for use or sale. In both cases, the water permeating the osmotic membrane is intended for reuse as process water because of its anticipated low content of salts and other components. This process thus can offer advantages in recovery of valuable chemicals and recuperation of soft water that may not require pretreatment, and, most important, the contamination of streams can thus be avoided.

In the recovery of water from municipal wastes, there is the expectancy that reverse osmosis will play a role in the production of potable water from the secondary effluent after removal of sludges and partial biological oxidation. We feel that the biggest hurdle in the utilization of this water will be psychological. The public will have to be convinced that the impurities in the original wastewater have essentially been removed.

EXPERIENCE IN THE UNITED STATES

I would like to present data from various pilot plants operating in the United States in the field of waste recovery. They are varied and all show that the process of reverse osmosis is coming of age at a rapid pace and will be used in the very near future on an economically sound basis in industry.

Gulf General Atomic (LARSEN, 1969) has installed a 5,000-gpd plant, using their spiral wound design, in Pomona, California, under a grant from the Federal Water Pollution Control Administration. The feed to the plant is the effluent from an activated carbon column after treatment by an activated sludge process used in municipal waste treatment. It has been in operation for 10,000 hours so far. A typical picture of the feed and product are given in Table 2. The plant is operated at 400 psi, with an 80% recovery of the feed stream.

Table 2. Gulf General Atomic pilot plant, Pomona, California

	PO_4	COD	NH_3-N	NO_3-N	TDS
Feed ppm	31	11	9	2.3	625
Product ppm	0.6	1.7	1.7	0.8	73

It should be noted that Mg and Ca are almost completely rejected, yielding basically a sodium chloride water of 73 ppm.

The Pulp and Paper Research League, of Appleton, Wisconsin, purchased a 50,000-gpd plant from Havens Industries, manufacturers of reverse osmosis— tube bundle units. The pilot plant is using as its feed a white wash liquor from the neutral bisulfite leaching of wood chips.

There are four large paper mills located on the Fox River. The State of Wisconsin has pressured the firms to cut down dumping of their wastes into the river. The Research League, supported by the paper mills of the state, undertook an extensive program to investigate methods of recovering these waste streams.

The pilot plant furnishes a product water (permeate) that is sent back as make-up water to the chip-leaching process, and the reject (concentrate) at 10% is sent to a spray drier where it is dried and sold locally.

The feed solution has a TDS of 10–15 g/l, including a total of 3 g/l BOD. The feed is dark brown in color and contains suspended solids. The only pretreatment is a very coarse screening to remove fibrous matter from the feed.

The permeate has a 99.8% rejection in color and the BOD is reduced by 95% on the average. Total solids rejection is 90%. The concentrate thus has a solids content of 10% and is sent to the spray drier and for subsequent sale.

Aerojet General ran a pilot plant on secondary sewage effluent under a contract with the Public Health Service.

The inlet to their unit had a TDS of 1,200 ppm containing 90 to 125 ppm COD and 6 to 10 ppm ABS. The product water contained only 10 ppm COD and 0.5 ppm ABS, with a TDS of 50 ppm. They claimed complete rejection of both bacteria and viruses in their system. The project was discontinued because of technical problems encountered in the mechanical design of their unit, these being unrelated to the membrane performance.

The U. S. Army (SCHMITT, 1969) at Fort Belvoir, Virginia, ran two pilot plants connected with decontamination.

In one of these plants, the feed to the unit was wastewater from the showers and kitchens at an army camp. The only pretreatment was coagulation. The information available indicated that the TDS was reduced from 3,550 to 105 ppm, phosphate from 35 to 1 ppm, and silica from 69 to 9 ppm.

The second plant used Potamac River water as feed. No filtration was used. In a bacteria test of the streams, the *E. coli* count was reduced from 2,000/ml to 0. This unit is still in operation.

CONCLUSIONS

The above cases represent only some of the extensive work being done in the United States today in the field of utilizing reverse osmosis as a system for recovery and purification of waste or contaminated streams. In general it should be stressed that when using the cellulose acetate Loeb-type membrane, most of the hardness and turbidity will be removed and rejection of both bacteria and viruses is almost complete. In the case of nitrogen compounds, 75–80% rejection may be expected.

There are many possibilities for the use of this system today, both for industry and in the decontamination of various water sources that are already contaminated irrespective of the reason. This could be a substantial contribution to the extension of potential water resources.

Below are listed some of the numerous areas of application where benefits can be derived:

a) In the metal-plating industries such as chromium, nickel, etc., where all the rinses can be reconcentrated to recover the expensive metal salts and the permeate reused as low-salinity clean water.

b) Wastewater from the bottle-washing industry.

c) Recovery of contaminated condensate from steam-stripping column operations.

d) Cooling tower blow-down recovery.

e) Paper mill wash liquor recovery.

f) Concentration of waste streams in the explosives industries.

g) Recovery of potable water from secondary sewage effluent.

h) Decontamination and salt reduction of contaminated water sources.

This list represents only a few examples where reverse osmosis may not only help industry reduce the problem of waste disposal but can also reduce their consumption of process water and, in certain cases, also recover valuable chemicals.

REFERENCES

AEROJET GENERAL CORPORATION, Azusa, California: Report of Research Done Under US Public Health Service Contract PH-86-63-227.

LARSEN, T.J. (1969): "Reverse osmosis pilot plant operation," Presented at U.S. Exhibition and International Conference on Water Purification and Desalination, Rome.

LOEB, S. and COHEN, H. (1969): "Reverse osmosis desalination plant, Yotvatah, preliminary report for period September 11 to December 31, 1968," Presented at Water Desalination Symposium, Eilat.

SCHMITT, R.P. (1969): "Use of reverse osmosis process for Army field water supplies," Notes from unpublished lecture presented at O.S.W. Second Symposium on Reverse Osmosis, Miami, Florida.

WILEY, A.J. and AMMERLAAN, A.C.F. (personal communication): "Membrane processing of dilute pulping wastes by reverse osmosis," Pulp Manufacturers' Research League, Appleton, Wisconsin.

MARINE POLLUTION

The Use of Radioisotope Tracers

in the Study of the Dispersion

and Inactivation of Bacteria

Discharged in Coastal Waters *

Ch. Gilat, H. I. Shuval,

Y. Yoshpe-Purer, N. Cohen

INTRODUCTION

The need to dispose of ever-increasing quantities of wastewater into coastal waters calls for the development of a rational approach to define the influence of various environmental factors which will aid in dispersing and inactivating microbiological pollutants such as pathogenic bacteria and viruses.

Scanty information is available on rates of bacterial die-away in the Mediterranean, and only very preliminary data have been gathered on bacterial dispersion patterns along the shores of Israel (SHUVAL et al., 1968). This study is a pre-

* This study was financed by grants from the Oceanographic and Limnological Research Co. of the Israel National Council for Research and Development and the Ministry of Health.

liminary attempt at determining bacterial disappearance rates and dispersion patterns *in situ* with the aid of radioisotope tracer techniques. The existing sewage outfall at Reading, north of Tel Aviv, was the locus of these studies since it provided a good model representative of typical coastal conditions along the southern half of Israel's Mediterranean shore. This site, in itself, is of considerable interest due to its proximity to some of the city's most popular bathing beaches.

HYDROGRAPHIC CHARACTERISTICS RELEVANT TO SEA POLLUTION ALONG THE CENTRAL AND SOUTHERN MEDITERRANEAN COAST OF ISRAEL

Geomorphology of the Sea Bed

The sea floor along the Israel coast south of Haifa slopes gently to a depth of about 20 meters at a distance of about one kilometer from the shore. North of Haifa, the shallow sea floor is mostly irregular due to the presence of rocky outcrops. The smooth profiles south of Haifa are characteristic of a sandy bottom (EMERY and NEEV, 1960).

Superimposed on the above gross topography are the submarine bars and troughs a few hundred meters from the shore. They run almost parallel to the shore and are interrupted at fairly regular distances by lower sections where the troughs turn seaward. The offshore zone, i. e., the zone from the submarine bars seawards to a depth of about 12 m, has a gentle slope of about 1:100. The foreshore, in contrast, is narrow and steep with numerous bars and troughs (STRIEM, 1969). All these topographic features contribute to the sea current map of the coastal region.

Tides

The mean tide amplitude is about 25 cm, but may be as high as about 50 cm. The fastest rates of change in the sea level are about 12 cm/hr. Usually the rate is 3–6 cm/hr (STRIEM, 1969). Therefore, tides are considered to be of very little importance to sea pollution as compared to other factors such as waves, winds, currents, etc.

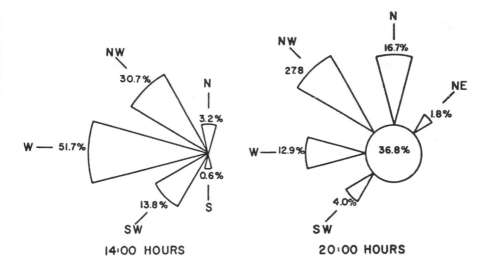

14:00 HOURS

20:00 HOURS

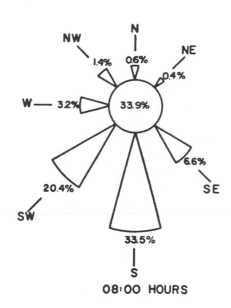

08:00 HOURS

Figure 1
Frequency of surface wind directions along the Tel Aviv shore

Waves

Wave heights, periods and direction affect the dispersion pattern of pollution agents and indirectly contribute to the sea currents. The wave height during summer rarely exceeds 2 m and varies with the direction from which the wave arrives. The highest waves come from WSW or W, and the wave height decreases the more northerly the direction of arrival. The wave periods range from 3–12 sec, but the majority fall between 3–6 sec. During summer about half of the waves come from the W and the rest from WNW and NW (STRIEM, 1969).

Winds

The frequency distribution of winds with respect to direction and velocity was considered mainly for the bathing season, i. e., from April to late November. The daily wind regime, excepting storms, shows that winds veer from S to SW in the morning to W at noon and NW to N in the afternoon. A typical series of wind roses for the month of August, based on statistics of data accumulated over an 8-year period (CLIMATOLOGICAL NORMALS, 1956), are shown in Figure 1. Most of the wind velocities fall between 2–4 on the Beaufort scale.

Currents

A few measurements of the currents near the shore of Israel have been published (EMERY and NEEV, 1960). These, together with certain indirect observations and an analysis of the parameters determining the currents, permitted the formulation of a general pattern (STRIEM, 1969). However, the sea currents in Israel coastal waters have not yet been fully determined, and the Oceanographic and Limnological Research Co. of Israel is planning systematic hydrographic studies in the future.

Offshore currents: The offshore current is composed of the general eastern Mediterranean current, wind drift and wave-induced currents.

The eastern Mediterranean current: This current is directed northward and is part of a general counterclockwise circulation pattern (EMERY and NEEV, 1960). Only a fringe of the current flows on top of the shelf, and its velocity decreases markedly in shallow water. A mean velocity of 0.17 m/sec has been indicated for this current (STRIEM, 1969).

Wind drift currents: The velocity of the wind drift current was estimated to be about 1/50 of the wind velocity (STRIEM, 1969). Thus, a weak wind (Beaufort scale 2, i.e., 4–6 knots) will produce a drift current of about 0.08 knots (0.04 m/sec). However, only the projection of this current on the general northward current direction will be effective. Due to the changes in wind direction explained above, the morning-noon component towards the north will be followed by a southerly directed component in the afternoon, leaving only a limited net northern effect.

Wave-induced current: These currents are the result of the change in direction of the waves as they obliquely approach the coast. Due to the changing azimuth of the Israel coastline and the frequency distribution of wave direction, the wave-induced current will essentially be northward south of Tel Aviv and southward north from Tel Aviv. The contribution of the wave currents to the overall offshore current is very important (STRIEM, 1969).

Nearshore currents (between the submarine bar and the shore): These currents are more complex as they are a function of the shoreward and return flow of the water and the topography of the region. The shoreward flow is usually perpendicular to the shore. The return flow results in a longshore current through the troughs adjacent to both the foreshore and submarine bars. The discontinuity of these bars gives rise to seaward rip currents which sometimes form turbulent eddies. The direction of the longshore currents in the nearshore zone is determined mainly by the local topography and sometimes by the direction of the waves (STRIEM, 1969).

THE READING (TEL AVIV) SEWAGE OUTFALL

The Reading sewer, operated by the Dan Region Association of Towns (Sewerage), disposes of the domestic and industrial sewage of the Dan area. Flow rates are in the range of 1,500–8,000 m^3/hr in the dry season and as much as 13,000 m^3/hr in the rainy season (MARKUZE, 1969).

The sewage is screened, comminuted and the grit removed. It is discharged into the sea via a pipe 1.5 meters in diameter and about 880 meters in length. The diffuser, 42 meters in length, has 11 ports, 10 of which are lateral (5 on each side of the pipe) and one at the end of the pipe. About 85% of the sewage is from domestic sources and the rest of industrial origin. The flow rate is minimum at night and maximum during the day.

OBSERVATIONS OF THE SEWAGE PLUME
AT THE READING OUTFALL

Observations of the sewage plume were made during May-July and November, 1968, from tall buildings in the vicinity of the Tel Aviv Reading outfall in order to determine the plume shape and direction as a function of winds. The plume, easily distinguished as a grayish patch, could be mapped with the help of navigation buoys located in the area.

Most observations were made during moderate seas (wave height 0.8–1.2 m) and wind intensities of 2–4 on the Beaufort scale. The sewage plume direction was observed to follow the direction of the wind (Figure 2). Furthermore, the plume followed the change in wind direction with minimal lag, e.g., over a 3-hour period in the afternoon the wind changed from NW, 310/12 (310° azimuth and 12 knots velocity) to N (010/10) and the plume changed accordingly at the same time.

Very few observations were made on calm seas (virtually no waves). However, on one such occasion, the wind was SSW (200/2), (0/0) and NW (300/7) during the morning, noon and afternoon, respectively, and the plume was directed towards NE and ENE. On another day with calm seas and a north wind (350/12 in the morning and 020/15 in the afternoon), the plume was directed south. These scant data indicated that, in the absence of both waves and a northerly wind, the current is northward, while a wind blowing from the north (350/12) cancels this current, at least in the upper layer where the major portion of the sewage is concentrated.

Although only semiquantitative, the observations of the sewage plume show that the sewage discharged through the Reading outfall spreads in a relatively stable thin layer on the surface of the sea. This floating layer is then transported to a large extent by the wind. Tracer experiments, described below, have confirmed these findings.

Future observations of the sewage plume are expected to assist in clarifying the mechanism of the sewage spread at Reading and will perhaps also assist in identifying the contribution of the different sea currents described above.

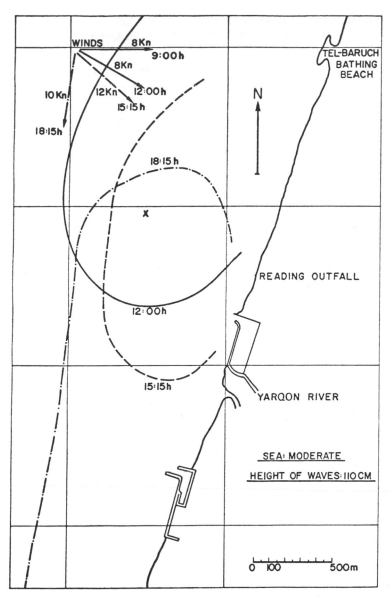

Figure 2
The sewage plume as observed at Reading on 7.7.1968 at 12:00, 15:15 and 18.15 h

METHOD FOR THE DETERMINATION OF SEWAGE DISPERSION AND BACTERIA DISAPPEARANCE

The reduction in the bacteria concentration of sewage discharged into the sea is due to three factors: an initial dilution of the waste as it passes vertically through a given depth of water; dilution and dispersion as it is transported by the sea current; and bacteria disappearance due to sedimentation, bacteria die-away and other removal causes.

The bacteria disappearance rate can be obtained by combined measurements of the "physical" dilution of sewage and of the bacteria concentration in seawater at different distances (i. e., travel times of the sewage) from an existing outfall.

Determination of Sewage Dispersion in the Sea

The initial dilution of the sewage from the sewer outlet ports to the sewage boil is calculable theoretically (HARREMOES, 1968). It can also be determined experimentally, by sampling in the area of the sewage boil. The transportation of the sewage can be evaluated either from sea current data or from observations on an existing sewage outlet plume. The combined effect of transportation and dilution can be studied by soluble tracer materials. Tracer experiments yield information which is both supplementary and complementary to current measurements.

Drift cards were used as tracers in an attempt to determine diffusion coefficients to be employed in connection with different diffusion models. It is likely that drift cards simulate transportation of flotables, while it is questionable whether they fully simulate transportation of suspended matter such as bacteria.

There is reason to believe that soluble tracers such as dyes or radioactive isotopes provide a good simulation of the transportation of suspended and soluble material. In many respects these two tracers are equally applicable and reveal the same results. Choice of tracer may be easy in certain extreme cases, e. g., for waters which carry a heavy load of suspended solids, where radioactive tracers are most suitable due to turbidity and adsorption of dye. When very large quantities of tracer are needed, dye is more suitable due to difficulties in handling large amounts of radioactivity. Except in such particular cases, the choice generally depends on local conditions and traditions, radioisotopes being preferred in Scandinavia and Britain, while dyes are favored especially in the USA. The availability of experienced personnel at the Soreq Nuclear Research Centre, trained and equipped to carry out radioisotope tracer studies, was an important factor in the decision to use radioisotopes in these studies in Israel.

The major advantages of using a radioactive tracer are the well-defined decay rate, this being a rather uncertain quantity for dyes, and the fact that measurements are made with standard field instruments.

Br^{82} is normally used as a radioactive tracer for studies in the sea. The instrumentation is sensitive enough to work below the level of concentrations of the radioisotope permitted by the international drinking water standards for all-year exposure. Thus, the use of radioactive tracers for sewage dispersion studies implies no health hazard.

On first thought, the most attractive approach to the study of dispersion of sewage in the sea would be to inject the radioisotope tracer at a constant rate into the sewer. However, this is a tedious and costly procedure to be adopted mainly in cases of extremely unsteady sea conditions. To overcome this problem, a pulse of radioisotope tracer of activity A is injected into the sewer, which is discharging sewage at a flow rate Q m^3/sec and an initial concentration C_o of the polluting agent (e.g., coliform organisms).

The radioactive cloud created in the sea is transported by the current and gradually diluted. The concentration of the radioisotope passing through a given point in the sea first increases and then decreases. It can be shown by standard convolution technique that the steady-state concentration C of the polluting agent at this point is:

$$C = \frac{QC_o}{A} \int_{-\infty}^{+\infty} c\,dt \tag{1}$$

where c is the concentration of the radioisotope at the given point as a function of time. In terms of count rate (proportional to the concentration c) Eq. 1 becomes

$$F = \frac{C}{C_o} = \frac{O}{As} \int_{-\infty}^{+\infty} (n - n')dt \tag{2}$$

where F is the dilution factor, and n and n' are the gross and background count rates, respectively, and s is the sensitivity of the detector. The proof of Eq. 2 has been given by HARREMOES (1966).

One should be able to find the count rate at any time at any point in the cloud. This, however, cannot be accomplished in practice. The radioactive cloud is continuously scanned by sailing a boat in and out of the cloud. Thus, it is measured several times at various points during the experiment. If more accurate data are required at a specific point, a fixed measuring station can be established (e.g., using an anchored boat).

The instrumentation aboard the boat consists of a scintillation detector with an HT power supply and a count rate meter coupled to a recording device (e.g., a strip chart recorder). Simultaneously, navigation data are collected in such a way that position and count rate can be synchronized. The course of the boat is immediately plotted on board, together with some rough information on the count rate. This is of extreme importance for gaining immediate knowledge of the cloud picture and for its proper mapping. The cloud is followed as far as it can be detected. Mappings of the cloud are made several times. Using standard instrumentation, e. g., $1'' \times 2''$ NaI (Tl) scintillator, and injecting an activity of 1 curie of Br^{82}, the activity can be followed till diluted in a volume of $10^7 \, m^3$, which usually corresponds to a distance of a few kilometers from the injection point.

The data is processed in several stages. First the course of the boat is plotted for each mapping of the cloud. This course is then corrected for the current prevailing during the experiment. (The current velocity and direction can be determined from the movement of the spot in the cloud where the isotope concentration is maximum.) Isocount curves are then plotted for every mapping of the cloud. A special integration technique (HARREMOES, 1966) is then employed in order to arrive at final dilution curves for the given sewage field.

If a fixed measuring station is employed, the direct result of the measurement is a count rate vs. time curve, which may be readily integrated.

The above-described technique is based on the linearity of the sewage disposal system and the presence of steady currents in the area during the experiment. As a by-product of the investigation, information is obtained on the currents prevailing in the measured layer (the detector senses within a radius of about 0.5 m) and the travel time from the sewage outlet to any point in the area.

Existing theories on diffusion were found to be not directly applicable to the prediction of dispersion of sewage discharged into the sea (HARREMOES, 1967). However, after carrying out some tracer experiments, a semiempirical mathematical model can be established. The model can then be used for prediction of dilution under different conditions.

Bacteriological Tests

Samples of seawater are taken from a moving boat during traverses through the radioactive cloud. The exact coordinates of the sampling points are recorded.

Samples are taken at depths of 20–30 cm below the surface and stored in sterile bottles at 10°C until examined in the laboratory within 3 hours.

The samples are examined for presence of members of the coliform group of bacteria. The multiple-fermentation tube method (AMERICAN PUBLIC HEALTH ASSOC., 1965) was used for the experiment on July 24, 1968. The membrane filter technique (AMERICAN PUBLIC HEALTH ASSOC., 1965) was employed in the experiment carried out on November 21, 1968. The results are reported as coliform bacteria per 100 ml.

Determination of Bacteria Disappearance Rate

From the measurements of the radioactive cloud a dilution map is constructed. The ratio of the "physical" dilution, obtained by the tracer experiment, to the bacterial dilution, obtained by sampling, is determined and plotted against travel time of the sewage from the outfall, in order to obtain the disappearance rate.

EXPERIMENTS AND RESULTS

Two experiments performed during 1968 are described below.

Experiment 1 (24.7.1968)

This experiment was performed under moderate sea conditions (wave height 120 cm); the wind was from the west (250/06 to 280/09). An activity of 3 curies of Br^{82} was injected into the sewage pipe on shore. The sewage flow rate was 6500 m^2/hr.

The activity in the sea was measured from the Israel Oceanographic and Limnological Research Co.'s research vessel "Shikmona", with the detector submerged 1 m below sea level. Navigation was by a Decca Hyfix radio navigation system. In addition to the scanning of the cloud, measurements were made from an anchored boat with a detector also submerged 1 m. Seawater was sampled for bacteria count at several positions which are indicated on Figure 3.

The current, as measured by the movement of the maximum activity in the cloud, was directed northward at a velocity of 8.5–10 m/min.

The physical dilution of the sewage is shown in Figure 3. Due to technical difficulties, the activity cloud could be followed for only a short time and therefore the dilution map is not very detailed. However, steady-state conditions prevailed

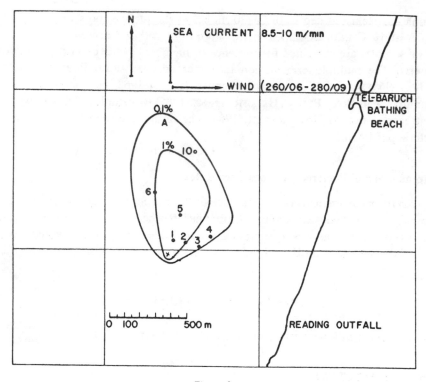

Figure 3
Isodilution curves determined from experiment 24.7.1968. Points 1 to 10 indicate sampling
positions. A is the position of the anchored boat

throughout the experiment, with almost no change in wind direction or intensity. This provided optimal conditions for the analysis of the data.

Theoretical bacteria concentrations were calculated by multiplying the initial coliform concentration in the sewage (prior to disposal through the outfall) by the physical dilution factors as determined in the tracer experiment. These concentrations were compared (see Figure 4) with the actual concentration of samples taken from the sea at various distances from the point of discharge. Bacteria disappearance factors of 30, 50 and 100 were determined for sewage travel times of 15, 40 and 105 minutes, respectively.

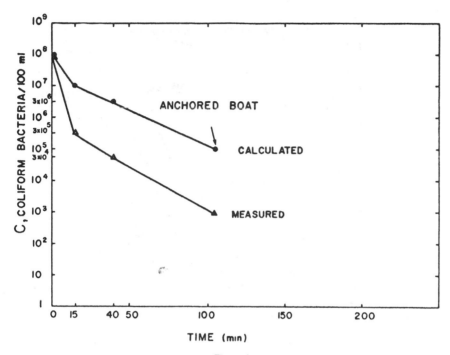

Figure 4
Actual concentration of coliform bacteria in the sea as a function of time compared with the
theoretical concentration due to dilution alone. Experiment of 24.7.1968. Initial coliform bacteria
conc: 10^8 ● calculated from physical dilution △ measured from samples

Experiment 2 (21.11.1968)

This experiment was performed under calm sea conditions (waves less than
30 cm). The wind was from the southeast (140/4) at the beginning of the experiment, changed to WNW (300/5) at noon, and by the end of the experiment (early
afternoon) was blowing from the north (360/6). These changing conditions
introduced serious limitations in the interpretation of the data, since steady-state
conditions did not prevail throughout the period of the experiment.

A pulse of 1.3 curies of Br^{82} was injected into the sewage which was flowing
at a rate of 6,500 m^3/hr. The activity in the sea was scanned from a boat equipped
with two detectors submerged 0.5 and 1.5 m, respectively. Navigation was by
theodolite measurement from the shore.

The current measured by the movement of the radioisotope cloud was north-

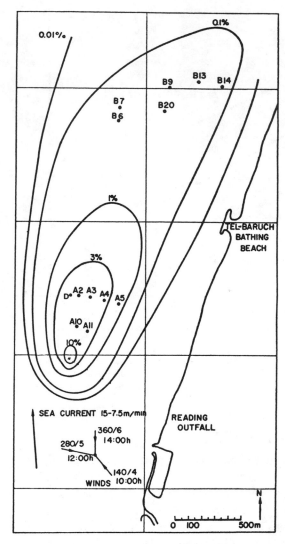

Figure 5

Isodilution curves in the upper layer of the sea. Detector at 0.5 m depth.
Experiment of 21.11.1968. Points A and B indicate sampling positions
of the first and second mapping of the activation of the cloud,
respectively. Measurements of activity distribution with depth were
made at point D. The 10 % dilution contour was evaluated from bacteria
dilution data only

ward. Due to the reversal of the wind direction during the experiment, the apparent average velocity changed from 15 m/min during the first mapping of the cloud (wind 140/4 to 300/5) to 7.5 m/min during the second run (wind 280/5 to 360/6). This information is of importance when trying to understand the pattern of sea currents in the area under study.

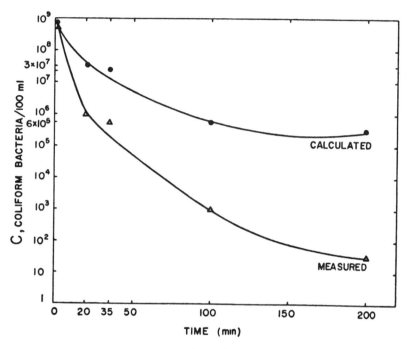

Figure 6
Actual concentration of coliform bacteria in the sea as a function of time compared with the theoretical concentration due to dilution alone. Experiment of 21.11.1968. Initial coliform bacteria conc: 6×10^8 ● calculated from physical dilution Δ measured from samples

The physical dilution of the sewage as measured by the upper detector (submerged 0.5 m) is seen in Figure 5. The 10% dilution contour, estimated from bacteria counts, indicates the sewage boil. The dilution contours in the region between the point of discharge up to the Tel Baruch bathing beach are felt to be more reliable than those north of Tel Baruch. The region near the point of discharge was monitored early in the day before major wind shifts occurred, and it is assumed that more or less steady-state conditions existed during that period.

The measurements made in the region north of Tel Baruch later in the day (second run) were probably influenced by the reversal of wind direction, with unknown effects on dilution patterns and sewage travelling time. The 0.01 % and 0.1 % contours in that area are therefore less reliable.

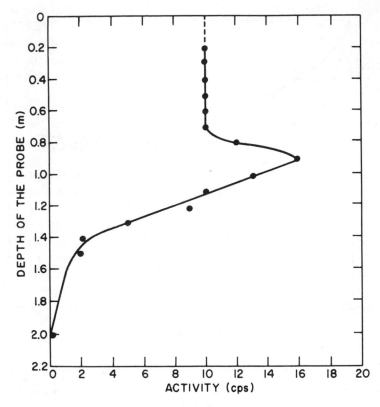

Figure 7
Distribution of radioisotope activity with depth,
measured at point D (see Figure 5)

The discrepancy between the actual concentration of coliform bacteria in the sea and the theoretical concentration due to dilution alone is shown in Figure 6. Bacteria disappearance factors of 30, 40, 600 and 10^4 were found for sewage travel times of 20, 35, 100 and 200 minutes, respectively. In view of the uncertain reliability of the measurements of the second run in the area north of Tel Baruch, the estimated bacteria disappearance factors of 600 and 10^4 at 100 and 200 minutes sewage travel times are less reliable.

Interesting results were obtained on the depth distribution of the active cloud. This distribution, measured at point D (Figure 5), is shown in Figure 7. In addition, the lower detector (submerged 1.5 m) registered almost no activity during the first mapping of the cloud. During the second run, activity patches were detected, starting from about 1 km north of the end of the outfall (in the region between 1% and 0.1% dilution on Figure 5). Quantitative treatment of the data provided by the submerged detector was not possible. However, qualitatively, it can be concluded that the floating sewage gradually mixes with the sea as it is carried away from the sewage boil.

DISCUSSION AND CONCLUSIONS

The two experiments described above were preliminary and further investiga- will be carried out in order to collect more information on both dispersion and bacteria disappearance.

Although the sea conditions and winds were quite different in the two experiments described, both are typical of the summer and fall seasons. On comparing the isodilution curves obtained, it appears that greater dilution of the sewage field occurred when the sea was moderate than when it was calm. The action of the waves seems to have a rather strong effect, which most probably also enhances the dispersion downward to deeper layers of the sea. The greatly improved dispersion in moderate seas can be seen at distances of about 800–1000 m from the sewage boil, where the dilution obtained on 24.7.1968 was ten times better than that on 21.11.1968.

In all probability, the dilution pattern determined on 21.11.1968 approaches the worst possible. Under the conditions existing on that day, the physical dilution opposite Tel Baruch bathing beach would be about 0.01% or less. If the cloud, as shown in Figure 5, would be thrown shoreward (e.g., by a wind blowing from the west), the conditions there would be even worse and the physical dilution in the range of 1% to 0.1%.

The observations of activity distribution with depth made on 21.11.68 confirm the existence of a floating layer of sewage. The rate of mixing of this layer with deeper water is relatively slow.

A summary of the bacteria disappearance data as a function of time is shown in Figure 8. There appear to be two distinct disappearance rates. The first rate

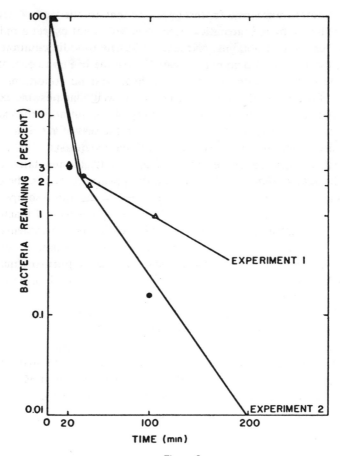

Figure 8
Bacteria disappearance as a function of time   Δ experiment of 24.7.1968
● experiment of 21.11.1968

has a T_{90} of 15–20 min in the immediate proximity of the outfall (radius of about 200 m from the outfall and travel times of 30–40 min). A second rate appears to extend from 30–40 to about 200 min (or traveling distances of 200–2,000 m), with calculated T_{90} values of 180 min in the experiment of 24.7.1968 and 70 min in the experiment of 21.11.1968. This latter figure is felt to be less reliable than that obtained in the first experiment due to the lack of steady-state conditions during the experiment.

The rapid disappearance rate in the area adjacent to the outfall can only partially be explained by sedimentation, since one would not expect a reduction of more than 50% in coliform concentration to be due to sedimentation alone. In both experiments, disappearance of about 97% of the bacteria concentration in about 20–40 minutes, independent of the hydrographic conditions of the experiments, is apparently related to other factors as well. One possible explanation for the high disappearance rate in the vicinity of the outfall is the existence of a higher concentration of antibacterial factors in the seawater rich in organic matter and microorganisms nurtured by the sewage (MITCHELL, 1968).

The above results, although preliminary and essentially of a qualitative nature, nevertheless indicate a relatively high bacteria disappearance rate in the coastal waters of Israel and demonstrate the application of the radioisotope tracer methods used for *in situ* study of bacterial dispersion patterns and inactivation kinetics in coastal waters. It is expected that with additional experiments and a more refined methodology it will be possible to determine parameters essential to the rational utilization of the natural capacity of the sea in purifying microbial contamination.

ACKNOWLEDGEMENTS

The contribution of Mr. H.L. Striem in the evaluation of the hydrographic parameters relevant to sea pollution and the active participation of Mr. Z. Stuhl in the performing of the experiments are gratefully acknowledged.

REFERENCES

AMERICAN PUBLIC HEALTH ASSOC. (1965): *Standard Methods for the Examination of Water and Waste-water*, 12 ed., New York.

Climatological Normals, (1956): Part Two, Series A., *Meteorological Notes*, published by the Meteorological Service of the State of Israel, Jerusalem.

EMERY, K.O. and NEEV, D. (1960): "Mediterranean beaches of Israel," Israel Ministry of Development, Geological Survey, Bulletin 26, Jerusalem.

HARREMOËS, P. (1966): "Prediction of pollution from planned wastewater outfalls," *J. Wat. Pollut. Control Fed.*, **38** (8), 1323.

HARREMOËS, P. (1967): "Theoretical treatment of data on turbulent dispersion related to disposal of industrial waste," Report No. 2 for Research Contract No. 402/RB, International Atomic Energy Agency, Vienna.

HARREMOËS, P. (1968): "Diffuser design for discharge to a stratified water," The Danish Isotope Centre, Copenhagen.

MARKUSE, M. (1969): "Dan Region Association of Towns (Sewerage) Tel Aviv," Personal communication.

MITCHELL, R. (1968): "Factors affecting the decline of non-marine microorganisms in seawater," *Water Research*, **2**: 535–543.

SHUVAL, H.I., COHEN, N. and FURER, Y. (1968): "The dispersion of bacterial pollution along the Tel-Aviv shore," *Rev. Intern. Oceanogr. Med.*, **9**, 107.

STRIEM, H.T. (1969): Soreq Nuclear Research Centre, personal communication.

Pollution Control

in the Raritan Bay Area

Lester M. Klashman, Kenneth H. Walker

and Richard T. Dewling

INTRODUCTION

The Federal Water Pollution Control Act, as amended, provides that pollution of interstate waters which endangers the health or welfare of any person is subject to abatement under procedures described in Section 10 (33 USC 466g) of the Act. A conference was called to review the existing water quality problems, establish a basis for future action by all parties concerned, and to give States, interstate agencies, localities and industries an opportunity to take any indicated remedial action under State and local law.

OBJECTIVE: CLEAN WATER

The objective of the Project was to develop the scientific data necessary for the conferees to establish an effective program for the abatement and control of pollution in the study area (Figure 1), which includes Lower, Sandy Hook and Raritan Bays, a portion of the Narrows, Arthur Kill, the tidal reach of the Raritan River and other small tributaries to the above-mentioned waterways.

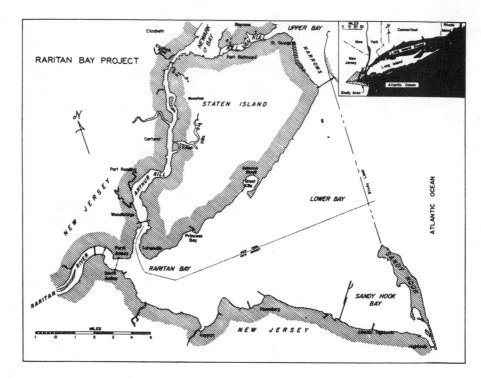

Figure 1
Raritan Bay study area

Waters of the study area are presently utilized for industrial water supply, navigation, commercial fin and shellfishing, and a variety of recreational activities. However, full utilization of these waters is presently restricted by unsuitable water quality. The present estimated annual value of water use is $2.0 million, 90% of which is associated with recreation. With suitable quality, the future potential value of these waters could be at least $19.0 million annually.

Studies of water currents and dispersion patterns indicate that Raritan Bay is affected by materials discharged into waters outside the immediate limits of the Project study area. Hence, the suggested control program considered the study area as a part of a system which includes Upper Bay, Kill Van Kull and Newark Bay.

SOURCES OF POLLUTION

Major pollutional loads to the study waters are presented in Table 1. Examination of these data indicates the large demand placed upon the assimilative capacity of these waters by the discharge of treated and untreated municipal and industrial wastes. Raritan Bay and Arthur Kill receive directly more than

Table 1. Municipal and industrial waste loadings*

Type source	Flow MGD	Loadings (lbs/day)		Tributary population	Population equivalent (BOD) discharged
		BOD	Suspended solids		
		Discharges to Raritan Bay			
Municipal	72.1	182.500	40,560	507,800	1,069,200
Industrial	0.1**	2,500			14,700
Total	72.2**	185,000			1,083,900
		Discharges to Arthur Kill			
Municipal	81.8	138,360	55,350	831,000	812,750
Industrial	367.3**	104,640			615,000
Total	449.1**	243,000			1,427,750
		Discharges to Raritan River			
Municipal	2.0	1,605	845	20,365	9,430
Industrial	85.7**	70,100			421,000
Total	87.7**	71,707			430,430
		Discharges to Study Area			
Municipal	155.9	322,465	96,755	1,359,165	1,891,380
Industrial	453.1	177,240			1,050,700
Total	609.0	499,705			2,942,080
		Discharges to Upper Bay			
Municipal	915.9	808,510	645,100	3,815,100	4,758,400
Industrial	N.D.†	N.D.†	N.D.†	N.D.†	N.D.†
Total	915.9	808,510	645,100	3,815,100	4,758,400

 * Does not include additional wastes loadings from recreational and commercial vessels, or from stormwater overflow.
 ** Excludes flow from power generating industry.
 † No data available.

480 million gallons per day (MGD) of wastes from a tributary population exceeding 1.3 million people. These discharges represent a Biochemical Oxygen Demand (BOD) loading of 430,000 lbs/day.

The discharge of additional wastes in adjacent waters increases the magnitude of impact of the direct loads. When discharges to Upper Bay and Raritan River are included, the total wastes volume approaches 1,500 MGD, which represents a BOD loading of greater than 1,300,000 lbs/day from a population exceeding 5.0 million people.

Contamination by pollutants other than BOD from these same sources is also a significant problem. Bacteriological pollution results from the discharge of more than 900 MGD of unchlorinated and raw municipal wastes emanating from a tributary population of 3.8 million. Such pollution constitutes a definite hazard to the health of persons having contact with these waters.

Nearly 75% of the total wastes volume is from industry. This results in pollution of study waters by a variety of contaminants in addition to oxygen-consuming material. Pollutants such as oil, phenol, phosphate and nitrogen result in unsightly conditions, destruction of desirable aquatic life, tainting of fish and shellfish, and eutrophication of the water.

Additional pollution results from the discharge of more than 1.0 billion gallons per day of "hot" cooling water from power-generating plants adjacent to these waters. Further contamination occurs in localized areas due to the discharge of wastes from recreational and commercial vessels. The overflow of sewage from combined storm-sanitary sewer systems also represents an important factor in pollution of these waters.

INVESTIGATIVE PROGRAM

A sampling program, based upon a review of existing data, was designed in order to permit an evaluation of the variations in water quality and long-term trends. The Project conducted an intensive program, with weekly sampling at each station (Figure 2) during the 13-month period from August 1962 through September 1963. From September 1963 to May 1966 the Project conducted a surveillance program which involved collection of monthly samples at selected stations in the Bay and Kill.

The intensive sampling program was designed to permit mathematical analyses of the variations noted in parameter values. The surveillance operation was pursued so as to maintain updated water quality data and to provide information

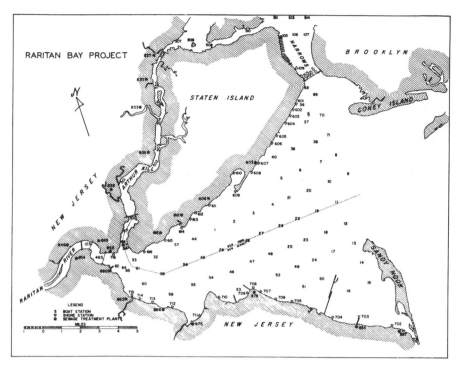

Figure 2
Sampling station locations, Raritan Bay, Arthur Kill and Upper Harbor

on any changes which might have occurred during the period of surveillance.

Major activities undertaken by the Project during this study included, but were not necessarily limited to:

(1) Simultaneous sampling of Raritan Bay, the Arthur Kill and waste treatment plant effluents emptying into these waters so as to permit assessment of relationships between the waste loads and water quality.

(2) Intensive bacteriological sampling of Raritan Bay and shoreline, entrant waters, and wastewater treatment plants discharging to the Bay in order to determine bacterial densities.

(3) Biological investigations designed to define the area of biological degradation, with particular emphasis on the benthic populations.

(4) Chemical evaluation of the existing water quality in the Bay as well as characterization of waste effluents, with particular emphasis on nutrients and the oxygen-demanding components.

A number of special investigations were undertaken by the Project to provide further data on water pollution problems in the study area. Included were an examination of water movement and dispersion patterns within Raritan Bay; an evaluation of the effects on water quality of combined sewer overflows; mathematical analyses to explain the variations found in the chemical and bacteriological analysis of Bay water samples; a study of the relationship between chlorination of wastewater treatment plant effluents and bacteriological densities in Raritan Bay; determination of the bacteriological and chemical quality of shellfish taken from the Bay; and isolation of certain pathogenic bacteria from study area waters, sewage effluents and shellfish. Results of certain of these special investigations are discussed later in this paper.

PHOTOSYNTHESIS—KEY ELEMENT IN MAINTAINING BAY DISSOLVED OXYGEN (DO)

Variation in dissolved oxygen throughout the Bay, which has an average chloride concentration of approximately 14,000 mg/l, was attributed to a predominant annual variation with secondary effects caused by tidal and diurnal cycles (Figure 3). During the winter, values throughout the Bay were 9–10 mg/l, with virtually no dissolved oxygen gradient. During the spring months, DO values remained at these levels; however, concentration gradients began to appear, with lower concentrations near the Narrows and near the confluence of the Raritan River and Arthur Kill. During the summer period, gradients were more pronounced, with DO values ranging from 10 mg/l in the center of the Bay to 4 mg/l in the vicinity of the Narrows, Raritan River and Arthur Kill. During autumn, the gradient essentially disappeared and DO concentrations throughout the Bay were of the order of 5 to 7 mg/l. From a dissolved oxygen standpoint, autumn appears to be the most critical period throughout the Bay, although near the Narrows and the junction of the Raritan River and Arthur Kill, equally critical DO levels were found during the summer.

Photosynthetic production of oxygen by marine organisms was a major factor in maintaining Bay DO levels. Biological surveys revealed that an increase in netplankton concentration was accompanied by an increase in DO levels. Increases in the zooplankton population, on the other hand, were accompanied by decreasing DO levels, with a simultaneous occurrence of lowest DO concentrations and peak zooplankton populations.

Respiration of the dominant zooplankters found during peak populations

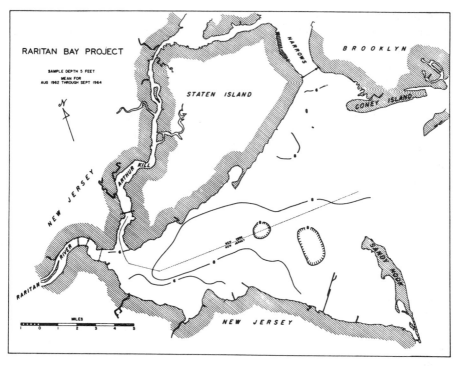

Figure 3
Dissolved oxygen (DO)

utilized as much as 37 mg/l per day of oxygen. This large loss of oxygen due to respiration was offset, at least partially, by simultaneous blooms of nanoplankton which are active oxygen producers.

Special studies were conducted at two stations in Raritan Bay to determine the net effect of photosynthetic production and respiration by marine organisms. The results, presented in Figure 4, suggest that oxygen production in the Bay is essentially limited to the top 11 feet, with peak production occurring in the upper 6 feet. Between 38 and 55% of the oxygen produced by photosynthesis was consumed by respiration, with the remainder being made available to the waters of the Bay.

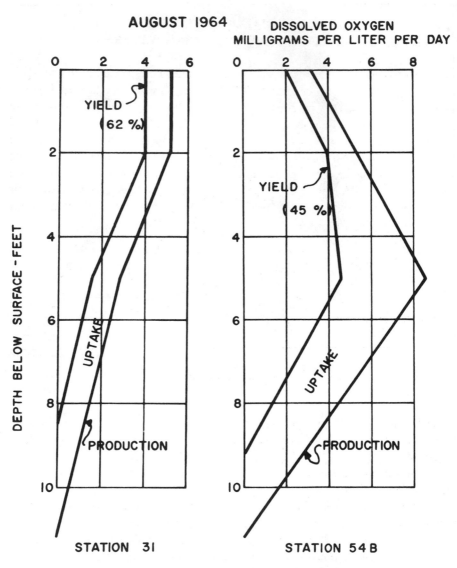

Figure 4
Oxygen production, uptake and yield, photosynthetic zone, Raritan Bay

BACTERIOLOGICAL STUDIES—
SHELLFISH PLUS OVERLYING WATERS

Analyses were performed for both total and fecal coliform by both the MPN and MF procedures, and for fecal streptococcus by only MF procedures. Figure 5 presents the mean MPN coliform count for the Bay. High densities were found both in the vicinity of the Narrows and at the junction of the Arthur Kill and Raritan River. From these two sources coliforms appear to radiate out into the Bay. Those stations with the lowest mean count formed an apparent edge between the two radiating sources, appearing as a straight band running from Princess Bay, Staten Island, New York to Sandy Hook Bay, New Jersey. Geometric mean counts for MPN confirmed a coliform range from 10,000/100 ml at the

Table 2. Results of bacteriological examination of shellfish meats

Station	No.	Total coliform, MPN/100 g			No.	Fecal coliform, MPN/100 g			No.	Salmonella isolations
		Min	Max.	Geom. mean		Min.	Max.	Geom. mean		Serotypes
1	8	<20	490	180	8	<20	330	120		
2	8	<20	1,700	550	8	<20	460	140		
3	8	<20	2,300	700	8	<20	2,300	370		
4	9	<20	24,000	3,200	9	<20	7,900	970		
6	7	<20	17,000	5,700	7	<20	13,000	3,100	4	S. st. paul; S. anatum; S. montevideo; S. litchfield
7	8	<20	160,000	39,000	8	<20	92,000	16,000	2	S. oranienburg; S. derby
10	7	<20	35,000	8,700	7	<20	11,000	2,600	2	S. derby; S. infantis
13	6	<20	7,900	1,400	6	<20	2,300	410		
14	8	<20	330	100	8	<20	130	45		
15	8	<20	330	120	8	<20	20	20		
16	8	<20	330	120	8	<20	230	52		
17	9	<20	2,300	580	9	<20	790	210		
18	7	<20	4,900	1,600	7	<20	1,300	350		
20	7	<20	13,000	4,000	7	<20	2,300	1,100		
21	6	<20	13,000	4,900	6	<20	3,300	1,300	1	S. derby
22	8	<20	3,300	1,200	8	<20	3,300	740	1	S. derby
23	8	<20	7,000	1,400	8	<20	790	260		
24	8	<20	4,900	1,300	8	<20	1,300	280		
25	9	<20	35,000	5,700	9	<20	3,300	1,000	1	S. tennessee
26	9	<20	16,000	2,800	9	<20	3,500	610		
27	8	<20	3,300	1,000	8	<20	2,200	620		
28	8	<20	1,300	600	8	<20	490	160	1	S. derby
29	7	<20	790	260	7	<20	490	110		
30	7	<20	460	200	7	<20	170	71		
31	8	<20	460	210	8	<20	230	95		

Table 2 cont'd.

| Station | No. | Total coliform, MPN/100 g | | | No. | Fecal coliform, MPN/100 g | | | Salmonella isolations | |
		Min	Max.	Geom. mean		Min.	Max.	Geom. mean	No.	Serotypes
32	8	<20	7,900	1,400	8	<20	950	320		
33	7	<20	2,300	930	7	<20	790	350		
36	8	<20	92,000	13,600	8	<20	35,000	4,700	1	S. derby
37	7	<20	24,000	6,600	7	<20	4,900	1,700	1	S. anatum
39	9	<20	24,000	5,200	9	<20	24,000	3,500	1	S. 6,7: K mono.
40	8	<20	22,000	5,600	9	<20	7,900	2,100	3	S. derby; S. anatum; S. 6,7 non.mot
41	9	<20	3,300	1,100	9	<20	490	150		
42	8	<20	3,500	540	8	<20	310	70		
43	7	<20	490	150	7	<20	140	67		
44	8	<20	2,300	630	8	<20	230	77		
45	7	<20	490	190	7	<20	140	52	1	S. typhimurium
46	8	<20	230	97	8	<20	80	31		
47	8	<20	1,300	350	8	<20	230	76	2	S. 6,7: non.mot; S. 6,7: K mono.
48	8	<20	3,300	780	8	<20	790	150		
49	8	<20	13,000	2,000	8	<20	1,300	300		
50	8	<20	3,300	600	8	<20	490	92		
51	7	<20	2,300	400	7	<20	2,300	340		
52	7	<20	4,900	860	7	<20	460	110		
53	8	<20	2,100	380	8	<20	130	·37		
54	7	<20	7,900	1,300	7	<20	490	90		
56	7	<20	490	180	7	<20	170	44	2	S. infantis; S. muenchen
57	8	<20	4,900	820	8	<20	490	160		
58	6	<20	3,300	1,200	6	<20	230	120		
61	6	110	7,000	1,400	6	<20	4,600	820		
73	6	<20	2,300	400	6	<20	170	45		

Narrows, and 7,000/100 ml at the mouth of the Raritan River to less than 50/100 ml in Sandy Hook Bay. The high fecal coliform densities and the ratio of fecal coliform to fecal streptococcus group organisms, which are characteristic of human feces, strongly suggested that contamination in the study area waters resulted from human sources.

The Project conducted bacteriological analyses on 391 shellfish samples taken from 50 stations throughout Raritan Bay. Analyses were performed for MPN total coliform. MPN fecal coliform, and for the presence of *Salmonella* bacteria. The results are summarized in Table 2.

Samples from 12 of the 50 stations had geometric mean total coliform densities greater than 2,400 per 100 grams of shellfish meat. The geometric mean fecal coliform density in shellfish taken from these same 12 stations ranged from

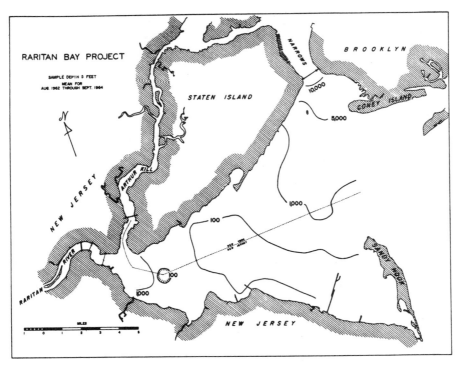

Figure 5
MPN confirmed coliform

610 to 16,000 per 100 grams. The presence of high total coliform densities appeared to show some correlation with water temperature. None of the shellfish taken from waters with temperatures less than 8.5°C had total coliform MPN's of 2,400 or more per 100 grams. The 12 stations having geometric mean coliform densities greater than 2,400 per 100 grams were located in the northerly sector of the Bay, in an area extending generally south of Staten Island to and across the New York-New Jersey state line.

Salmonellae were isolated from clam meats collected at 14 of the 50 sampling stations. Of these 14 stations, nine also showed geometric mean total coliform densities greater than 2,400 per 100 grams of clam meat. The geometric mean coliform density in shellfish from the other five stations ranged from 180 to 1,200 per 100 grams. A total of 23 *Salmonella* isolations were made with 13 serotypes identified. *Salmonella derby* was the predominant serotype and was isolated in shellfish from seven of the 14 stations. Stations which showed the presence of

Salmonella in the clam meats covered two general areas, one of which corresponded with the location of high coliform counts in the clam meats as described above. The second area was located along the New York-New Jersey state line, in an area bounded roughly by Great Kills, Staten Island, N.Y., and Keyport and Keansburg, N.J.

Chemical analyses of meats from shellfish taken from these 50 sampling stations indicated high phenol and mineral oil concentrations from a number of stations in the western sector of the Bay, with highest values associated with those stations nearest the mouths of the Arthur Kill and Raritan River. Specific analyses for a number of metals, including copper, chromium, zinc and lead, and for pesticide residues, revealed trace amounts in clam meats.

PATHOGEN ISOLATIONS FROM SEWAGE AND BAY WATERS

In an attempt to further evaluate the effects of Upper Bay and the Narrows on the eastern portion of Raritan Bay, studies were undertaken to isolate *Salmonella* and *Shigella* from sewers discharging into the Narrows, and from the waters of Raritan Bay and the Narrows.

No isolations could be made of *Shigella* organisms, but a number of positive results were obtained for *Salmonella*. From October 1963 through April 1964, these organisms were isolated in four of seven samples taken from a sewer which discharges raw municipal wastes from Staten Island into Upper Bay just above the Narrows. Between October 1963 and July 1964, a total of 20 samples in the Narrows were analyzed, 40% of which were positive for *Salmonella*. A total of 15 different serotypes were identified, and as many as seven different serotypes were isolated from one sample. Areas of Staten Island shore closest to the Narrows showed the greatest frequency of *Salmonella* isolation. Five of 13 samples taken at South Beach were positive; at Midland Beach two of 14 samples showed *Salmonella*. No *Salmonellae* were recovered from samples further west at the Miller Field beach areas. Some of the same serotypes found in the Narrows were isolated from the bathing area samples. Although a limited number of samples were analyzed, the relatively small sample volume (2 liters) which was used for these determinations suggests a substantial density in these areas.

Attempts were made to isolate *Salmonella* from various locations in eastern Raritan Bay (see Figure 6), extending on a line from the Narrows southward toward Sandy Hook. Of the 16 stations sampled, 10 were positive. Of the 48 samples processed, 27% contained *Salmonella*, and a total of 25 *Salmonella*

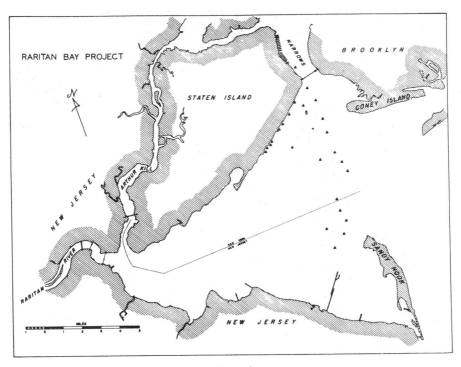

Figure 6
Location of *Salmonella* isolations

isolations were made. *S. derby* was the predominant serotype, being isolated on eight different occasions, and was also the predominant serotype in the samples collected at the Narrows. *Salmonellae* were isolated below the Narrows as far as approximately six miles south of the Verrazano-Narrows Bridge.

PLANKTON AND BENTHIC POPULATIONS STUDIED

During the period of study, nanoplankton comprised 94% or more of the total phytoplankton population. At all sampling stations (see Figure 7) the nano-plankton population was high during the summer and low in the winter. Nano-plankton blooms developed as water temperatures increased sharply in May and June and showed peak densities coincident with peak water temperatures. During summer blooms, nanoplankton comprised as much as 99.9% of the total

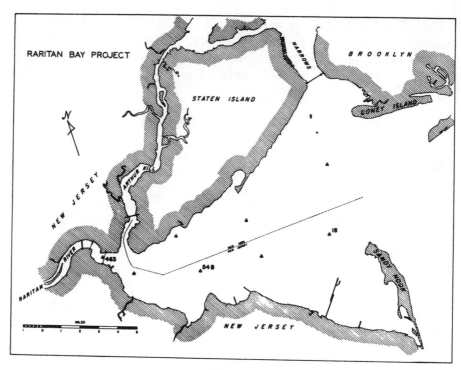

Figure 7
Plankton sampling station locations

plankton population. Netplankton blooms occurred during the colder months, disappearing as temperatures reached 8 or 9°C; hence, netplankton densities were lowest during the summer and greatest in the spring. At their peak, spring blooms of netplankton constituted 27 to 48% of the total plankton population. In both 1962 and 1963, blooms of netplankton occurred during the first week of October at Station 18. Such fall blooms are a normal occurrence in coastal waters.

Phytoplankton populations were dominated by two algal species, *Nanochloris atomus* and *Skeletonema costatum*. The former, a green alga, comprised more than 50 to 99.9% of the nanoplankton community. *Skeletonema costatum*, a diatom, comprised from less than 1.0 to more than 99% of the netplankton population. During August and September 1962, and again in 1964, a dinoflagellate, *Peridinium trochoidum*, numerically dominated the netplankton population. This alga was not observed in quantitative samples collected during the summer of 1963.

Coincidental with plankton studies, levels of selected nutrients were determined at each of the plankton stations. These selected nutrients—total phosphorous, nitrate, organic nitrogen, ammonia—were always present in amounts sufficient to support the observed plankton populations.

BENTHIC STUDIES: KEY BIOLOGICAL TOOL

Benthic samples were collected in Raritan Bay (see Figure 8) and subjected to both chemical and biological analysis. Sediments were classified according to median grain size. Those stations with sediment composed of the smallest size particles had fewer animals than those areas with the larger grain size.

The type of benthic organisms and their relative numbers are presented in

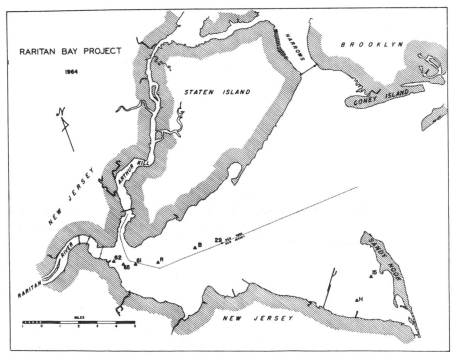

Figure 8
Benthic sampling station locations

Table 3. Percentage of benthos at representative stations

1964	Station 62				Station B				Station 29				Station H			
	PW	AC	SC	O	PW	AC	SC	O	PW	AC	SC	O	PW	AC	SC	O
February	0	0	0	0	76	6	0	18	67	17	0	16	8	92	0	0
May	100	0	0	0	65	15	0	20	33	66	0	1	15	85	0	0
August	0	0	100	0	35	28	10	27	74	19	7	0	55	38	0	7

PW = Polychaete worms
AC = Amphipod crustaceans
SC = Soft-shell clams
O = Others: all types of organisms that comprised separately less than 5% of the total

Table 3. Polychaete (segmented worms) and amphipod crustaceans were the dominant benthic organisms. Tube-dwelling worms, regarded as pollution-tolerant organisms, were more numerous towards Stations 62 and B, indicating a greater degree of pollution in that area.

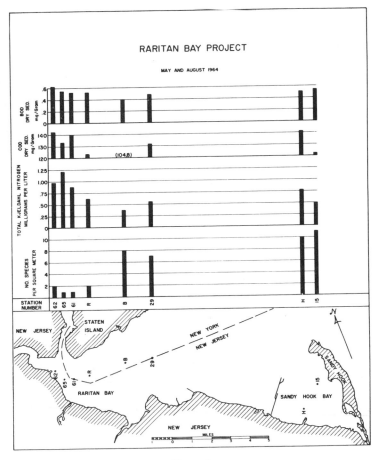

Figure 9
Chemical and biological sediment analysis

In May and August 1964, certain chemical analyses were performed on samples of bottom sediment. A comparison was made between these data and the average number of benthic species found at each station. With the exception of Station

H, the results presented in Figure 9 indicate a general decline in the level of Total Kjeldahl Nitrogen, BOD and COD with increasing distance from the more polluted stations. The higher concentrations at H were attributed to a small sewer outfall located in the immediate vicinity. In general, fewer benthic species were found at those stations having the higher concentrations of nitrogen.

WATER MOVEMENT AND DISPERSION

Examination of the geographical structure of the study area suggests the hydraulic complexity of the system, due to interconnections between the bodies of water as well as other waters external to Raritan Bay and Arthur Kill. Any satisfactory pollution control program developed for Raritan Bay and Arthur Kill must be based on knowledge of the movement of waters between these various bodies so as to recognize probable paths of flow of pollutional materials. Accordingly, the Project conducted investigations of water movement by tracer dye studies, geological investigations, and by reviewing available hydraulic model data.

Dye studies provided information on water movement and dispersion characteristics under conditions actually observed at the time of each dye release.

Dye release studies were made in the Raritan River, Arthur Kill, the westerly portion of Raritan Bay and in Upper Bay to observe the interrelationship of these waters. Rhodamine B dye, used in all studies conducted by the Project, was added to the water as an instantaneous release. In all studies, except upper Raritan River, resulting movement of dye was monitored visually and by the use of fluorometers for as long as deemed advisable. During the monitoring phase, boats equipped with fluorometers and continuously recording meters cruised the dye mass to determine its movement, location of the limits, and the peak concentrations. Monitoring boats proceeded on a predetermined course, established between known navigational aids, at a fixed rate of speed. In addition to recording dye concentration, records were also maintained on time and boat course so as to permit proper correlation between an observed dye concentration and the exact location and time of such reading.

Results of the largest (1,000 pounds) dye release, conducted in Upper Bay at high water slack, are shown in Figure 10 and summarized as follows:

(1) Material introduced in the northwest sector of the Upper Bay affects a broad area of Lower Bay, and is found on the Staten Island shore from Midland Beach to the Narrows within 6 hours of release;

(2) Within 32 hours of release such material affects a large area of Raritan Bay, and is found on the Staten Island shore from the Narrows to Great Kills, as well as on the Coney Island shore of Brooklyn, N.Y.;

(3) On an ebb current there was little lateral mixing across the Narrows, but lateral mixing does occur on the first flood current following release;

(4) Material moving from the release point on the first ebb passes along the western edge of the channel and the Staten Island shore before passing through the Narrows.

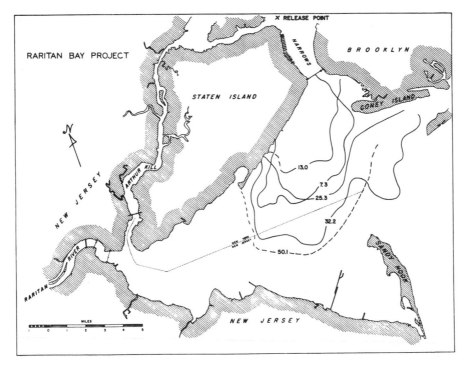

Figure 10
Upper Hudson dye study (contours show edge of dye mass at various slack tide; numbers indicate hours after release)

A geological investigation of Raritan Bay was carried out to obtain information on long-term water movement and sediment distribution. In summary, the investigation found, on the basis of the sediment distribution within the Bay, that:

(1) Freshwater inflow from the Raritan River moves along the southern section of the Bay towards Sandy Hook;
(2) Particles introduced into the Bay at widely varying locales were eventually transported throughout the Bay, with the finer particles gravitating toward the area bounded by Seguine Point and Great Kills, Staten Island, N.Y., and Keyport and Keansburg, N.J.

Project studies, as well as those performed by the U.S. Army Corps of Engineers on the Vicksburg model of New York Harbor, which have been reported previously by other agencies, indicated the complexity of the Raritan Bay system. Essentially, the waters of Raritan Bay may be affected by materials discharged into waters outside the immediate limits of the study area. Hence, any effective control program for pollution control in Raritan Bay must consider the Bay not as an independent estuary, but as part of a larger interconnected system which includes Upper Bay, Kill Van Kull, Newark Bay, Arthur Kill and the Raritan River.

RECOMMENDATIONS FOR REMEDIAL ACTION

On the basis of Project studies, the following recommendations were made in order to reclaim study area waters for maximum beneficial uses:

(1) Municipal treatment facilities should provide a minimum of 80% removal of BOD and suspended solids at all times, including any four-hour period of the day when the strength of the raw wastes might be expected to exceed average conditions. Effective year-round disinfection (effluent coliform count of no greater than one per ml in more than 10% of samples examined) at all municipal plants discharging directly to these waters shall be provided.

Unless existing orders specify earlier completion dates, in which case the earlier dates must be met, all improvements are to be completed by 1970.
(2) Industrial plants shall improve practices for the segregation and treatment of wastes so as to effect maximum reduction of the following:
   a) acid and alkalis;
   b) oil and tarry substances;
   c) phenolic and other compounds that contribute to taste, odor and tainting of fin and shellfish meat;
   d) nutrient materials, including nitrogenous and phosphorous compounds;
   e) suspended material;

f) toxic and highly colored wastes;

g) oxygen-requiring substances;

h) heat;

i) foam-producing discharges;

j) bacteria;

k) wastes which detract from optimum use and enjoyment of receiving waters.

Industrial treatment facilities, to accomplish such reduction, must provide removals at least the equivalent of those required for municipal treatment plants. Such facilities or reduction methods must be provided by 1970 unless existing orders specify earlier compliance dates, in which case the earlier dates must be met.

(3) Facilities and procedures be established at each treatment facility to provide laboratory control.

(4) State regulations be extended to require waste treatment facilities or holding tanks on all vessels and recreational boats using the area. If holding tanks are to be used, adequate dockside facilities should be required to ensure proper disposal of wastes.

(5) Investigate additional proposals to safeguard water quality in the study area. These studies are to include, but not be limited to:

a) relocation of the main shipping channel through Raritan Bay to improve circulation characteristics;

b) selection of areas for dredging for construction materials;

c) suitable outfall locations for waste effluents to include possible trunk systems to divert effluents from the Arthur Kill.

Conferees, who include representatives from FWPCA, the States of New York and New Jersey, and the Interstate Sanitation Commission, meet every six months to review and initiate progress on the water quality improvements outlined above.

ACKNOWLEDGEMENTS

The authors wish to acknowledge the contributions of Mr. Paul De Falco, Jr., Regional Director, Southwest Region, FWPCA, who was the Project Director of the Raritan Bay Study, and Mr. Merrill S. Hohman, Director, Planning and Program Management, Northeast Region, FWPCA, who was Chief of Planning and Evaluation for this investigation.

REFERENCES

DE FALCO, PAUL JR. AND KANDLE, ROSCOE P.: "Effect of effluent chlorination on bacterial populations in Raritan Bay Waters."

Proceedings Volume 1, Conference on Pollution of Raritan Bay and Adjacent Interstate Waters, Third Session, 1967, FWPCA.

Proceedings Volume 2, Conference on Pollution of Raritan Bay and Adjacent Interstate Waters, Third Session, 1967, FWPCA.

Proceedings Volume 3, Conference on Pollution of Raritan Bay and Adjacent Interstate Waters, Third Session, 1967, FWCPA.

Progress Report for the Conference on Pollution of Raritan Bay and Adjacent Interstate Waters, Second Session, 1963, PHS, Dept. of Health, Education and Welfare.

Report on the Pollution of Raritan Bay, Raritan Bay Conference, 1961, PHS Dept. of Health, Education and Welfare.

INDEX